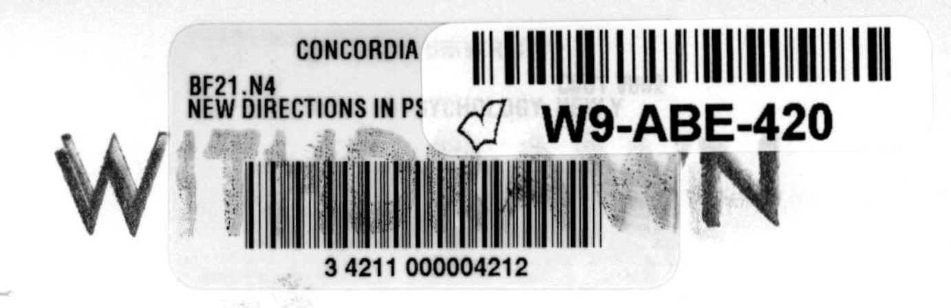

# NEW DIRECTIONS IN PSYCHOLOGY II

FRANK BARRON
UNIVERSITY OF CALIFORNIA, BERKELEY

WILLIAM C. DEMENT
STANFORD UNIVERSITY

WARD EDWARDS, HAROLD LINDMAN, AND
LAWRENCE D. PHILLIPS UNIVERSITY OF MICHIGAN

JAMES AND MARIANNE OLDS
UNIVERSITY OF MICHIGAN

# NEW DIRECTIONS IN PSYCHOLOGY II

*The Psychology of Creativity*

 *An Essay on Dreams: The Role of Physiology in Understanding Their Nature*

*Emerging Technologies for Making Decisions*

*Drives, Rewards, and the Brain*

FOREWORD BY THEODORE M. NEWCOMB

Holt, Rinehart and Winston, Inc.
*New York Chicago San Francisco Toronto London*

*Library of Congress Catalog Card Number: 65-17710*

20812-0115

*Printed in the United States of America*

# FOREWORD

Psychology, as Galileo is said to have remarked about the planet Earth, does move. But its course is less predictable than that of *orbis terrarum;* some of its many fronts move now rapidly, now at a modest, walking pace, while others seem barely to hold their own. The present venture attempts to plot some of the movements.

Professional psychologists have their journals; within the United States alone some dozens of them are family members or close relatives. The American Psychological Association's *Psychological Abstracts* can direct the sophisticated inquirer just where to go to find just what, and its monthly *Contemporary Psychology* reviews most of the important new books. The *Annual Review of Psychology* provides condensed, encyclopedic overviews of important developments of the past year in each of a dozen or more areas of psychology. Such are the resources that professional psychologists provide for one another. For our students and apprentices we have no dearth of textbooks, handbooks, and volumes of selected readings, but the informed instructor—and, sometimes, even the alert student—knows about the publication lag that is compounded of multiple delays, first in the journals and then in the textbooks. Occasionally the student-apprentice, along with the scientifically oriented nonpsychologist, can titillate his appetite for "what's news in psychology" from the pages of *The Scientific American.* What none of these sources has yet managed to do is to present to the student or layman an account, fresh and informed but not highly technical, of recent contributions to a few problem-areas that lie somewhere between "the science of psychology" and "the change from trichromatic to dichromatic vision in the human retina."

The four contributions that follow, like those in *New Directions I*, report new developments of special interest, against older and more familiar backdrops, and have been deliberately chosen to range across psychology's broad spectrum. The contributors are uncommonly familiar with their respective problems—and this in large part because they have themselves done much to extend the frontiers of those problems.

Each of the four contributions was written in 1964. They are not only still warm; they are authoritative and they are readable. The students for whom they are primarily written might do well to call them to the attention both of their teachers and of their friends.

ANN ARBOR, MICHIGAN
JANUARY 1965

THEODORE M. NEWCOMB

# CONTENTS

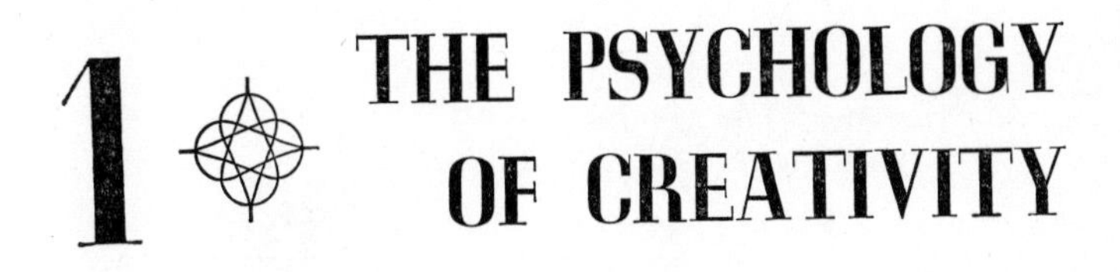

# 1 THE PSYCHOLOGY OF CREATIVITY

FRANK BARRON
UNIVERSITY OF CALIFORNIA, BERKELEY

The problem of psychic creation is a special case of the problem of novelty in all of nature. By what process do new forms come into being? The specification of the conditions under which novelty appears in human psychical functioning is the task to which the psychology of creativity addresses itself. In doing so, it links itself to the general scientific enterprise of describing the evolution of forms in the natural world.

Such an attempt at a purely naturalistic description of creation is itself relatively new. Creation has long been thought of as a mystery and has been deemed the province of religion, or more broadly, of the supernatural. Supernaturalism includes magic as well as religion, and may be described as an attitude of mind in which the occurrence of the unfamiliar is prone to be interpreted as an interruption of the natural course of events, or as evidence of the existence of another world. The radically novel occurrence thus borders on the uncanny and properly arouses awe.

This sense of the mystery surrounding creation is close to a universal sentiment, and certainly it may be found in the breasts of even the most scientific of psychologists as they approach the phenomenon of psychic creativity. Creativity may be defined, quite simply, as the ability to bring something new into existence. The archetype of the creator is the Divine Being; Aristotle defined the principle of generation of the universe as *Nous Poetikos*, the Poetic or Creative Reason. But in the divine creative act something is made to exist where nothing existed before. Since human beings are not able to make something out of nothing, the human act of creation always involves a reshaping of given materials, whether physical or mental. The "something new," then, is a form made by the reconstitution of, or generation from, something old.

To step from the putative divine case to the relatively familiar human case seems at first to remove much of the mystery. It is quickly restored, however, by considering a most common human participation in the creative act: the making of a baby. New flesh is made from old, a new form that has never lived before now comes into being. But the question quickly comes, as indeed it comes to every mother and father, even if fleetingly and darkly, "What on earth had *we* to do with this?" One speaks then of "the miracle of birth," meaning really the miracle of conception and gestation as well as parturition, and the miracle of sexuality, the male and the female principles of generation. The most primitive of emotions participate in the human act of procreation, and the sense of awe and blessedness which the mother and father may feel at the birth of their child derives in part from their recognition that a cosmic process has worked through them in a way they can only dimly understand.

In view of this universal sense of the mystery of creation, we should not be surprised if the techniques of modern psychology can offer only the most modest of beginnings to scientific knowledge in the area of psychic creativity. Indeed, the whole question of mystery may be irrelevant; certainly molecular biology in its unraveling of the genetic code has not diminished the awesomeness of the process of reproduction of living forms, nor have theoretical physics and astronomy in the picture they give us of the magnitude and age and workings, both vast and tiny, of the physical universe diminished our wonder. Quite the contrary; the revelations of science might instead lead all of us, in the back of our minds if not consciously, to be, as an intimate of Franz Kafka's once described him, "constantly amazed."

Psychology cannot as yet promise such amazing revelations

concerning the process of creation in the psychic sphere, and it must still follow the older branches of science at a respectful distance. Yet since 1950 there has been substantial progress in this area of psychological study, much of it stemming from new efforts at measurement, as well as new substantive inquiries directed toward the delineation of personality characteristics of highly creative human beings. To present the results of some of these studies is the aim of this chapter. First, however, let us consider some of the problems of measurement posed by the nature of human creativity.

## THE MEASUREMENT OF CREATIVITY

We might begin by returning to that newborn baby, and its wondering parents. Once the wonder has worn off a bit and the baby is claimed from the cosmos and made their own, the parents are likely to begin to look for the evidence that they did indeed have something to do with it, as revealed in resemblances. While each baby is absolutely new and unique and is truly a form that has never lived before, it can sometimes seem almost a replica of one of its progenitors, or at least a mosaic with recognizable contributions from only a very few sources. Besides that, one baby is very much like every other baby, so that even as we say "new and unique" we must add "similar" or "almost a repetition."

The same is true of thoughts. Perhaps we should have said that the making of thoughts is the most common human participation in the creative process. The two processes may in fact be not so far apart. It has often been noted that in some sense a man's ideas are his children, and when one studies closely a particular act of psychic creation, such as the writing of a story or the development of an invention, one can see the psychological analogues to those biological generative processes of conception, gestation, and parturition—and even, on occasion, post-partum moodiness.

And just as every baby is both unique and typical, so is almost every thought. A man may think a thought which for him is a new thought, yet it may be one of the most common thoughts in the world when all thinkers are taken into account. His act is a creative act, but the "something new" that is produced is something new in the population of thoughts he can claim as his own, not something new for mankind as a whole.

These considerations are relevant to the problem of the measurement of creativity, since the statistical frequency with which a given response occurs in a defined population of responses is one kind of handy measure or index of originality. We must be careful, however, to specify accurately the population of responses that is being made to serve as a base of reference. Confusion on this point has led to much vain argumentation over whether a given individual is "creative" or not. All of us are both creatures and creators, but we vary both in our quality as a creation and in our power to create.

Great original thoughts or ideas are those that are not only new to the person who thinks them but new to almost everyone. These rare contributions are creative in perhaps a stronger sense of the term; not only are they the results of a creative act, but they themselves in turn create new conditions of human existence. The theory of relativity was such a creative act; so was the invention of the wheel. Both resulted in new forms of power, and human life was changed thereby.

Creative power of an outstanding order is marked by the voluminous production of acts that can claim a notable degree of originality, and the occasional production of acts of radical originality. It is instructive to read in a good encyclopedia the history of the basic scientific disciplines; one soon finds the same great names cropping up in field after field, for it is the nature of genius to range with fresh interest over the whole of natural phenomena and to see interrelationships which for others go unnoticed.

Indeed, there is reason to believe that originality is almost habitual with individuals who produce a really singular idea. What this implies is that a highly organized mode of responding to experience is a precondition for consistent creativity. And from what we know in general about the relationship between thinking and behavior, we certainly should expect that some aspects of an individual's personality will play an important role in his capacity to think and act creatively.

The kinds of behavioral products we may designate as creative are of course quite various: a novel solution to a problem in mathematics; a mechanical invention; the discovery of a new chemical process; the composition of a piece of music, or a poem, or a painting; the forming of a new philosophical or religious system; an innovation in law; a fresh way of thinking about social problems; a breakthrough in ways of treating or preventing a disease; even, heaven help us, the invention of mighty new armaments or new methods of controlling the minds of others. The important defining properties of these creative products are their originality, their aptness, their validity, their adequacy in meeting a need, and a rather subtle additional quality which for the time being perhaps we can call "esthetic fit" or "elegance." The emphasis is upon whatever is fresh, novel, unusual, ingenious, divergent, clever, and apt.

## RESEARCH BEGINNINGS

The end of the first half of the twentieth century saw the profession of psychology well furnished with tests of "intelligence" but as yet poorly furnished with tests of that aspect of intelligence we call creativity. But the conclusion of World War II had left a number of psychologists with the conviction that efforts at measurement were badly needed in such trait areas as flexibility, initiative, ingenuity, adaptability, spontaneity, and originality. The psychologists who headed testing and selection programs in branches or special arms of the military establishment, such as the U. S. Air Corps and the Office of

Strategic Services, returned to their academic positions with the determination to do something about the research gap in this whole set of valued human potentialities. Many other psychologists were feeling the same stir, and by 1951 several important research programs were in full swing.

J. P. Guilford, who had directed the Air Corps research on the selection of combat crews, may fairly be said to have launched much of this effort with his address as retiring president of the American Psychological Association in September, 1950. In that address he systematically surveyed the gaps in knowledge in the domain of intellectual abilities and listed dozens of new tests then being developed by him and his colleagues in the Psychological Laboratory of the University of Southern California. Donald W. MacKinnon and Nevitt Sanford, both of them former students of Henry A. Murray at Harvard and Murray's collaborators in the germinal "Explorations in Personality" (1938), were simultaneously launching the Institute of Personality Assessment and Research at the University of California, with the assessment of originality as one of their main goals. John Flanagan, through the critical incident technique, was establishing the basis for his later comprehensive testing programs; most relevant in the present context was his development of performance tests of ingenuity, which combined open-endedness with mechanical scoring (1963). Murray himself, at Harvard, had already contributed an important instrument of observation in the study of imagination, the Thematic Apperception Test (1943), and students of his now set to work on studies of the creative process in poetry and the arts. L. L. Thurstone's influence continued to be felt, both through his own writings (1952) and the writings and organizational activities of his colleagues. Especially noteworthy was the role of Calvin W. Taylor, then in charge of the fellowship program of the National Science Foundation and presently director of a very active program of research in creativity at the University of Utah. Taylor's importance in the definition of this research area has come not only through his research but also through his organization of national conferences of researchers, his establishment of effective lines of communication among them, and his periodic issuance of reports on progress.

A welcome contribution from another source was the clinically oriented studies of Ann Roe, who brought a depth-psychology approach to the study of imagery and motivation in creative artists and scientists. By the time of Guilford's 1950 address she had already begun her pioneer researches in the study of scientific creativity that resulted in her 1952 book, *The Making of a Scientist.*

We ourselves have had a hand in the work at the Institute of Personality Assessment and Research at the University of California since 1950, and upon it we shall draw most heavily in presenting evidence as to the personality characteristics associated with creativity. Most of the observations made there depend upon the method of research known as living-in assessment, and a description of its origins and its philosophy of inquiry will be helpful to the reader in judging the adequacy and validity of its program. There are many other excellent methods that have contributed substantially to scientific knowledge of creativity, of course; we select this as an example at the risk of overemphasizing its general importance.

## ORIGINS OF THE ASSESSMENT METHOD

The method of research known now as "living-in assessment" was originally not a method of research at all. Rather, as the word assessment implies, it was a way of appraising persons, or of judging how a person would fit the requirements of a certain job. In American psychology, it grew out of the need for selecting men for hazardous irregular warfare assignments in World War II, assignments calling for courage, ingenuity, initiative, and the ability to take responsibility for grave actions in rapidly changing circumstances in which usually a go-ahead from superiors could not be sought.

Psychological tests available at that time simply could not do the job of assessing the fitness of men for such assignments. Complex judgments were called for, and they had to be made by men of maturity on the basis of observation of the candidates in stressful circumstances. Thus was born the Selection Service of the Office of Strategic Services. A distinguished psychologist and psychiatrist, Henry A. Murray, successor to Morton Prince as head of the Harvard Psychological Clinic, was chosen to be acting head. He in turn rounded up an outstanding group of psychologists to serve as assessors.

With war's end, some of these psychologists did try to evaluate the program of assessment itself, and the results of that retrospective research is reported in a book by the assessment staff of the Office of Strategic Services, *The Assessment of Men* (1948). This evaluation served to clarify some of the virtues as well as shortcomings of the method, and it prompted some of the government agency's staff to seek ways of applying living-in assessment to research problems. This was the origin of the Institute of Personality Assessment and Research, launched as a research division of the University of California in 1949, with Donald W. MacKinnon as director.

Shortly thereafter, MacKinnon was to write, in an essay (1953) that set forth some guidelines for the Institute's approach to data-gathering in the ensuing years:

"In the 1930s it was considered appropriate to make explorations in personality, but today one is made to feel pedestrian unless in his investigations he is testing so-called deductions from a theoretical model . . . In some fields and in respect of some problems, even in personality, such a demand is legitimate, but in other areas we would be more honest with ourselves and more faithful to the true meaning of theory if we admitted that what we proposed was an exploration.

Another indication of our underestimation of the significance of the fact-finding process is the common tendency to treat the laborious task of collecting data as a chore to be given, whenever possible, to someone else. The notion that anyone can collect data, but that only a few can think creatively about them, and that the two processes can always and everywhere be carried out entirely apart from one another is widespread. Collecting data is regarded as a job for a technician, for the graduate research assistant, but not for the professor or high-powered researcher.

In the more venerable fields of science such a division of labor can often be made advantageously, but not so easily or so often in new fields and especially not in fields where the data are the interactions of individuals in complex situations and where the collector of data must, of necessity, be a participant observer, not only listening with a third ear but seeing with a third eye. The neglect would not be so serious if we would ourselves make the first observations or pretest the instruments of our invention before turning these tasks over to research assistants, but frequently even these preliminary interactions with our subjects are omitted.

Such disregard of the sources of our data is difficult to interpret except as the consequence of the social hierarchy in our science which grants greater prestige to activities the farther removed they are from data. If, as we know, even the performance of rats in mazes is influenced by the way in which they are handled, on what grounds do we believe that human subjects, infinitely more sensitive and subtle, will be any less affected in their behavior by the way in which they are treated in interview, test, or experimental situation?"

In practice, what this boiled down to was a decision that the close-in work of personality study of individuals was to be accomplished by persons as highly qualified as possible, and by a method that brought them into as direct contact as possible with the individuals who were to be chosen as subjects of study.

We have written elsewhere in considerable detail of the method itself (see especially Chapter 4, "An Odd Fellow," in Barron, 1963, *Creativity and Psychological Health*). A single "assessment" generally ran from Friday through Sunday, and took place in a large, comfortably furnished, former fraternity house located on a pleasant tree-lined street of such houses on the edge of the Berkeley campus. In the early days of the Institute the subjects and staff members slept in on Friday and Saturday nights, and of course took all their meals in the house and in general made it a comfortable place of residence for the week-end. A wine cellar and a fireplace added to the amenities, and in as many ways as possible the situation was defined not as test-taking but as a mutually open situation in which staff and subjects could get to know each other.

How the subjects recorded *their* observations, or whether they did at all, is not known (for the most part), but what *the staff* did at the end of the three days was this: each senior staff member wrote down all his impressions of each subject, then used a 300-word adjective checklist to characterize each subject as accurately and tersely as possible, and finally employed a 100-item set of sentences, each of them representing a clinical inference, to describe the subject in somewhat more technical and psychodynamically "deeper" terms. The Gough Adjective Checklist (Gough, 1962) was used for this first task, and the Block Clinical Q-sort (MacKinnon *et al.*, 1958) for the second.

These descriptions were given without knowledge of test results and were intended to represent what could be observed from the subject's actions and words during the three days. The full intuitive capacity of the staff observer was thus called into play, and eventually also was brought to bear on each case through the medium of a case conference and final case write-up, with test results and interview data taken into account as well. Finally, when all cases in a given sample had been studied, they were rated relative to one another on a set of 40 personality traits, based largely on the earlier conceptual formulations of Murray and of Gordon Allport (1937).

Much of the work of the Institute to be described in this chapter has already been published in professional journals and is appropriately referenced. At this writing, however, a considerable body of data remains unpublished and is available only in mimeographed form and to qualified professionals. The present senior staff of the Institute has been very generous in giving permission for the inclusion in this chapter of some material hitherto presented only in the mimeographed preliminary report, *The Creative Person*, a staff report given at a University of California Extension Conference. More specifically, we should like to acknowledge our gratitude to Donald W.

MacKinnon and Wallace B. Hall, who had primary staff responsibility for the study of architects; Harrison G. Gough, who conducted the studies of research scientists and of engineers; Richard S. Crutchfield, both for his work with mathematicians and his studies of conformity behavior; and Ravenna Helson, for her research on creative potential in women as well as for the special study of women mathematicians.

The permanent senior staff of the Institute has served not only as observers in assessment and as project directors for specific studies; they set themselves also the task of developing new instruments of observation, in the form of tests, experiments, interview schedules, and techniques of description. In doing so, they faced a series of interesting technical problems that it may be instructive to consider.

## PROBLEMS OF TEST CONSTRUCTION

A primary strategic consideration in building tests of creativity derives from the practical need for tests which (a) can be administered to groups of subjects rather than to one subject at a time, (b) can be mechanically scored without the intermediation of a rater, and (c) depend on simple enumeration which can yield frequency distributions readily susceptible of statistical analysis. (Elimination of the need for a rater is desirable since it can lead both to greater objectivity and to replicability; raters have their good days and their bad days and they tend to come and go, but a mechanical scoring system behaves the same way all the time and will stay put.)

This set of requirements, however, immediately bumps head-on into the nature of the creative act, which most commonly is quite complex and to be recognized must have an observer capable of embracing its complexities. Emerson once declared that the person closest to the thinker of an original thought is he who first recognizes its originality. Thomas Huxley is reputed to have exclaimed, upon first hearing the statement of Darwin's theory of natural selection, "Now why didn't

I think of that!" Even though he hadn't thought of it, he recognized immediately its originality and validity. A mechanical scoring system, so far as we know, could not have done the same.

This difficulty applies to the evaluation of any complex symbolic production. Consider the four following examples from the writer's own experience.

1. As the concluding section of a three-hour-long examination for a course in the Department of Social Relations at Harvard University, we asked the following question of the students (both Radcliffe and Harvard students were included in the class):

"In Part I of his 'Notes from the Underground,' Dostoevski supposes a world in which 'the psychologists' shall have finally catalogued all the responses of which human beings are capable, and all the functional relationships among such responses, so that, given the history of the entire series of events in the life of a person, or a complete description of his state at a given moment, all his subsequent actions would be predictable. Dostoevski supposes such a world in order to deny the possibility of its existence, for there is always, he says, an 'except'—a final, unpredictable, unclassifiable element, which will never behave according to rational formula and in the interest of calculated advantage. And so into the state of unrelieved order and prosperity that he had imagined, Dostoevski injects 'a gentleman with an ignoble, or rather with a reactionary and ironical, countenance,' who arises and 'putting his arms akimbo says to us all: I say, gentlemen, hadn't we better kick over the whole show and scatter rationalism to the winds, simply to send these logarithms to the devil, and to enable us to live once more at our own sweet foolish will?' "

In the audience to whom this question is addressed there are sitting a factorially complex factor analyst and a thoroughly analyzed and simplified psychoanalyst. The factor analyst turns to the psychoanalyst and whispers, "He's just the sort of person who would say that." "Yes," replies the psychoanalyst with an air of secret knowledge, "and at just this moment too."

What is there left now for the gentleman with the ignoble or perhaps reactionary and ironical countenance to say?

This final question in the examination, which was otherwise conventional in content and easily graded, was received without alarm or undue notice by most of the class, who answered it at length with varying degrees of originality. The response most difficult to evaluate, however, was the following, in its entirety, by a Harvard student: "Nothing; but if he were a Radcliffe girl he would fill two more blue books."

2. A graduate student who was serving as a subject in an assessment study was asked to construct a mosaic out of 1-inch-square pieces of colored cardboard, each piece being solid-colored with a dozen or so colors available. The instructions were to build the mosaic design in a defined area rectangular in shape, the dimensions being 8 inches in height and 10 inches in width. This particular subject, however, turned the frame around, so that the vertical dimension was 10 inches and the horizontal dimension 8 inches. He then proceeded to construct a question mark in yellow on a light gray background.

3. Another research subject was presented with cards of the Rorschach Psychodiagnostic, a set of inkblots of somewhat ambiguous form, and was asked to tell what he saw in each blot. Unlike most subjects who take the test card and look at the blot straight-on, he proceeded to inspect the card edgewise and even to bend cards in the middle to produce alterations in the area he could see. He gave responses never before heard of by the examining psychologist, a veteran of several thousand Rorschach testings.

4. A subject in a study of dreaming reported no dreams with visual content; all her dreams were of voices.

In all these cases, the rater or raters were in a quandary as to how to evaluate the response. In the study of dreams, for example, the dreams of 150 subjects had been rated for originality with very high inter-rater agreement, but this particular subject's dreams were rated either quite high or quite low. The Rorschach scorer was certain that his subject's responses were "originals," for the test manual defines an original response as one that occurs no more often than once in 100 examinations; but whether to score the responses 0+ (a "good" original) or

0– (an original response that does not sufficiently respect the inkblot reality) was difficult to decide. The artists who later rated a large set of mosaics gathered in similar fashion from research subjects gave the "question-mark" a very low rating, feeling that it was simply manneristic and that the subject had not really done the job he was asked to do. One of the readers of the course examination gave the student a "D" for his response to that question, while another reader graded it "A."

This point is made at such length because of its crucial importance in the evaluation of the creative act. The merely eccentric is not creative, even though it is in a statistical sense uncommon. But at the same time one must be wary of dismissing all eccentricity that is tinged with mannerism as "mere eccentricity." As we have written elsewhere (Barron, 1963) in response to a question put by the late Albert Deutsch:

> People who think oddly often act and dress oddly as well, although this is by no means always true. As children, creative people frequently realize that in some way they are different from those around them, and this inner difference in perception may readily give rise, intentionally or unintentionally, to outer differences. Sometimes, of course, the outer differences go along hand-in-glove with the inner. It is only when a person puts on differences, when he tries self-consciously to act or dress differently, that we begin to wonder whether the eccentricity is superficial and simply an act. In important movements in art, there are usually a certain number of untalented hangers-on who talk, dress, and act like the real artists, and may even be accepted as real artists, but who actually do not create. Frequently, however, the genuine artist or creative scientist is really distinctive in bearing, dress and manner; therefore it would be a mistake to interpret even consciously adopted eccentricities as pretentious. The unusual individual often feels isolated, and he may be pardoned for flying the flag of his individuality."

In brief, in scoring tests of creativity in which considerable latitude of interpretation is permitted both the testee and the evaluator or assessor, it is a good policy to be lenient in accepting the "far-out" response. Still, the optimal practical situation is one in which a derivative measure, one not requiring a creative behavior, can be employed with equal accuracy. If careful and complex ratings can be done just once, and then correlates of those ratings discovered in mechanically scored questionnaires, the problems of objectivity, large scale sampling, and replicability will be solved.

All the behaviors that presented these difficulties of evaluation were, it should be noted, "free responses," and the possibility of variation in response was quite considerable. Is it not too much to expect that a set of responses whose possibilities are rigidly limited and predetermined by the tester could tap such dimensions as esthetic sensitivity (as the mosaic designs test is thought to do), or independence of judgment, or originality?

To answer this question we shall have to get a bit ahead of our story by citing partial results of substantive investigations rather than limiting ourselves at this point to methods of measurement. In practice, of course, the development of methods and their refinement by the scrutiny of initial results always went along together, so it is not unnatural that in this account of a developing program of research they should do the same.

We shall take as examples some of the efforts at the Institute of Personality Assessment and Research to measure the three variables discussed above: esthetic discrimination, independence of judgment, and originality.

## ESTHETIC DISCRIMINATION

From the outset of our work on the psychology of creativity we had posited *sensitivity to esthetic values* as an important index to creative potential. We assembled a variety of tests of "good taste" and constructed several others of our own, all of them consisting of materials such as paintings, sculptured forms, pictures of building or of furniture, geometric figures, and so on; in brief, artifacts that arouse in the observer the esthetic sentiment and which readily elicit expressions of *like* or *dislike*.

The materials that we finally found most useful were the line drawings that comprised the Welsh Figure Preference Test. In 1948 George Welsh, then a graduate student at the University of Minnesota, had attempted to develop a non-verbal analogue to the Minnesota Multiphasic Personality Inventory (MMPI). For this purpose, he had assembled several hundred line drawings, both ruled and free-hand, constructed in black ink on 3-by-5-inch white cards. One hundred and forty-three persons, including 6 artists, were asked to sort these figures into 2 classes, those they *liked* and those they *disliked*.

A factor analysis of the standardization group sortings showed that two factors accounted for most of the variance in the scores: an acceptance-rejection factor (general tendency of the subject either to *like* or to *dislike* the figures, identified by number of items in "don't like"), and a second bipolar factor, orthogonal to the first, whose poles (as determined by inspection of the figures) seemed to be simplicity-symmetry and complexity-asymmetry.

In other words, there are some drawings about which people agree: if one person likes them, almost everyone will like them, and vice-versa. But also, there are some drawings about which people disagree: they are either liked very much or disliked very much. These drawings define the bipolar factor and may be said to divide people into two camps.

When one looks at the drawings that arouse such strong disagreement, one sees that some people are especially fond of simple and symmetrical designs, while others much prefer complex and asymmetrical ones. The simple-symmetrical figures usually are drawn according to some easily recognized geometrical principle, and they are described by such adjectives as clean, regular, neat, well-ordered; the complex-asymmetrical figures are more commonly freehand drawings and may be described as dynamic, irregular, whimsical, complicated, messy, or even chaotic.

Because he was interested mainly in individual differences,

and especially in how esthetic choice is related to personality, Welsh extended his analysis of the data to an investigation of the personalities of those who preferred simple-symmetrical figures as contrasted with those who preferred the complex-asymmetrical. The persons themselves proved as groups to be as different from one another as the figures they preferred, and in rather similar ways. Those who preferred the simple figures to the exclusion of the complex ones were described by other people as conservative, organized, conventional, occasionally even rigid; those who preferred the complex figures and rejected the simple figures (and this included all the artists in the sample) were described by such terms as unconventional, original, dynamic, and sometimes as radical and rebellious. There seem to be both positive and negative aspects of each kind of preference (Barron, 1953).

Several implications of these findings suggested themselves. In the first place, the artists may have clustered together at the complex-asymmetrical pole simply because their critical artistic judgment led them to prefer figures that in fact better satisfied certain principles of composition. On the other hand, the artists may have been very like one another in personality, obtaining similar scores chiefly because the test tapped those personality variables in which they were alike. Then again, there may exist some higher-order determinant of both artistic taste and personality style, with both of the lower-order variables having found expression in these test scores.

It seemed that a systematic exploration of these possibilities should begin with a comparison of the figure preferences of artists and non-artists. A necessary condition for the confirmation of any one of the three possibilities was that artists and non-artists must differ significantly in their preferences for the figures. If that condition were established, then one could seek to discover whether the observed differences were due to: (a) simple differences in esthetic judgment; (b) simple differences in the personalities of artists and non-artists; or (c) related differences in both esthetic judgment and personality. At this point the present writer entered the research and carried through the next step in conjunction with Welsh.

In addition to the theoretical interest in a comparison of the figure preferences of artists and non-artists, there was of course the important methodological advantage for future research to be gained from the construction of an objective, easily obtained measure of artistic discrimination. Previous work in the field of personality testing suggested that the use of external criterion groups would best insure the derivation of a valid measure. With the dual aim, then, of constructing a scale of artistic discrimination while, at the same time, discovering what systematic differences in figure preferences might exist between artists and non-artists, the set of figures used in the previous study, expanded now to a total of 400 such drawings, was given to a group of artists, 37 in all. As in the previous study, they were asked to indicate which ones they preferred. An analysis then was made to discover which figures were liked more often by artists and which by non-artists.

It became clear immediately that artists preferred the complex-asymmetrical figures significantly more often, while in comparison with artists the man on the street preferred simple-symmetrical figures. Sixty-five figures were found to be especially differentiating, and these were therefore made to constitute a scale, called later the Barron-Welsh Art Scale, in which preferences similar to those of artists brought a high score.

When applied back again to the original standardization group, this scale separated the artists from the non-artists quite effectively. The average score of the non-artists was 16.9 of a possible score of 65; the average score of the artists was 40.25. The observed difference was so great that it would occur by chance less than one time out of a thousand. Only four of the 150 non-artists scored above the average of the artists.

When the scale was tested on two new groups, 30 artists and 30 non-artists, it again discriminated the groups effectively. The averages in this cross-validation sample were 18.37 for the non-artists and 39.07 for the artists. Again the artists differ significantly from the non-artists at a level of confidence beyond .001. Only 4 of the 30 artists scored below the average of the non-artists, and only 5 of the non-artists scored above the average of the artists. The scale appeared therefore to give promise as a valid test at least of the propensity to become an artist.

When the scale was tested on 2 new groups, 30 artists and 30 non-artists, it again discriminated the groups effectively. The means of the cross-validation samples were 18.37 for the non-artists, and 39.07 for the artists. These values do not differ significantly from the comparable values in the original standardization groups. They do, however, differ significantly from one another (critical ratio of 3.97, level of confidence better than .001). Four of the 30 artists scored below the mean of the 30 non-artists, while 5 of the non-artists scored above the mean of the artists. Eight artists and 22 non-artists scored below the mean of the total distribution. In a new sample of 80 non-artists, the reliability of the scale, as determined by correlating the odd-numbered items with the even-numbered, was .96. In a further study of reliability, 26 group psychotherapy patients at the Kaiser Foundation Hospital in Oakland, California, were administered the scale a second time after an interval of 6 months. The test-retest reliability was .91. This highly satisfactory estimate of reliability, as well as the early validity evidence, were encouraging indications that a useful scale had resulted from the approach we had adopted.

Experience with the scale in the years since then has borne out this expectation. Further validity evidence will be presented when appropriate in this chapter. Meanwhile, an inspection of Table 1.1 will show in terms of group averages that the interpretation of the scale as relevant to the esthetic factor in creativity is a reasonable one.

Table 1.1 shows means and standard deviations on the Barron-Welsh Art Scale for various samples of subjects studied at the Institute of Personality Assessment and Research from 1950 to the present.

TABLE 1.1. MEAN SCORES ON THE BARRON-WELSH ART SCALE FOR THE SAMPLES INDICATED

| *Sample* | *Number of subjects* | *Mean* | *Standard deviation* |
|---|---|---|---|
| Artists (standardization group)* | 80 | 40.3 | 12.9 |
| Artists (first cross-validation group)* | 30 | 39.1 | 13.8 |
| Architects I ("creative" architects) | 40 | 37.1 | 9.8 |
| Mills College "creatives" | 21 | 35.86 | 7.6 |
| Writers ("creative") | 19 | 32.9 | 11.1 |
| Team members of first American expedition to attempt Mount Everest | 15 | 31.5 | 12.1 |
| Mills College "controls" | 30 | 30.9 | 11.0 |
| Research scientists I ("creative" scientists) | 15 | 30.7 | 6.3 |
| Architects II (comparison sample for creative architects above) | 43 | 29.5 | 10.1 |
| Women mathematicians I ("creative") | 16 | 28.1 | 12.5 |
| Women mathematicians II ("representative") | 28 | 26.9 | 15.4 |
| Men mathematicians I ("creative") | 26 | 26.9 | 12.7 |
| Architects III ("representative" American architects) | 41 | 26.1 | 12.1 |
| Research scientists II ("less creative") | 15 | 22.1 | 14.1 |
| Men mathematicians II ("less creative") | 21 | 19.4 | 10.1 |
| Scientists III ("least creative") | 15 | 19.2 | 8.7 |
| Unselected adult males | 343 | 13.9 | 11.2 |

* After the initial standardization, 3 items were found to be nondiscriminating on further item-analysis and therefore were dropped from the scale, which now consists of 62 items, 38 *disliked* by artists and 24 *liked* by artists.

Personality correlates of this scale, as determined in several subsequent studies, may be summed up briefly as follows:

1. Artistic preference is related positively to rapid personal tempo, verbal fluency, impulsiveness, and expansiveness.
2. It is related negatively to rigidity, control of impulse by repression, social conformity, ethnocentrism, and political-economic conservatism.

3. It is related positively to independence of judgment, originality, and breadth of interest.

## INDEPENDENCE OF JUDGMENT

A situational test to measure independence of judgment or, conversely, susceptibility to conformity pressures, in the face of a false group consensus was developed by one of the Institute's staff members, Richard S. Crutchfield, for use in the living-in assessment setting. It will be remembered that in living-in assessment the subjects of study are brought together in groups of 5 or 10 in the assessment house, where they make their residence for 2 or 3 days.

The Crutchfield technique is an adaptation for this particular setting of an experimental procedure used earlier by Solomon Asch in his well-known studies of independence of judgment (1952). The basic experimental technique employed by Asch was to place an individual in radical conflict of judgment with all the other members of a group and to express quantitatively certain aspects of his mode of resolution of the conflict.

Here is a prototypic situation in one of the Asch experiments: there are 8 ostensible subjects in a perceptual discrimination problem, all seated in a row, all of whom are asked to respond orally one at a time in a sequence determined by the seating arrangement. Of these 8 ostensible subjects, however, only 1 is naïve; the rest are confederates of the experimenter, and in conspiracy with him they produce the crucial conflict situation. The apparent experimental task is to judge which of 3 lines of variable length meets a standard line; or, to state it otherwise, to match the length of a given line with 1 of 3 other lines not equal to one another. The naïve subject is so placed that he will always be one of the last respondents. On the critical trials, the hired majority gives a prearranged false answer.

In the living-in assessment situation, this experiment is not feasible, since each assessee is himself a subject of study. The Asch experiment also suffers from certain limitations because of the nature of the stimulus material, which permits of only 1 "true" answer; susceptibility to influence in judgments in which reality is less unambiguous cannot be studied under this condition.

In the Crutchfield technique, subjects are seated in groups of 5 in front of an apparatus consisting of 5 adjacent electrical panels. Each subject can see the face of the panel directly in front of him, but cannot see the panels of the other 4 subjects. Each panel contains five rows of signal lights, labeled A,B,C,D, and E. The experimenter explains that the panels themselves may receive similar designations, as A,B,C,D, or E, and that the subject at Panel A, for example, may send information to the other subjects by throwing switches provided for him at the bottom of his panel. This information would appear on the other panels in the form of green signal lights in the row labeled A. If the subject at Panel B threw the switches on his panel, lights would appear on the other panels in the rows labeled B, and so on. The subjects were informed that the designation of their panel, as A,B,C,D, or E, would change throughout the experiment and that they would know what panel they had at any given time by the appearance of a red signal light to the left of the appropriate letter.

Slides were now projected on a wall directly facing the subjects. Each slide called for some judgment by the subject. He was instructed to indicate his choice of one of several multiple-alternative answers by closing the appropriately numbered switch on his panel. The subjects were further instructed that the person at Panel A was to respond first, followed by B,C,D, and E *in order*. Thus each subject was able to see from the pattern of lights on his panel what answers were being given by the other subjects.

On the critical trials, in which the subjects were to be put under pressure to conform, the red light appeared on every panel to the left of E. Thus each subject thought himself called upon to respond *last*. The experimenter, through a device of wiring that enabled him to control the signal lights on all the panels, now put in prearranged false answers in rows A,B,C, and D. If the subject now agreed with the false answer apparently being given by his fellow subjects, he was said to *yield;* if he gave the right answer, he was said to have remained *independent*. Thus the basic psychological situation in the Asch experiment was reproduced, but with much greater flexibility inherent in the experimental procedure, and with more potential for rigor in the control of variables.

Scores for independence of judgment in the Crutchfield technique had a possible range from 0 to 21, and the kinds of judgments called for in the critical trials were more varied than in the Asch experiment, which used only line judgments. Crutchfield asked for judgments on areas of figures, logical completion of number series, vocabulary items, estimates of the opinions of others, expression of attitudes on controversial issues, esthetic preferences and so on. (See Crutchfield, 1955, 1962, and 1963, for a full description of the technique and its results.)

This experimental measure, like the Barron-Welsh Art Scale, is important because it places the subject in a situation where he is called upon *to choose*, and moreover to choose in terms of values that are central to his way of being. It is interesting as a sidelight on the centrality of esthetic choice that figures of the Art Scale are more impervious to pressure from a fabricated consensus in the Crutchfield procedure than are any other stimulus materials; although about 75 percent of all subjects will yield to group pressure in other matters, less than 10 percent will yield when the judgment involves simple-symmetrical figures versus complex-asymmetrical ones.

The personality correlates of independence of judgment have been described for the Asch experiment in a 1953 paper by the present writer (1953), and for the Crutchfield experiment in the several papers by Crutchfield. They bear an interesting relationship to the findings that emerge in studies of the correlates of originality and creativity, as we shall see. Stated briefly, they are as follows: the independent individual sometimes gives an appearance of greater instability than the individual who conforms, but actually he scores higher on various measures of inner resources and of ego strength; he tends to value creative work and is receptive to new ideas, even when they are at first apparently impractical or controversial; he is like artists in his esthetic preferences; when deprived of some of the usual perceptual cues by which we orient ourselves spatially he is less perplexed and can continue to make accurate spatial judgments; and he scores somewhat higher on standardized tests of intelligence, but the difference is slight and accounts for no more than 10 percent of the variance one observes in reaction to conformity pressures. Independence of judgment is thus in part a matter of personal stance and reflects social and individual values in ethics and in esthetics.

In exploring further the correlates of independence of judgment, the present writer used a technique which combined hypothesis-testing as to the meaning of the criterion variable with new-scale development that could provide an additional objective and easily scored measure of the variable in question. Remember the general tactical problem in this area of psychological measurement: to develop mechanically scorable tests that can be administered to large groups and for which reliable standard scores can readily be derived.

The goal chosen by the investigator in this instance was the development of a personality inventory scale of the True-False variety; that is, a set of simple declarative sentences to which the testee could respond either True or False. Such sentences should of course be constructed so as to reflect the dynamic quality and the centrality of the criterion variable itself; in this case, being able to give the right answer when everyone around you is giving the wrong, and where there is at least implicit pressure to agree with the consensus. The experiment devised by Asch, let it be noted, is one step away from the real-life situation, and Crutchfield in fact called his own procedure a "quasi-group interaction technique." A questionnaire is even further removed from "real" behavior. This makes the problem all the more challenging for the questionnaire item-writer or item-gatherer, since many relevant items already exist in the literature. The need is to find or invent items that are able to stir within the respondent the feelings or the motivational organization that produced the significant act.

The testing situation itself as the situational context for the new behavior, that is, answering an item True or False, must also be taken into account. Thus while the questionnaire seems to call for self-report, it need not do so naïvely. The item may represent a guess on the part of the experimenter that a certain kind of person will in the testing situation assent to a certain kind of sentence; it need not matter whether the subject is reporting correctly on his own experience or actual opinions, since the guess made by the psychologist takes the situational context into account. Items may be written with different degrees of clarity or ambiguity of meaning, and it is possible to embody considerable projective elements in a seemingly objective questionnaire.

On the whole, however, the questionnaire-maker does expect that self-report will occur and will be fairly accurate and candid. Very often the subject himself will be so positive about his response that he can hardly conceive that another individual will respond differently. This phenomenon has been noted repeatedly in testing individuals with the Figure Preference Art Scale, and it occurs also in attitude questionnaires if one goes over the subject's responses with him one at a time to see whether he cannot be induced to change his answer.

With these considerations in mind, the present writer developed a set of 84 items hypothesized by himself and Asch to be relevant to independence of judgment in the Asch experiment. The items were given as a questionnaire to Asch's subjects, and the correctness of the hypothesis embodied in each item was checked by determining whether subjects who answered it in the hypothesized direction had in fact been independent under pressure.

The great majority of the hypotheses proved to be correct. Indeed, when the items were now made to constitute a scale by selecting those which in fact differentiated Independents from Yielders at the .01 level of confidence, 20 out of 22 differentiating items were answered in the hypothesized direction. The resulting scale and direction of scored response is given below, and the two items that did not turn out as hypothesized are noted.

*At the* .01 *level:*

(1) What the youth needs most is strict discipline, rugged determination, and the will to work and fight for family and country. (False)

(2) Some of my friends think that my ideas are impractical, if not a bit wild. (True)

(3) Kindness and generosity are the most important qualities for a wife to have. (False)

(4) I have seen some things so sad that I almost felt like crying. (True)

(5) I don't understand how men in some European countries can be so demonstrative to one another. (False)

(6) I must admit that I would find it hard to have for a close friend a person whose manners or appearance made him somewhat repulsive, no matter how brilliant or kind he might be. (False)

(7) A person should not probe too deeply into his own and other people's feelings, but take things as they are. (False)

(8) I prefer team games to games in which one individual competes against another. (False)

(9) I could cut my moorings—quit my home, my family, and my friends—without suffering great regrets. (True)

*At the .05 level:*

(10) What this country needs most, more than laws and political programs, is a few courageous, tireless, devoted leaders in whom the people can put their faith. (False)

(11) I acquired a strong interest in intellectual and esthetic matters from my mother. (False) (Contrary to hypothesis)

(12) Human nature being what it is, there will always be war and conflict. (True) (Contrary to hypothesis)

(13) I believe you should ignore other people's faults and make an effort to get along with almost everyone. (False)

(14) The best theory is the one that has the best practical applications. (False)

(15) I like to fool around with new ideas, even if they turn out later to be a total waste of time. (True)

(16) The unfinished and the imperfect often have greater appeal for me than the completed and polished. (True)

(17) I would rather have a few intense friendships than a great many friendly but casual relationships. (True)

(18) Perfect balance is the essence of all good composition. (False)

(19) Science should have as much to say about moral values as religion does. (True)

(20) The happy person tends always to be poised, courteous, outgoing, and emotionally controlled. (False)

(21) Young people sometimes get rebellious ideas, but as they grow up they ought to get over them and settle down. (False)

(22) It is easy for me to take orders and do what I am told. (False)

Such questionnaire scale development, then, is another tactic that can be used successfully in preparing for the task of discovering the correlates of creativity. Essentially it consists in developing an instrument of observation based on a tentative theory and capable of giving extensive observations when applied in further research.

## ORIGINALITY

The Independence of Judgment scale is a questionnaire or inventory-type scale developed in two steps: (1) the culling or inventing of items which on the basis of theory were hypothesized to relate to independent behavior in an experiment designed to simulate or reproduce in essence a common real-life conflict situation requiring serious choice; and (2) the selection from such an a priori scale of those items, and only those items, that did in fact prove to be significantly related to the behavior in question—in this case, remaining independent when under implicit group pressure to conform to a false group opinion.

Inventory-type scales to measure "the disposition toward originality" were also developed at the Institute, but by a method that differed from the above in an important way. In Step 1 the items were not chosen on an a priori basis; theory played no part in making items eligible for inclusion in the scale. Instead, a very large number of items written for some other purpose were routinely correlated with scores or ratings on tests designed to elicit originality of response to a specific problem. The resulting set of correlation coefficients was then scrutinized for statistically significant degrees of association, and the items revealed by this scrutiny were selected for inclusion in the scale.

We shall present examples of two such scales: one drawn from the items of the Strong Vocational Interest Blank (Strong, 1943), and the other drawn from items comprising the California Psychological Inventory (Gough, 1957).

The initial form of both these scales utilized as a criterion of originality a measure that consisted of the summed standard scores on 8 separate performance measures that purported to elicit behaviors relevant to originality. The sum of the 8 measures was dubbed "Composite Originality," and its full correlates have been reported elsewhere (Barron, 1957); we shall have occasion to refer to them later when we discuss the relationship of originality to intelligence. The sample under study consisted of 100 military officers who took part in 3 days of living-in assessment at the Institute.

Three of the eight tests that were presumed to measure originality (or at any rate to provide the medium for its expression by the respondents and its discernment by raters) were developed by Wilson, Guilford *et al.* (1953) and have been shown by them to emerge with high loadings on a factor identifiable as originality. (The Guilford tests are discussed more fully in the next section of this chapter.) The three tests are: (a) Unusual Uses; (b) Consequences B; (c) Plot Titles B. Unusual Uses calls upon the *S* to list 6 uses to which each of several common objects can be put, and it is scored for infrequency, in the sample under study, of the uses proposed. In Consequences B the respondent is asked to write down what would happen if certain changes were suddenly to take place, and a score reflecting the cleverness or remoteness of the consequences suggested is obtained. In Plot Titles B the *S*'s score is the number of clever, as opposed to obvious or ordinary, titles he suggests for 2 story plots.

In addition to the 3 tests from the Guilford creativity battery, 2 standard projective tests, the Rorschach (1942) and the Thematic Apperception Test (TAT) were used. The Rorschach 0+ count was taken as one measure of originality, and the TAT scores were rated for originality by two raters working independently. A sixth test measure was provided by a Rorschach-like set of inkblots which had been developed by the present writer to measure the threshold for the human movement response (1955), but which in this context was scored simply for infrequency of the percepts reported by the *S* in protocols of the sample studied. A count of highly infrequent but correct anagram solutions to the test word "generation" provided a seventh measure; and a rating of the originality of a story composed by the *S*, in which he was called upon to use all the words in a standard list of 50 randomly selected common nouns, adjectives, and adverbs provided the eighth. These measures, their reliabilities, and their interrelations have been described in the report already cited (Barron, 1957).

The Strong Vocational Interest Blank (SVIB) is designed to measure the similarity of a respondent's interests to the interests of successful members of some 40 different vocations. To this end, it asks direct questions about the sorts of activities one likes to engage in, ranging from school subjects to social activities to hobbies; the sorts of people one likes; and the kinds of vocational roles one would enjoy. The respondent indicates in order of preference that he *likes, dislikes*, or *is indifferent to* the prospect presented.

To select items for the Originality scale, we now compared the 27 most original officers (as determined by scores on the Originality Composite) with the 27 least original. Eighty-five items were discovered which had significant associations (at the .05 level of confidence) with Composite Originality. Since it could be expected that many of these had occurred by chance, a cross-validation, or a check on the findings in a second sample, was desirable. The only comparable sample readily available was a group of 242 military officers of the same rank who had taken Tests 1, 2, 3, and 7 of the Originality Composite. The 85 items resulting from the first analysis were therefore checked for significant associations in this second sample. Of the 85 items found initially, 36 did not have significant correlations with the criterion while 49 continued to do so. These 49 items were therefore chosen for inclusion in the final version of the scale.

It will be noted that the second criterion was forced to omit the more perceptual, as opposed to verbal, of the originality measures. To be on the safe side, therefore, we called the scale a measure of the disposition toward originality in verbal expression or, more simply, *Verbal Originality*.

While it would not be appropriate to present the entire scale here, its content, in terms of the values of persons who are original in verbal expression, may be summarized as follows.

*Vocations.* They like such vocational roles as actor, artist, consul, editor, and musician, and they would dislike being a factory manager, a jeweler, a mining superintendent, a rancher, a toolmaker, or a watchmaker; they would either like or be indifferent to, but at any rate not dislike being a magazine writer; and they would either dislike or be indifferent to the job of office clerk; to the job of wholesaler they would simply be indifferent.

*School subjects.* They like Art, Botany, Dramatics, English Composition, Geology, Music, Philosophy, Public Speaking, and Zoology, and they either like or are indifferent to but do not dislike Literature; they dislike only Physical Training.

*Leisure-time activities.* They like tennis but dislike hunting and fishing; they like full-dress affairs and symphony concerts but they dislike making a radio set and are indifferent to adjusting a carburetor and repairing electrical wiring; they like to argue, make speeches, interview clients, organize a play, or be pitted against someone else in a political or athletic race.

*Miscellaneous.* They like optimists, but they dislike or are indifferent to religious people; they are indifferent to whether their work is outside or inside, but they would rather read a book than go to a movie, be a headwaiter rather than a lighthouse tender, and be a policeman rather than a fireman. They usually start activities of their group, have more than their share of novel ideas, and can write a concise, well-organized report.

The final 49-item version of this Verbal Originality Scale of the Strong Vocational Interest Blank was found to correlate .64 with Composite Originality on the first sample of 100 officers and .43 with the second composite criterion on the sample of 242 officers.

Other scales, consisting of True-False items from such inventories as the California Psychological Inventory (Gough, 1957) and the Minnesota Multiphasic Personality Inventory (Hathaway and McKinley, 1943) were developed in similar fashion. A total of 132 items (out of an item pool of 957 items) correlated significantly at the .05 level of confidence with the four-measure composite score for verbal originality. A scale composed of items from the California Psychological Inventory alone may serve as an example comparable to the SVIB scale. The kinds of opinions, interests, and preferences expressed by persons high on Verbal Originality are as follows.

*Verbal and intellectual interests and skills.* They like work involving the use of words, such as teaching school, being a journalist, or, more adventurously, being a foreign correspondent. They like to talk before groups of people and to belong to discussion clubs; they have at one time or another written poetry; they read fast, talk well, and they *like* to read and to talk.

*Persuasiveness and self-assertion.* They have strong political opinions, and they describe themselves as persuasive, decisive, generally in charge of things; they are "strong personalities"; they confess that they wouldn't mind fighting in a boxing match. The self-assertion may even shade off into a fondness for personal exhibition: they like to be the center of attention, to show off a bit now and then. They would like the profession of acting.

*Candidness.* They admit to various imperfections and difficulties: their home life was not always pleasant; they don't always tell the truth; they can remember "playing sick" in order to get out of something. They see some faults in the American way of life, and they say that disobedience to government is sometimes justified.

The validity of the Originality Composite upon which the scale derivation is based may be seen both from its correlation with a staff rating of Originality, given of course without knowledge of the subjects' scores on the test measures (the staff ratings were based entirely on observations of social behavior and of group discussions, charades, and improvisations) and its correlates with staff Q-sorts and adjective descriptions of the subjects.

The correlation with the averaged staff rating of Originality, based on ratings by 11 psychologists of the originality of 100 military officers each of whom had been seen for 3 days of living-in assessment, is .55. This is one of the highest validity coefficients we have observed for any set of test predictors assembled on an a priori basis.

The 25 highest scorers on the Originality Composite were compared with the 25 lowest scorers on both the Q-sort descriptions and the adjective checklist (Gough, 1962). The Q-sort items that showed statistically significant differences follow. The results for the high scorers were:

*At the* .001 *level:*

1. Verbally fluent, conversationally facile
2. High degree of intellect
3. Communicates ideas clearly and effectively
4. Highly cathects intellectual activity
5. Is an effective leader
6. Is persuasive; wins others over to this point of view

*At the* .01 *level:*

7. Is concerned with philosophical problems and the meaning of life
8. Takes an ascendant role in his relations with others

The low scorers revealed the following characteristics:

*At the* .001 *level:*

1. Conforming; tends to do the things that are prescribed
2. Is stereotyped and unoriginal in his approach to problems

3. Has a narrow range of interests
4. Tends not to become involved in things
5. Lacks social poise and presence
6. Is unaware of his own social stimulus value

*At the* .01 *level:*

7. Slow personal tempo
8. With respect to authority, is submissive, compliant, and overly accepting
9. Lacks confidence in self
10. Is rigid, inflexible
11. Lacks insight into own motives
12. Is suggestible
13. Is unable to make decisions without vacillation, hesitation, and delay

Adjectives that were applied differentially (at the .05 level or better) by the assessment staff to high and low scorers are given below, with the frequencies (number of cases out of 25 to which the adjective was applied) stated in parentheses after the adjective. Frequencies for the high scorers were:

interests wide (12-1)
clever (9-1)
imaginative (9-1)
planful (9-1)
poised (11-2)
determined (10-2)
talkative (10-2)
logical (9-2)
rational (9-2)
shrewd (9-2)
civilized (8-2)
loyal (8-2)
mature (8-2)
versatile (7-0)
efficient (14-3)
initiative (13-3)
resourceful (12-3)
reflective (9-3)
quick (9-3)
enterprising (11-4)
energetic (10-4)
organized (10-4)
fair-minded (13-6)

For the low scorers, the frequencies were:

| | |
|---|---|
| dull (0-8) | apathetic (1-8) |
| commonplace (1-11) | rigid (1-7) |
| simple (1-11) | unassuming (5-12) |
| slow (1-10) | conventional (7-13) |

These Q-sort and adjective descriptions support once again the validity of the Originality Composite. In brief, high scorers are seen as intelligent, widely informed, concerned with basic problems, clever and imaginative, socially effective and personally dominant, verbally fluent, and possessed of initiative. Low scorers are seen as conforming, rigid and stereotyped, uninsightful, commonplace, apathetic, and dull.

The contribution of verbal ability to this set of correlated personality traits is clearly considerable. Since we were interested especially in originality as distinct from verbal intelligence or facility in verbal comprehension, it seemed desirable to remove statistically the effect of verbal ability upon the correlations between the Originality Composite and the other assessment measures. When the relationship of these other measures to the Concept Mastery Test is partialed out, the statistically significant partial *r*'s shown in Table 1.2 are discovered. (In Table 1.2 the variables are grouped, and the groups named, simply in a way that makes sense subjectively to the present writer; these are not clusters established statistically.)

The best single measure of verbal intelligence used in the study was the Concept Mastery Test (Terman and Odin, 1947). It was significantly correlated with the Originality Composite (Pearsonian *r* of .33). Thus, part of the observed correlates of the latter might well be due to verbal intelligence alone. By applying partial correlation techniques it proved possible to identify clearly the variables related to originality when verbal intelligence was held constant. Six clusters of variables emerged from this analysis. In Table 1.2 the variables themselves are

TABLE 1.2. Variables Significantly Associated with the Originality Composite when Concept Mastery Test Scores Are Partialed Out

| | *Partial r's* |
|---|---|
| Disposition toward integration of diverse stimuli: | |
| 1. Rorschach: W | .52 |
| 2. Rorschach: number of different determinants used | .37 |
| 3. Idea Classification Test: number of classes discerned in sets of varied objects and properties | .31 |
| Energy, fluent output, involvement: | |
| 4. Improvisations: degree of participation | .35 |
| 5. Word Fluency Test: total output | .41 |
| 6. Charades: motility | .39 |
| 7. Charades: fluency | .28 |
| 8. Staff rating: fluency of ideas | .49 |
| 9. Staff rating: drive | .42 |
| Personal dominance and self-assertion: | |
| 10. Improvisations: dominance | .37 |
| 11. Staff rating: dominance | .37 |
| 12. CPI: Dominance scale | .29 |
| 13. Personal Preference Scale: Active Phallic | .47 |
| Responsiveness to impulse and emotion: | |
| 14. CPI: Impulsivity scale | .39 |
| 15. Block Ego-control Scale: undercontrol | .40 |
| 16. Rorschach: sum C | .38 |
| Expressed femininity of interests: | |
| 17. Charades: over-all performance | .39 |
| 18. Improvisations: total effectiveness | .34 |
| 19. Staff rating: Over-all effectiveness in command functions in the Air Force | .36 |
| 20. Staff rating: Over-all effectiveness in staff function in the Air Force | .37 |
| General effectiveness of performance: | |
| 21. SVIB: Masculinity | −.31 |
| 22. MMPI: Femininity (Mf) | .33 |
| 23. Personal Preference Scale: Feminine Identification | .30 |

named and the partial *r*'s are given; in the paragraphs below each cluster is discussed in terms of the *meaning* of the variables.

*Disposition toward integration of diverse stimuli.* This was shown on the Rorschach inkblot test in two ways: the subject's tendency to interpret the blot as a whole rather than to attend to details in isolation, and his tendency to use many aspects of the blot in his interpretations, such as color, shape, textural qualities such as mottling, suggestions of motion, and so on. It was also shown in performance on a test where the subject was presented with many varied objects and asked to classify them in as many ways as possible; the ability to see many classes goes along with originality even when verbal intelligence is not operative.

What this cluster suggests is an openness in the more original *S*s to a variety of phenomena, combined with a strong need to organize those phenomena into some coherent pattern. This might best be described as a resistance to premature closure, combined with a persistent effort to achieve closure in an elegant fashion. In brief, everything that can be perceived must be taken cognizance of before a configuration is recognized as a possibly final one.

*Energy, fluent output, involvement.* This was shown in social behavior, in games such as charades, in a word fluency test, and in a psychodrama where each *S* acted out a part that he was creating as he went along; the more original *S*'s had been rated as much more participative in the psychodrama, and as having more fluency, drive, and behavioral output as shown in other ways.

This cluster would seem to indicate a higher level of drive, as well as ease of expression of the drive in work. This might well be a generic factor that shows itself interpersonally in the form of dominance and striving for power. The behavior apparently is effective as well, judging from the correlations with various ratings of effectiveness of performance.

*Personal dominance and self-assertion.* This was shown by scores on the Dominance scale of the California Psychological Inventory, by staff ratings of Dominance, and by scores on a scale to measure so-called "phallic" behavior.

*Responsiveness to impulse and emotion.* This was shown on the Rorschach by a tendency to use color freely in interpreting the blot, which according to Rorschach theory is related to emotional spontaneity; on the California Psychological Inventory by high scores on the Impulsivity Scale (later renamed the Self-control Scale and of course scored backwards); and on another inventory scale designed to measure control of impulse, with the finding again being that the more original subjects tended to be more impulsive.

*General effectiveness of performance.* This was shown particularly in staff ratings of the officer's potential for both command and staff functions in the Air Force. The more original officers were rated as being probably more effective. They were also more effective in psychodrama and in charades.

*Expressed femininity of interests.* This was shown in several test performances, including the Minnesota Multiphasic Personality Inventory and the Strong Vocational Interest Blank. More original men expressed interests that are more typical of women than of men in our society. Yet the high scorers on the Originality Composite were of normal masculinity, or perhaps even more masculine than the average, by the usual behavioral standards. Perhaps "integration of diverse stimuli" is involved here. In a sense, the recognition by men of impulses or interests that are considered more appropriate in women, or at least more characteristic of women than of men in this culture, may be seen as one aspect of the more basic disposition toward inclusiveness and complex integration. A firmly established personal identity should be most free of the social stereotypes of masculinity and femininity.

The question itself is a complex one, however, and we shall return to it later and treat at greater length of the perplexing problem of creativity and sexual identity. Meanwhile, still another approach to the development of differential measurement within the domain of creative-thinking abilities must be considered. This is the factor analytic approach, deriving mostly from the work of the British psychologists, Karl Pearson, Charles Spearman, and Cyril Burt. It has been represented most substantially in recent years in research on creativity by Raymond B. Cattell and J. P. Guilford.

## THE FACTOR ANALYTIC APPROACH

When in 1950 Professor Guilford marked his retirement as president of the American Psychological Association by listing and describing several dozen possible new tests in the general domain of creative thinking, few in the audience of psychologists who sat quietly through what to many seemed a boringly detailed enumeration of untried intellectual tasks realized that what was to be retired was not Professor Guilford but the concept of the IQ. It was not news that many intellectual abilities were quite specific in the sense that they might be possessed to an outstanding degree by an individual undistinguished for general intellectual power, but not very many had grasped the fact that an entire domain of intellectual abilities of the utmost importance had been excluded from consideration by the builders of standardized tests designed to measure "intellectual quotient," presumably a single comprehensive summary of general intellectual ability.

The excluded intellectual abilities were precisely those that are important in the production of new ideas, or broadly speaking, in psychic creation. What Guilford was proposing was that a full picture of the structure of intellect required a comprehensive study of many abilities for which useful tests did not then exist; he suggested that psychology as a scientific discipline needed to multiply instruments of observation in the area of intellectual abilities in order to study the factorial composition of intelligence and hence to begin differentiating the structure of intellect. Since from the first it had appeared to him that creative-thinking abilities were largely untapped in current intelligence tests, he offered ideas for the construction of such tests.

Guilford and his associates in the Project on Aptitudes of

High-level Personnel, University of Southern California, went on from the construction of new tests to the study of their relationship to well-known "marker" tests for established factors in intellectual functioning. By subjecting to factor analysis a matrix of intercorrelations of some 54 test measures covering 8 abilities hypothesized as being important in creative thinking, they succeeded in identifying 7 creativity factors in addition to 7 already established and expected factors in perception and cognition in general. The 7 creativity factors were named as follows: associational fluency, ideational fluency, originality, adaptive flexibility, spontaneous flexibility, redefinition, and sensitivity to problems.

At the time these results became generally available, the Institute of Personality Assessment and Research (IPAR) was planning its study, by the living-in assessment method, of the 100 military officers. The results of this study with regard to correlates of the Originality Composite have just been described. It will be remembered that several of the tests that make up the Originality Composite were drawn from the Guilford battery on the basis of their loadings on the Originality factor. Three tests with high loadings on the Originality factor were chosen: Unusual Uses, Plot Titles, and Consequences.

In addition to this use of the results of the factor analytic approach, it was considered desirable to bring the Guilford findings from these short and simple tests into relationship with the complex data of living-in assessment. To this end, a collaboration was proposed and carried through, whereby the Project on Aptitudes of High-Level Personnel would make available to the Institute a selected battery of the newly developed tests for factors in creativity, and the Institute in turn would make available to the Project a set of ratings, based on three days of observation of the subjects, of variables closely related to the creativity factors, as well as sets of scores on other tests that might serve to extend the meaning of the factors.

The IPAR staff ratings were given at the end of the three-day, living-in assessment period. Three trait ratings especially were named and defined in such a way as to make them relevant to the Guilford work: Originality, Adaptive Flexibility, and Fluency of Ideas. The definitions of these variables used by the staff raters are as follows.

*Originality.* "Originality and creativity in thinking and in approaches to practical problems; constructive ingenuity; ability to set aside established conventions and procedures when appropriate."

*Adaptive flexibility.* "Ability to adapt one's approach to meet changing conditions; openness to new ideas. Ability to take a new approach in an attempt to obtain a solution if the approach previously being used has failed to bring about the desired result."

*Fluency of ideas.* "Ability to produce rapidly a lot of ideas when one is faced with a question or problem. For this trait it does not matter whether the ideas are good or not; it is the number of ideas per unit of time that counts here."

These definitions do not differentiate as sharply among the three traits as the corresponding factor definitions do. The rating on Adaptive Flexibility, for example, has more reference to novelty of approach than does the factor definition, which stresses change of set but with rather more emphasis on taking a *different and more effective* tack than on taking a *new* tack. The rating on Adaptive Flexibility does in fact correlate .76 with the rating on Originality, and also .76 with the rating on Fluency of Ideas. Originality in turn correlates .85 with Fluency of Ideas.

Regardless of the extent to which differential measurement of these 3 factors by the factor tests is reproduced by staff ratings, some idea of the validity of the tests and of the ratings may be obtained by considering the correlations between the factor tests and the corresponding ratings based on 3 days of observation of the subjects in living-in assessments. These correlations are shown in Table 1.3.

TABLE 1.3. CORRELATIONS BETWEEN STAFF RATINGS AND CORRESPONDING FACTOR TESTS*

| *Staff rating* | *Unusual uses* | *Consequences B* | *Plot titles B* | *Consequences A* | *Plot titles A* | *Match problems* | *Controlled associations* |
|---|---|---|---|---|---|---|---|
| 1. Originality | .30 | .35 | .32 | .16 | .09 | .10 | .35 |
| 2. Adaptive Flexibility | .33 | .28 | .26 | .27 | .04 | .15 | .37 |
| 3. Fluency of Ideas | .32 | .34 | .26 | .21 | .07 | .07 | .32 |

* Correlations between factor-test scores and corresponding factor ratings have been underlined.

The relationship of the Originality rating to the four tests having significant loadings on the Originality factor is certainly an important confirmation of the validity of the factor and of the tests that measure it. The multiple correlation of the 4 factor tests with the staff rating on Originality is .45. This is a reasonably satisfactory degree of relationship, which indicates that the prospects are good of developing a battery of short, objective, easily administered tests that require a minimum of skilled time but which correlate highly with ratings based on several days of observation by skilled observers. (See Barron, 1957, 1958, for tests subsequently developed for this battery.)

The rating of Adaptive Flexibility, it will be noted, produces correlations substantially like those of the Originality rating, as was expected from the .85 correlation between the two ratings. It is fair to say that Adaptive Flexibility as the latter is defined in the earlier factor analytic investigation was essentially not rated in this study; apparently what *was* being rated in the three ratings under consideration was some complex trait that might best be called the fluent production of original ideas. Differentiation of these traits can perhaps best be achieved by tests especially designed to call for one ability at a time. Ratings of complex social behavior are bound to be more highly intercorrelated than tests that have isolated the appropriate variables and measured them reliably. These findings cannot therefore be construed as showing valid differential measurement by the factor tests; what they do show is that the Originality factor was probably correctly named, and that the tests for it do have substantial variance in Originality as the latter is discerned by psychologists who observe subjects behaving socially. Or to turn the matter about, these data provide evidence that originality as rated by psychologists from social behavior of the subjects is significantly correlated with operationally defined originality of response in a test situation.

However, the matter is far from unambiguous, since most of the factor tests are not univocal, usually having more than one significant factor loading. It might be the case, for example, that one part of the variance in the Originality rating which is associated with variance in the Controlled Associations Test is actually associated with that part of the variance in the latter which is unrelated to the loading of the Controlled Association Test on the Originality factor. Perhaps it is the Associational Fluency variance in Controlled Associations which is producing the correlation of the test with the Originality rating. Clearly what is required is a factor analysis in which not only test scores but also relevant ratings are included.

A further factor analysis was therefore carried out, but since the sample size was relatively small and there were numerous ambiguities of interpretation, the analysis was not considered sufficiently well based to warrant firm conclusions. What did emerge from an analysis of 34 variables, including the eight Guilford factor-test measures and a variety of IPAR measures and ratings, was a moderately strong confirmation of such previously discovered factors as Verbal Comprehension, Originality, Adaptive Flexibility, Word Fluency, Ideational Fluency, Expressional Fluency, Spontaneous Flexibility, and Redefinition. Several tests used regularly as part of the IPAR battery strengthened the understanding of these factors: the Gottschaldt Figures Test for the Adaptive Flexibility factor, the

Arthur Stencil Design Test for the Redefinition factor, the Word Rearrangement Test for the Word Fluency factor, and the Concept Mastery Test for Verbal Comprehension. Moreover, a Complexity factor emerged, its highest loading being on the Barron-Welsh Art Scale.

In this further analysis the staff ratings had most of their variance absorbed by a Staff Rating factor, which in part no doubt reflects the usual halo effect. On the basis of other evidence, however, the Staff Rating factor was interpretable as a second-order creativity factor observable uniquely in complex social interaction and different in kind from test-evidenced creativity.

The interested reader may find a detailed technical report of the factor analysis in Barron *et al.*, 1957, and a description of the assessment variables in MacKinnon *et al.*, 1958.

The joint study here described served to illustrate some of the difficulties of interpretation that beset all efforts at differentiating the structure of a domain of abilities. By bringing the Guilford creativity factor tests into conjunction with the data of the living-in assessment ratings, as well as with certain test measures that ordinarily would not have been used in common with the type of short, group-administered tests depended upon most heavily by Guilford and his associates, the study sought to advance both approaches. Guilford's work on the structure of intellect has proceeded apace and is now considerably more complex than it was at the time of this study; the approach to creativity through the study of the personalities of highly creative individuals has also advanced vigorously in its own way. It is the findings of the latter approach that we shall now consider.

# THE STUDY OF HIGHLY CREATIVE PERSONS

With considerable work already accomplished in the development of simple measures and the exploration of their interrelationships and their external correlates, the Institute staff turned to a method of study of exceptional promise but full of challenge and difficulties: the study by the living-in assessment method of highly creative individuals whose accomplishments in the arts and sciences had already brought them renown.

It had of course long been recognized that the study of genius was the most direct psychological approach to an understanding of the genetic and environmental forces contributing to superior achievement. Sir Francis Galton (1869) had shown the way in this as in many other areas of the psychology of individual differences by his forthright approach to biographical material in a hunt for evidence of hereditary predisposition. The volume in which his work was summed up, *Hereditary Genius* (1869), remains the most systematic and provocative analysis of the effect of family lineage on the appearance of high talent. In *Hereditary Genius* he relied on biographies for his raw data; he followed that work immediately with a study of 180 contemporary scientists to whom he sent questionnaires about their family backgrounds and their experiences in childhood, and the tabulations he made from their responses to the questions he had put to them were published in 1874 in his *English Men of Science: Their Nature and Nurture*.

It was to Galton that the monumental work of James McKeen Cattell, issuing as it has in *American Men of Science*, owes its inspiration; Cattell employed a combination of the questionnaire method and a criterion of eminence based not on biography but on current reputation within the community of science, a system of evaluation based on "voting" by one's peers which has resulted in the system of "starring" those scientists listed in American Men of Science who are judged to have attained eminence by this criterion. Cattell also developed a method for establishing relative degrees of eminence of historical personages and by it assembled a list of carefully ranked *1000 Eminent Men.*

Galton's work with life histories was followed on the Continent by a rash of biographical studies of men of genius, many of them written from a psychiatric point of view and with a strong emphasis on psychopathology; these so-called "pathographies of genius" helped draw clinic and drawing room together in the consensus that "great wits are sure to madness near allied," as Dryden, following Seneca, had said. Havelock Ellis turned from such slanted interpretations of individual life histories to a more objective and statistical method based on a specific criterion of eminence (space devoted to the biographee in the *Dictionary of National Biography*), and his detailed analysis of over 900 eminent lives (*British Men of Genius*, 1904) showed that the incidence of psychosis among them was certainly no greater than in the general population. (A very readable though not quite so systematic recent study, *Cradles of Eminence* (Goertzel and Goertzel, 1962), makes the point even more strongly; the incidence of psychosis was found to be considerably lower among the eminent, although eccentric behavior and various forms of behavioral pathology other than psychosis, including suicide, are much more common.)

These early studies thus broke new ground in establishing a method of investigation, and they lent two distinctive substantive emphases as well: (1) to the relationship between rare creative abilities and mental illness, or, more broadly, the relationship between intellectual talents and individual personality; and (2) to the relative contribution of environment, especially early environment, and heredity. These methods and these emphases came together to give form to the living-in assessment studies of highly creative contemporary authors, architects, and mathematicians in the years 1957-1962 at the Institute of Personality Assessment and Research.

## ARCHITECTS

As a model of the systematic development of criterion information, we shall present first a study of the professional group selected for intensive investigation at the midpoint of the Institute's program: American master architects. A study of renowned writers chosen for their originality had already been completed, and studies of several other groups had been launched, all these under the direction of various staff members of the Institute (Richard S. Crutchfield, Harrison G. Gough, Ravenna Helson, and the present writer). The study of architects was undertaken by Donald W. MacKinnon, director of the over-all program of research, and Wallace B. Hall. Although each study differed slightly from the others, this particular investigation combined the features of all and may properly be considered a prototype.

The first step in the definition of a sample was establishment of a rule for deciding who should be considered highly creative in the field of architecture. Recourse was had to the "nomination and voting" method introduced by Cattell. Five senior architects of the faculty of the College of Architecture at the University of California, Berkeley, were asked individually to nominate, without consulting with one another, the 40 most creative architects in the United States, and then to rate each of the 40 relative to all the others. The following deliberately loose definition of creativity in architecture was given as a working guide: "originality of thinking and freshness of approach to architectural problems; constructive ingenuity; ability to set aside established conventions and procedures when appropriate; a flair for devising effective and original fulfillments of the major demands of architecture: the demands of technology, visual form, planning, human awareness, and social purpose."

With the task thus set for them, the 5 nominators produced a total of 86 names; of these, 13 were nominated by all five members of the panel, 9 by four members, 11 by three, 13 by two, and exactly 40, as it happened, by single panel members. All the modern giants of American architecture who were active at that time were included in this listing.

The initial request for 40 names was linked somehow to a decision on the part of the staff that 40 subjects would be studied by the living-in assessment method, although in retrospect it seems likely that some unanalyzed weakness for number magic must have lain behind this decision rather than any rational basis for choosing a right number for sampling. (We have, it seems, almost always studied either 40 cases or 100 cases.) In any event, 86 names were now on the invitation list, with 40 guests desired. Subjects were now informed of their nomination, and their cooperation was sought, beginning with the most frequently nominated. Sixty-four in all were invited before the desired complement of 40 was filled.

The question naturally arises, was there any tendency for the more, or perhaps the less, creative to turn down the invitation? To check on this, the ratings of each of the 86 architects by the nominating panel were now re-examined and the 40 who had decided to take part in the research were compared with the 24 who had decided (for quite a variety of good reasons, it might be added) not to participate. The average ratings for the two groups were found to be virtually identical: in standard score terms, 50.00 (standard deviation 9.9) for the 24 not assessed, and 50.1 (standard deviation 9.5) for the 40 who did participate in the study.

To check further on this point, since it is such a crucial one in the selection of a sample, 11 editors of the major American architectural journals, *Architectural Forum*, *Architectural Record*, *Journal of the American Institute of Architects*, and *Progressive Architecture*, were asked to rank the 64 invited architects from most to least creative. These ranks too were converted to standard scores and average values for each architect determined; when the mean of the 40 assessed architects was compared now with the mean of the 24 who were invited but did not participate, the difference was slight and not statistically significant (51.9 for the 24; 48.7 for the 40). The slight difference that did exist could be accounted for by one case: that famous non-attender, Frank Lloyd Wright!

The architects who did take part in the assessment were also asked to rate one another (and to include themselves in the sample they were rating). Interestingly, their averaged evaluations of one another correlated .88 with the average evaluation of them by the 11 editors of architectural journals. This is an extremely high degree of agreement and approaches the reliability coefficient of the ratings themselves. It leaves little doubt that the criterion of creativity is a highly accurate one. With such fine discriminations even among the most select of master architects, the chances are very good of establishing a valid picture from the pattern of correlations with assessment variables.

The logic of the research design called for more than just correlations within a highly select sample, however. When the range of variation in the criterion variable has been so radically restricted, we can expect markedly lower estimates, from observations in such a selected sample, of the true degree of association between the criterion and its potential predictors than we might find if the entire population of architects were studied. So, even if no correlations were to appear between such ratings of creativity and the assessment variables, there might still be revealed certain group traits relevant to creative personality when the highly creative were compared with other architects unselected for creativity.

To put this another way, we might say that a comparison group of representative architects is essential if we are to be certain that the characteristics of highly creative architects are related to their creativity rather than to the fact of their being architects. And we might add that if the differences between highly creative and indifferently creative architects are similar to the correlations we find within the highly creative sample, we have strong additional grounds for believing that such differences are related to creativity.

Accordingly, another sample of architects was drawn by locating in the *Directory of Architects* 41 architects who were not numbered among the 86 earlier nominees but who were identical with them in age and in geographic location of practice. Then a further group of 43 was drawn for additional comparative purposes by adding the requirement that they should have at least 2 years of work experience and association with one of the nominated creative architects.

Thus three samples were drawn: (1) representative architects who were entirely unselected for creativity; (2) highly creative and renowned architects; and (3) architects undistinguished for creativity who nevertheless had shared space and time closely with a creative architect, and who in some sense might be thought of as "near misses."

MacKinnon and Hall, having employed both the nomination and voting technique as well as ratings, and having sampled finely to achieve interesting comparison groups, now added the further step of establishing an index of eminence by measurement of the amount of printer's ink of which the individual had been found worthy. Taking references in the *Architectural Index* as their criterion, they computed: (a) a weighted index of the number of articles by or about each architect and his work in the years 1950-1958; and (b) a weighted index of the number of pages devoted to the architect and his work for that same period. A comparison of representative with creative architects shows a clear difference.

| | *Articles by or about each architect* | *Pages* |
|---|---|---|
| Representative Architects | 2 | 3 |
| Creative Architects | 97 | 131 |

Finally, in order to be absolutely sure that these groups chosen for comparison purposes were really different in creativity, all 124 architects were cast into a single list. This list was then sent to 19 professors of architecture throughout the United States, as well as to the 5 professors of architecture who comprised the original nominating panel. It was also sent to every architect on the list itself, and to 6 editors of the major architectural journals. All these individuals were asked to rate all 124 architects on a 7-point scale in terms of creativity.

The results, when all ratings were averaged appropriately, were quite clear-cut; the "creative architects" as designated above were markedly superior to the other 2 groups, and the comparison group was significantly (the observed difference would occur by chance less than 1 time in 1000) more creative than the group of representative architects.

A valid criterion can therefore fairly be said to have been established. Not only is the sample of creative architects unique, since it includes a high percentage of the most distinguished architects of the United States, but even within such a distinguished group it proved possible to make fine discriminations in terms of creative ability. A criterion of this sort augurs well for the task of discovering associated patterns of temperament, motivation, and intellectual ability.

## WRITERS AND MATHEMATICIANS

Two other groups of eminent individuals were studied by the living-in assessment method: writers and mathematicians. The study of writers, which came first in this sequence of researches, suffered from some of the vicissitudes of initial research. For psychologists to attempt to study the creative process through first-hand contact with highly creative persons in a research setting was something new. There was by no means any assurance that such individuals would consider it worth their time and effort to make the trip to Berkeley and to spend 3 days taking tests. Although they were to be offered an honorarium, in itself it could not compensate them for their time. The seriousness of the enterprise was of course vouched for by the reputation of the University of California, and also by the sponsorship of the Carnegie Corporation, as well as by the positions of responsibility held by staff members of the Institute; but to some creative writers, for whom the stuff of both literature and life was revolt against society and contempt for the "academy," these vouchsafers were but red flags before the bull. One of the creative writers who was invited because of his early importance in the "beat" literature of the preceding decade was so little impressed by the seriousness of intent on the part of the psychologists that he used the invitation to garner a commission from *The Nation* for a piece, "The Vivisection of a Poet," exposing the folly of the study (Rexroth, 1958). Testy reactions to the first letter of invitation were not uncommon, and in some cases an exchange of four or five letters occurred before the creative writer decided whether or not to participate.

Student writers taking courses in creative writing were even touchier than their elders, and university professors teaching courses in creative writing were the most sensitive of all. On one occasion the psychologist in charge of the research, seeking the help of student writers for a study preliminary to the work with writers of high reputation, was permitted to address his request to a creative writing class, but was introduced by the instructor with this remark, "So far as I am concerned I would like to see all psychologists buried with Freud and Jung in a boxcar a hundred feet deep," evidence of an associational process so intriguing that the bemused psychologist forgot for a moment why he was there.

But it was possible to remain philosophical about such rebuffs and to get on with the task. These of course were the extreme reactions of distaste, and they were not typical even of the invited writers who did not elect to participate in the research. Actually, architects too produced a few denunciatory rejections of the whole idea of such research, although among them, as among writers, the majority recognized the possible worth of the study and were willing to put themselves out in order to make a contribution to it. MacKinnon (1962) spoke of this as follows in the 1962 Walter Van Dyke Bingham Lecture:

"The response of creative persons to the invitation to reveal themselves under such trying circumstances has varied considerably. At the one extreme there have been those who replied in anger at what they perceived to be the audacity of psychologists in presuming to study so ineffable and mysterious a thing as the creative process and so sensitive a being as a creative person. At the other extreme were those who replied courteously and warmheartedly, welcoming the invitation to be studied, and manifesting an eagerness to contribute to a better understanding of the creative person and the creative process."

It seemed, indeed, that the very greatest of the writers, who were great human beings as well, found the three days of living-in assessment profoundly engaging. Most seriously they entered into the task of looking at their work in relation to their lives and their deepest self. The psychologists and psychiatrists who interviewed these writers about their work and their life had of course studied the work intensively beforehand, that they might know the most significant questions to ask.

In all, a total of 56 writers participated in the research, out of 101 who were invited. Of these 56 writers, 30 were writers of high reputation whose names had been secured by a similar process to that already described for the architect study. Three professors of English, themselves creative writers, and one editor of a literary review, were asked to suggest names of writers who should be invited to take part, although they were not, as the architect nominators were, asked to suggest a specific number. Their nominations did show considerable agreement among themselves, however, and a list was drawn up consisting of 48 writers who had been suggested by at least 2 nominators. These writers were accordingly invited, and 26 of them accepted the invitation. Of these 26, only 17 finally did come to Berkeley for the living-in assessments, because of difficulties of scheduling groups; some last minute changes resulted in filling out the groups with 3 writers who had been nominated by only 1 nominator. Later, 10 other writers were seen either individually at Berkeley or in their own homes, giving a total of 30 participants in this phase of the research.

A comparison group was chosen from California writers who were members of a writers' association; these writers did not participate in living-in assessment, however. Most of the statistical comparisons to be drawn, therefore, will be based upon test data obtained from the comparison group by mail. The writers' study itself must be considered incomplete at this point and a full report on it will not be attempted here, but it does yield enough interesting data to justify a preliminary report.

The study of mathematicians also suffers from a certain lack of symmetry in the design, again stemming from practical difficulties. A total of 48 male mathematicians and 44 female mathematicians participated. The men, however, did not take part in living-in assessments, but were administered the test battery individually by the project director, Richard S. Crutchfield. The 44 women were studied by the living-in assessment method under the direction of Ravenna Helson.

Of the male sample, 26 were nominated as unusually creative by a panel of fellow mathematicians, while 22 were considered competent representatives of the profession (all held the Ph.D. in mathematics from reputable universities). The female sample is believed to include virtually every productive woman mathematician in the United States and Canada. Again a nomination technique was used to obtain the list of subjects to be invited; in this case, it consisted of 52 individuals, of whom only 8 declined to, or were not able to, participate. The 44 participants were later rated by mathematicians in their own research specialties throughout the United States. From these ratings and accumulated professional opinions it seemed clear that 16 of the women mathematicians stood out from the rest of the sample as being the most original and important women mathematicians in this country and Canada; the data analysis therefore concentrates on observed differences between them and the other 28 in terms of performance in living-in assessment. (Incidentally, it should be noted that fully half of the creative women mathematicians, as was true also of the men, are foreign-born. Visher's (1947) study of men starred in American Men of Science shows that the percentage of eminent men who are foreign-born is higher in mathematics (32 percent) than in scientific fields as a whole (17 percent).)

We turn now to a sampling of the results of these studies. A comprehensive review of the results must await publication of full reports on each study separately, and these are not yet available. Even a thorough first-level correlational analysis based on test measures in relationship to the criterion ratings has not yet appeared in print. Nevertheless, from several papers (Gough and Woodworth, 1960; Helson, 1965, in press; Hall, 1958), as well as from an earlier chapter in a book by the present writer (Barron, 1963) and from the mimeographed proceedings of the University Extension conference at which the first public reporting of results was made by the entire Institute staff (MacKinnon *et al.*, 1961), it is possible to pull together a wealth of findings that are of scientific interest even though they have not yet been cross-validated.

Let us begin with staff descriptions of highly creative individuals as contrasted with less creative or merely representative members of the same profession. The assessment of women mathematicians can readily be made to yield such data, since 16 women of unusual creative ability were assessed, together with 28 women undistinguished for creativity. The assessment staff was of course kept in ignorance of the ratings, and, besides, eminent women mathematicians, unlike eminent architects or writers, are rarely known by reputation to anyone outside the profession. None of the psychologists except the project director had any grounds for identifying a given subject as one of the nominated "creatives." Consequently, the staff adjective descriptions and Q-sorts obtained from the assessment staff immediately upon conclusion of the three days of assessment were free of bias and preconceptions; the task was simply to give a candid and objective description of each assessee, and the assessee's standing in terms of nominations or criterion ratings was unknown. The results of the Gough Adjective Checklist analysis are presented in Table 1.4, and of the Block Q-sort analysis in Table 1.5.

TABLE 1.4. Staff Adjective Descriptions of Women Mathematicians

| *Creative women mathematicians* | *Representative women mathematicians* |
|---|---|
| *at .01 level:* | |
| individualistic | cheerful |
| original | |
| preoccupied | |
| *at .05 level:* | |
| artistic | active |
| complicated | appreciative |
| courageous | considerate |
| emotional | conventional |
| imaginative | cooperative |
| self-centered | helpful |
| | obliging |
| | organized |
| | practical |
| | realistic |
| | reliable |
| | sympathetic |

The emphasis is upon genuine unconventionality, high intellectual ability, vividness or even flamboyance of character, moodiness and preoccupation, courage, and self-centeredness. These are people who stand out, and who probably are willing to strike out if impelled to do so. Creative people have an edge to them, it would seem from these first results.

Since no comparison group was available for the living-in

TABLE 1.5. Clinical Q-sort Items Correlated with Creativity

| *r with creativity rating* | *Q-sort item* |
|---|---|
| *Positive correlations:* | |
| .64 | Thinks and associates to ideas in unusual ways; has unconventional thought processes. |
| .55 | Is an interesting, arresting person. |
| .51 | Tends to be rebellious and nonconforming. |
| .49 | Genuinely values intellectual and cognitive matters. |
| .46 | Appears to have a high degree of intellectual capacity. |
| .42 | Is self-dramatizing; histrionic. |
| .40 | Has fluctuating moods. |
| *Negative correlations:* | |
| −.62 | Judges self and others in conventional terms like "popularity," the "correct thing to do," "social pressures," and so forth. |
| −.45 | Is a genuinely dependable and responsible person. |
| −.43 | Behaves in a sympathetic or considerate manner. |
| −.40 | Favors conservative values in a variety of areas. |
| −.40 | Is moralistic. |

assessment portion of the study of writers, it is not possible to present comparable Q-sort data for them. However, the composite staff description does convey a picture of their personal style. The items whose averaged Q-sort values were either 9 or 8 on a 9-point scale are given in Table 1.6.

TABLE 1.6. Composite Staff Q-sort Description of Creative Writers

*9's*

Appears to have a high degree of intellectual capacity.
Genuinely values intellectual and cognitive matters.
Values own independence and autonomy.
Is verbally fluent; can express ideas well.
Enjoys esthetic impressions; is esthetically reactive.

*8's*

Is productive; gets things done.
Is concerned with philosophical problems; for example, religion, values, the meaning of life, and so forth.
Has high aspiration level for self.
Has a wide range of interests.
Thinks and associates to ideas in unusual ways; has unconventional thought processes.
Is an interesting, arresting person.
Appears straightforward, forthright, candid in dealings with others.
Behaves in an ethically consistent manner; is consistent with own personal standards.

This composite Staff Q-sort description of writers is not altogether unique to writers, however; a somewhat similar picture emerges in the staff's description of creative architects. Of these 13 "most descriptive" sentences, 8 are also among the most descriptive for architects; the notable exceptions, pertaining to writers but not to architects, are: "is verbally fluent; can express ideas well"; "is concerned with philosophical problems"; "thinks and associates to ideas in unusual ways"; "is an interesting, arresting person"; and "appears straightforward, forthright, candid in dealings with others." These items are replaced, in the staff description of architects, by the following:

"enjoys sensuous experiences (including touch, taste, smell, physical contact)"; "has social poise and presence; appears socially at ease"; "is a genuinely dependable and responsible person"; "is critical, skeptical, not easily impressed"; and "concerned with own adequacy as a person, either at conscious or unconscious levels." (This latter item, it should be added, does appear in the fifteenth place for the writers as well, and it reflects for both groups a common finding from both interviews and psychological test results. The evidence is convergent from a number of sources: creative individuals are very much concerned about their personal adequacy, and one of their strongest motivations is to prove themselves.)

The differences between creative writers and creative architects do make good sense. Architects are businessmen as well as artists, and they convey a sense of practicality, dependability, and social ease that one does not find among creative writers, on the whole. Also, architects are not notably fluent talkers, though of course there are some striking exceptions; the architect is more likely to be sensitive to physical materials and to sense impressions than to the flow of ideas in words. Writers are dramatists or singers, architects are builders and designers, and so one finds consistent differences in their style of being creative; but the two groups are alike in being productive and in having high standards, a wide range of interests, high intellectual ability and a high valuation of the role of intellect in human affairs, a definite sense of personal independence, and an internally consistent ethical basis for action.

So much for staff description; but what do personality and intelligence tests themselves show? What basis is there for thinking that creative individuals have an unusual amount of concern for their own adequacy as persons? What is the psychometric evidence in terms of measures of psychopathology, such as tendencies towards neurosis and psychosis? And what of intelligence? Do the tests of intellectual aptitude used in the research support the notion that creative individuals as a class are of high intellectual ability? How important is measured intelligence in determining originality, and what contribution do motivational and temperamental variables distinct from intelligence make to creativity?

For at least partial answers to these questions, we turn to the results obtained from the use of objective tests. First, there are such questionnaires as the Minnesota Multiphasic Personality Inventory and the California Psychological Inventory, as well as the Type Indicator based on C. G. Jung's theory of psychological types, to give some idea of the differences between creative individuals and comparison groups from the same professions in terms of personality traits, both normal and abnormal. Consider first the evidence from the MMPI, which yields measures on such psychiatric dimensions as Depression, Hypochondriasis, Hysteria, Psychopathic Deviation, Paranoia, Psychasthenia, and Hypomania.

The MMPI comparisons for the samples of mathematicians are among the data not yet available in published form, but we do have such information for both writers and architects. The creative groups consistently emerge as having *more* psychopathology than do the more representative members of the same profession. The *average* creative writer, in fact, is in the upper 15 percent of the general population on *all* measures of psychopathology furnished by this test! The average creative architect is less markedly deviant, but still is consistently and substantially higher than the average for the general population on these indices of psychopathological dispositions. (See MacKinnon *et al.*, 1961, for statistics in the architect sample; the relevant average scores of the two groups of writers on the MMPI are shown in Table 1.7.)

From these data one might be led to conclude that creative writers are, as the common man has long suspected them to be, a bit "dotty." And of course it has always been a matter of pride in self-consciously artistic and intellectual circles to be, at the least, eccentric. "Mad as a hatter" is a term of high praise when applied to a person of marked intellectual endowments.

TABLE 1.7. AVERAGE MMPI SCORES OF CREATIVE AND REPRESENTATIVE WRITERS

| *MMPI Scale* | *Creative Writers* | *Representative Writers* |
|---|---|---|
| L | 47 | 45 |
| F | 62 | 55 |
| K | 56 | 54 |
| Hypochondriasis | 63 | 57 |
| Depression | 65 | 59 |
| Hysteria | 68 | 58 |
| Psychopathic Deviation | 65 | 56 |
| Paranoia | 61 | 57 |
| Psychasthenia | 64 | 55 |
| Schizophrenia | 67 | 56 |
| Hypomania | 61 | 51 |
| Ego-strength | 58 | 52 |

But the "divine madness" that the Greeks considered a gift of the gods and an essential ingredient in the poet was not, like psychosis, something subtracted from normality; rather, it was something added. Genuine psychosis is stifling and imprisoning; the divine madness is a liberation from "the consensus."

If this is so, then we should expect to find evidence of an enhancement of ego strength in our creative individuals, so that greater psychopathology and greater personal effectiveness would exist side by side. Psychometrically, such a pattern would be quite unusual; the Ego-strength scale of the MMPI, for example, correlates −.60 with Schizophrenia in the general population, and −.50 with such other variables as Hysteria, Hypochondriasis, and Psychopathic Deviation.

Nevertheless, just such an unusual pattern is found, not only in relation to ego strength but in relation to the scales of the California Psychological Inventory, most of which are themselves aspects of ego strength and negatively related to the psychopathological dimensions measured by the MMPI. The average Ego-strength score for the nominated creatives among the writers is 58, and among the creative architects is 61. In brief, they are almost as superior to the general population in ego strength as they are deviant on such pathological dispositions as Schizophrenia, Depression, Hysteria, and Psychopathic Deviation. This finding is reinforced by evidence from the California Psychological Inventory, as shown in Table 1.8, which also gives the mean scores of the representative professionals for comparison purposes.

These CPI profiles are indicative of a high degree of personal effectiveness. Creative writers are outstanding in terms of flexibility, psychological-mindedness, and the ability to achieve through independent effort as opposed to achievement through conformance; they are high also in self-acceptance, social participativeness, and capacity for gaining high social status. Creative architects are outstanding in rather similar ways: in self-acceptance, in capacity for status, in achievement through independence, in flexibility, in social participativeness, and in personal dominance.

Of this unusual patterning of psychopathology and personal effectiveness we have written elsewhere (1963) as follows:

". . . if one is to take these tests results seriously, (creative individuals) appear to be both sicker and healthier psychologically than people in general. Or, to put it another way, they are much more troubled psychologically, but they also have far greater resources with which to deal with their troubles. This jibes rather well with their social behavior, as a matter of fact. They are clearly effective people who handle themselves with pride and distinctiveness, but the face they turn to the world is sometimes one of pain, often of protest, sometimes of distance and withdrawal; and certainly they are emotional. All of these are, of course, the intensely normal traits indicated by the peaks on their profile of diagnostic scores."

"The CPI profiles reveal also certain consistent differences between the highly creative and less creative members of the two professions. In both writing and architecture, the more creative individuals are more self-accepting and more flexible. Yet they score lower on socialization and on self-control, report less 'sense of well-being,' and on a scale that was developed to measure 'effort to make a good impression' they score significantly lower than the general population. This latter finding probably goes along with their lower scores on "achievement through conformance." On the

TABLE 1.8

| *CPI scale* | *Creative architects* | *Representative architects* | *Creative writers* | *Representative writers* | *Creative women mathematicians* | *Representative women mathematicians* |
|---|---|---|---|---|---|---|
| Dominance | 59 | 56 | 55 | 54 | 46 | 50 |
| Capacity for status | 60 | 57 | 60 | 57 | 52 | 54 |
| Sociability | 48 | 51 | 52 | 49 | 42 | 47 |
| Social participation | 58 | 53 | 60 | 57 | 52 | 52 |
| Self-acceptance | 61 | 56 | 63 | 54 | 44 | 51 |
| Sense of well-being | 48 | 54 | 41 | 48 | 50 | 50 |
| Responsibility | 51 | 54 | 52 | 50 | 55 | 55 |
| Socialization | 47 | 52 | 42 | 46 | 45 | 48 |
| Self-control | 45 | 53 | 45 | 52 | 51 | 53 |
| Tolerance | 50 | 54 | 53 | 47 | 56 | 56 |
| Good impression | 43 | 52 | 44 | 51 | 46 | 47 |
| Communality | 48 | 53 | 49 | 51 | 41 | 47 |
| Achievement thru conformance | 50 | 56 | 50 | 54 | 46 | 54 |
| Achievement thru independence | 59 | 58 | 63 | 60 | 65 | 64 |
| Intellectual efficiency | 51 | 54 | 54 | 52 | 54 | 55 |
| Psychological-mindedness | 61 | 57 | 60 | 59 | 68 | 65 |
| Flexibility | 59 | 51 | 60 | 55 | 69 | 56 |
| Femininity | 57 | 52 | 62 | 55 | 53 | 49 |

independence of judgment scale described earlier, being creative in the profession is substantially correlated with greater independence; the correlation is .43 in the architect total sample, and among the writers there is a highly significant difference in that direction. The average score of the general populaton on the Independence of Judgment scale is 8.12; representative writers scored 11.69, and creative writers 15.69."

In terms of C. G. Jung's theory of psychological types, there are again consistent differences between the more creative and the less creative members of these two professions. Creative writers and creative architects are markedly "intuitive" as opposed to "sensation" types, and are "perceptual" rather than "judging" in their orientations; in both respects they are different both from the general population and their professional colleagues. These findings are based on the Myers-Briggs Type Indicator, a questionnaire developed from Jung's theories and following quite closely his formulation in his book *Psychological Types*. This questionnaire yields scores on Introversion-Extraversion, Feeling-Thinking, Judging-Perceiving, and Intuition vs. Sensation. Only 25 percent of the general population is classified as "intuition" types by this test, yet 100 percent of the creative architects (as opposed to 59 percent of representative architects) and 92 percent of creative writers (as opposed to 84 percent of representative writers) were so classified. In terms of perception vs. judgment, 58 percent of the creative architects are the former, compared with 17 percent of representative architects.

MacKinnon discusses these test findings as follows (1962):

"Employing the language of the test, though in doing so I oversimplify both it and the theory upon which it is based, one might say that whenever a person uses his mind for any purpose, he performs either an act of perception (he becomes aware of something) or an act of judgment (he comes to a conclusion about something). And most persons tend to show a rather consistent preference for and greater pleasure in one or the other of these, preferring either to perceive or to judge, though everyone both perceives and judges.

"An habitual preference for the judging attitude may lead to some prejudging and at the very least to the living of a life that is orderly, controlled, and carefully planned. A preference for the perceptive attitude results in a life that is more open to experience both from within and from without, and characterized by flexibility and spontaneity. A judging type places more emphasis upon the control and regulation of experience, while a perceptive type is inclined to be more open and receptive to all experience.

"The majority of our creative writers, mathematicians, and architects are perceptive types. Only among research scientists do we find the majority to be judging types, and even in this group it is interesting to note that there is a positive correlation (.25) between a scientist's preference for perception and his rated creativity as a scientific researcher. For architects, preference for perception correlates .41 with rated creativity.

"The second preference measured by the Type Indicator is for one of two types of perception: sense perception or sensation, which is a direct becoming aware of things by way of the senses versus intuitive perception or intuition, which is an indirect perception of the deeper meanings and possibilities inherent in things and situations. Again, everyone senses and intuits, but preliminary norms for the test suggest that in the United States three out of four persons show a preference for sense perception, concentrating upon immediate sensory experience and centering their attention upon existing facts. The one out of every four who shows a preference for intuitive perception, on the other hand, looks expectantly for a bridge or link between that which is given and present and that which is not yet thought of, focusing habitually upon possibilities.

"One would expect creative persons not to be bound to the stimulus and the object but to be ever alert to the as-yet-not-realized. And that is precisely the way they show themselves to be on the Type Indicator . . ."

## CREATIVITY AND INTELLIGENCE

So much for findings based on techniques of measurement and description of personality. We shall return to them at a later point in this chapter, when we look through other means, such as analyses of biographical material, at the psychodynamics of the creative person. Before taking leave of these recent researches by the living-in assessment method, however, let us consider briefly the findings on the relationship of creativity to measured intelligence. Table 1.9 shows descriptive statistics for a variety of samples studied with the Concept Mastery Test. Those studied at the Institute are shown by the designation (IPAR).

TABLE 1.9. CONCEPT MASTERY TEST, FORM T

| *Sample* | *N* | *Mean* | *Sigma* |
|---|---|---|---|
| 1. Creative Writers (IPAR) | 20 | 156.4 | 21.9 |
| 2. Creative Women Mathematicians (IPAR) | 16 | 144.0 | |
| 3. Stanford Gifted Study | 1004 | 136.7 | 33.8 |
| 4. Representative Women Mathematicians (IPAR) | 28 | 124.5 | |
| 5. Graduate students, University of California | 125 | 119.2 | 33.0 |
| 6. Research Scientists (IPAR) | 45 | 118.2 | 29.4 |
| 7. Medical students, University of California | 161 | 118.2 | 33.1 |
| 8. Ford Foundation fellowship applicants | 83 | 117.9 | 35.1 |
| 9. Creative Architects (IPAR) | 40 | 113.2 | 37.7 |
| 10. College Graduates, University of California | 75 | 112.0 | 32.0 |
| 11. Public Health Education applicants, University of California | 54 | 97.1 | 29.0 |
| 12. Spouses of Stanford Gifted | 690 | 95.3 | 42.7 |
| 13. Electronic engineers | 95 | 94.5 | 37.0 |
| 14. Undergraduates, lower division, Stanford University | 97 | 77.6 | 25.7 |
| 15. Military officers | 343 | 60.3 | 31.6 |

As Table 1.9 shows quite clearly, the three groups of creative individuals studied at the Institute are of quite superior verbal ability. The Concept Mastery Test is considered in some quarters to be a very good test of general intelligence—in fact it was developed by Lewis M. Terman and his associates specifically with the goal of providing differential measurement of general intelligence in the high IQ ranges represented by the highly gifted individuals in the famous Stanford studies. In Guilford's factor analytic studies of the structure of intellect, the test is construed as primarily a measure of verbal comprehension. However, scores on the Concept Mastery Test in adulthood are known to be highly correlated with Stanford-Binet IQ scores of the same individuals in childhood; if one accepts the Stanford-Binet IQ as a good measure of general intelligence, then the Concept Mastery Test would qualify as the same. While only rough IQ equivalences have been established for the Concept Mastery Test, we can accept the mean of the Stanford Gifted sample as descriptive of a group whose IQ range is from about 135 to about 180. The scores of our creative writers and creative mathematicians are therefore well up in this range; in fact, only two of the creative writers made scores below the mean of the Stanford Gifted sample. The lowest scoring group of creative individuals, architects, are in the general range represented by university medical students and graduate students as well as adult research scientists, and they are markedly superior to such groups as the spouses of the Stanford Gifted and a large group of military officers, all of them of the rank of captain and at the time of testing under consideration for promotion to field grade.

Because of security regulations governing the use of the Concept Mastery Test, it could not be administered either to the comparison group of writers or to the comparison groups of architects. The only sample for which a true comparison group is available is the Creative Women Mathematician sample, and the observed difference between the "creatives" and the "representatives" among women mathematicians favors the former and is statistically significant. In view of the correlation we have already noted in the military officer sample between the Concept Mastery Test and the Originality Composite, and considering also the report of Meer and Stein (1955) of a significant positive association between measured intelligence and creativity ratings among industrial chemists, this result is not surprising. The most probable state of affairs is that a low positive relationship exists between general intelligence and creativity.

The observed correlation in the sample of creative architects, however, between Concept Mastery scores and over-all rating of creativity for the 40 highly creative architects is not significantly different from zero (−.08). A similar value was discovered in the research scientist sample studied by Gough (1961). The extremely restricted range of creativity represented by the highly distinguished architects might be expected to produce considerable attenuation in the observed correlation, of course, but as we have seen there were a substantial number of findings of a theoretically sensible sort in that sample, and there is no reason for this particular relationship to be more attenuated than the others.

## BESIDES INTELLECT, WHAT?

The suspicion that in most standardized intelligence tests the very important domain of intellectual ability, creativity, was being neglected existed in informed quarters long before Guilford made so explicit in his 1950 address the kinds of testable functions for which new tests were needed. In 1898 G. V. Dearborn had published in the American Journal of Psychology an article titled "A Study of Imagination," in which he reported the responses of Harvard students and faculty to a series of inkblots; one of his observations was that some of his more "intellectual" subjects were least imaginative. The same sort of observation was made sporadically by a variety of experimenters in the ensuing 20 years. R. M. Simpson, in a 1922 article in the American Journal of Psychology (1922), several years after the development of the psychometrically sophisticated Stanford-Binet Intelligence Test, was perspicuous enough to write: "Tests . . . to ascertain either native intelligence or acquired knowledge . . . (have) no elements in them to extract from the mind of the individual his powers of creative productivity and his tendencies toward originality."

Simpson proceeded to invent a number of tests of imagination for school children, and he was followed in this effort by several other psychologists, such as McCloy and Meier (1931), Andrews (1930), and Welch (1946). Correlations averaging about .25 between IQ and imaginativeness or originality were found. By the time psychologists were called upon in World War II to select men for assignments calling for a high degree of flexibility and ingenuity, it was commonly recognized that standardized measures for such traits were missing from the selection psychologist's armamentarium.

In the years since 1950 this state of affairs has become well understood among psychologists, and it has been dramatized for professional educators and intelligent laymen by a provocative study by Getzels and Jackson, published as a book in 1962 under the title *Creativity and Intelligence.* Their actual findings, unfortunately, have been somewhat misunderstood and do not entirely support the popular interpretation that has been placed upon them. There has even been a tendency to conclude that having a high IQ is a sign of *lack of creativeness.* The strongest statement that any reported finding to date would warrant is that there is no relationship at all between certain purported measures of intelligence and measures or ratings of certain aspects of creativity. Even this statement, however, is open to criticism on statistical grounds, and more definitive studies are needed.

The Getzels-Jackson study is provocative in part because that academic underdog, the student with the low IQ, seems to run off with the prize in the end, as if in reply to the pigeonholers who had given him a label based on their own notions of neat problem-solving. The most quotable portions of the study have been TAT stories told by the students who, in the nomenclature of the research, are "high creatives" *as opposed to* "high IQ's." Here are a few of the stories from a "high creativity" child as opposed to a "high IQ" child. (Getzels and Jackson, 1962, p. 107.)

*High IQ*

This is a story of counterfeiters. The man with the hat is the printer. The other man is the big boss. They are in danger of being captured by the police. They want to get out of the house. The police will arrive too late. The man and the evidence will be gone.

*High creativity*

The man in the foreground is the leader of a counterfeiting ring. They have abducted the older man in the background. The older man is an excellent artist. They have kidnapped him so that they can force him to engrave the plates. He is very reluctant but they threaten to harm his wife and children so he gives in. But he draws George Washington cross-eyed and the counterfeiters are captured and he is released.

*High IQ*

There's ambitious Bob, down at the office at 6:30 in the morning. Every morning it's the same. He's trying to show his boss how energetic he is. Now, thinks Bob, maybe the boss will give me a raise for all my extra work. The trouble is that Bob has been doing this for the last three years, and the boss still hasn't given him a raise. He'll come in at 9:00, not even noticing that Bob has been there so long, and poor Bob won't get his raise.

*High creativity*

This man has just broken into the office of a new cereal company. He is a private eye employed by a competitor firm to find out the formula that makes the cereal bend, sag, and sway. After a thorough search of the office he comes upon what he thinks is the current formula. He is now copying it. It turns out that it is the wrong formula and the competitor's factory blows up. Poetic justice!

These and a few other examples of contrasting qualities of imagination in high "IQ" and "high Creativity" *S*'s leave the casual reader with the impression that the high IQ child is something of a mole while the high Creativity child is spontaneous, amusing, unconventional, and free. Findings that are given in statistical terms, employing usually the chi-square test applied to observational categories derived from inspection of the data, include the following that were reported to be statistically significant differences between the two groups:

1. Standardized achievement measures of verbal and numerical-mathematical achievement show that both experimental groups are superior to the average of the student body, and to about the same extent—this in spite of an average IQ of 150 in the "high IQ" group and 127 in the "high Creativity" (high C) group. Verbal achievement particularly is correlated with the creativity measures.

2. There were no differences between the two groups in terms of achievement-motive.

3. Teachers enjoy teaching the "high IQ" *S*'s significantly more than they do the average student, although this difference, while in the same direction, is not statistically significant for the "high C's."

4. In terms of such values as moral character, creativity, goal-directedness, intelligence, superior school performance, wide range of interest, emotional stability, and sense of humor, the high IQ's believe that the traits they prefer for themselves are the ones that will lead to adult success and are favored by teachers, in contrast to the opinion held by the high C's that there is no relationship between the traits they prefer for themselves and the ones favorable to adult success, and a negative relationship between traits they prefer for themselves and traits regarded favorably by teachers.

5. In the use of imagination for the creation of fantasy, high C's show significantly more stimulus-free themes, unexpected endings, humor, incongruities, and playfulness, and a marked tendency toward more violence.

6. In terms of career aspirations, the high C's see more occupational possibilities as open to them, as well as many more unconventional ones: adventurer, inventor, or writer, for example, as opposed to lawyer, doctor, or professor.

Getzels and Jackson attempted also to discover variables in family background that would differentiate the two groups. The findings here were sparse. The number of parents (either father or mother) who had graduated from college did not differentiate the groups, but more mothers of high IQ *S*'s had had some graduate training, and more fathers of high IQ *S*'s were employed in university teaching, in research, or in editing; high C fathers were more often in business. There was a slight tendency for the parents of high IQ *S*'s to have a greater age difference between them. High IQ mothers tended to notice more unfavorable things about their children and to emphasize "external" qualities as desirable in their children's friends, while high C mothers emphasized more "internal" qualities (such as standards of value, and so on).

On the whole, then, the findings do suggest more openness to experience, more flexibility, more unconventionality, more playfulness, more aggression, and more independence and inner-directedness in the "high Creatives" than in the "high IQ's," and thus they seem to fit in well with the pattern of results obtained in various other studies. The only trouble is that the Getzels-Jackson results cannot really be so neatly assimilated to other findings, simply because the labels "high IQ" and "high Creative" are not quite accurate. The results must be entertained with certain important reservations, as the authors themselves point out. To be clear about these reservations we must keep in mind the methods the investigators employed in constituting the two groups on which they concentrated.

The subjects were 449 students in the sixth through twelfth grades in a private urban school. The mean IQ of the students, as determined or estimated from existing records (Stanford-Binet, Henmon-Nelson, or Wechsler-Bellevue Scale for Children), was 132. So, the average student in the school was in about the upper 1 percent of the general population to begin with, a crucial point in understanding the findings.

The creativity measure was a summation of 5 tests, 4 of them having considerable verbal component and all of them being significantly correlated with the IQ measure. The correlation between IQ and the summated creativity score is not given, but one of the creativity measures alone (Word Association) correlates .38 with IQ.

Both the IQ and the creativity score distributions were now dichotomized at the 80th percentile, and 4 groups thus defined: high-high (upper 20 percent on both measures); low-low (lower 80 percent on both measures); high-low (upper 20 percent on the IQ measure and lower 80 percent on the creativity measure); and low-high (lower 80 percent on the IQ measure and upper 20 percent on the creativity measure).

Such a procedure results in considerable reduction of sample size, of course; in this particular case, only 52 subjects of the original 449 qualified for study when these extreme groups were thus selected. The missing 90 percent includes the high-highs, who could be expected to be a small group (no more than 90, no fewer than none, and probably about 30, considering the correlations of IQ with the components of the creativity score). The high-highs are an extremely interesting group and their exclusion results in considerable loss of information.

This kind of decision on the part of the investigators is perfectly appropriate, however, and Getzels and Jackson made quite clear what they were doing, and why, and have in addition promised a further report on the high-highs. What is misleading are the labels: "high intelligence group," giving the impression that all the high intelligence subjects are included, whereas actually a subject of high intelligence would be excluded if he were also of high creativity; and "high creativity," giving the impression that all subjects of high creativity are included, whereas actually a subject of high creativity would be excluded if he happened also to have a high IQ. And besides this source of confusion, as we have already indicated, even a person designated as of "low intelligence" could have an IQ considerably above 132, since that represented the 50th percentile and hence 60 percent of the subjects with IQ's greater than 132 were eligible for classification as "low intelligence"!

These considerations certainly limit the value of the findings the investigators report, especially since the information that might allow the reader to disentangle himself from the misleading nomenclature is not given. While we might agree that it is high time that the public become aware of the abuses to which indiscriminate use of IQ testing may lead, it should be clear that what advances the scientific question will in the long run be of more use to society. Yet the findings are likely finally to prove valid; E. Paul Torrance at the University of Minnesota has replicated some of the more important ones, and his work we shall take up later. Repeated studies employing careful measurement offer the best hope for clarification of the degree of relationship between various aspects of intellectual functioning.

## STUDIES OF INTELLIGENCE BY HISTORIOMETRY

So far as we know, the Institute of Personality Assessment and Research Study is unique in having obtained intelligence test data on living individuals who are by Galton's standards "eminent," or perhaps even "illustrious." In fact, the only research offering comparable IQ estimates of persons of eminence is that reported by Catherine Cox in *Genetic Studies of Genius, The Early Mental Traits of 300 Geniuses* (1926). Her extremely painstaking research depended upon the reconstruction from biographical data, and by application of the method of historiometry, of the picture of early mental development of intellectually eminent or illustrious individuals who were born in the 400-year span between 1450 and 1850. The IQ estimate that she and her colleagues arrived at was then correlated with rank order of eminence in a sample of 282 cases. (Rank order of eminence is an index of position on Cattell's list of 1000 eminent historical personages.) The correlation proved to be .25, plus or minus .038. She presents carefully analyzed data showing that this is not due either to halo effect or to greater information about the early mental development of the more eminent.

These historiometrical studies are utterly fascinating in the details they present of the mental achievement of young geniuses. Fittingly enough, Terman himself tackled the begetter of this entire line of inquiry, Francis Galton, and the interested student might read the brief article in which he presents the evidence on Galton's IQ, which he estimates at 200 (see Terman, 1917). Here are some brief excerpts:

*The earliest period of instruction*

"From early childhood Galton was under the instruction of his sister Adele, herself a mere child. She taught him letters in play, and he could point to them all before he could speak. Adele had a wonderful power of teaching and gaining attention without fatiguing. She taught herself Latin and Greek that she might teach him. She never had him learn by heart, but made him read his lesson, bit by bit, eight times over, when he could say it. He could repeat much of Scott's *Marmion*, and understood it all by the time he was 5.

"Francis knew his capital letters by twelve months and both his alphabets by eighteen months; . . . he could read a little book, *Cobwebs to Catch Flies*, when he was 2½ years old, and could sign his name before three years.

"A letter written to his sister the day before his 5th birthday runs as follows:

'My dear Adele,

I am 4 years old and I can read any English book. I can say all the Latin substantives and adjectives and active verbs besides 52 lines of Latin poetry. I can cast up any sum in addition and can multiply by 2, 3, 4, 5, 6, 7, 8, (9), 10, (11).

I can also say the pence table. I read French a little and I know the clock.

Francis Galton
Febuary 15, 1827.'

We are told by Terman, "The only misspelling is in the date. The numbers 9 and 11 are bracketed above, because little Francis, evidently feeling that he had claimed too much, had scratched out one of these numbers with a knife and pasted some paper over the other.

"By six, under the tutelage of Adele, Galton had become thoroughly conversant with the *Iliad* and the *Odyssey*.

"It seems that Adele also taught Francis a good deal about entomology, and at 6 and 7 years he was active and persistent in collecting insects and minerals . . .

"Francis's interests . . . were not wholly literary, for at the age of 13 he gave us *Francis Galton's Aerostatis Project* . . . a series of drawings representing a flying machine. It was to work by large, flapping wings with a sort of revolving steam engine, and was supposed to carry five passengers, a pilot, and an engineer."

These are fascinating facts about young Francis Galton, and certainly we should not be surprised to learn that so brilliant and so favored a youngster became illustrious. But we might wonder, whatever became of Adele . . . ? Of this, more later.

## HISTORIOMETRY APPLIED TO PERSONALITY

The historiometric method in the Terman studies consisted in the application of mental test standards to behavior and intellectual performance in childhood as reported in history and biography. The same method has been employed, with varying degrees of painstakingness and probable accuracy, in the study of personality. Ostwald, for example, in an early study (1909) compared six scientists with one another in terms of their "romantic" versus "classical" orientations. Davenport (1919) developed a dichotomous typology of heroism, the "hyperkinetic" and the "hypokinetic," and brought the historiometric method to bear on biographies of naval heroes to check his theories.

The essential steps in the method are these two: (1) a preliminary psychogram or set of numerical trait ratings or counts, based on a search in biographical material or historical records for evidence of certain character traits; and (2) a statistical analysis of group averages in order to establish significant differences in accord with theory.

Many of the early studies grew out of an interest in the inheritance of unusual mental abilities, and personality traits as we now think of them were not in the foreground. James McKeen Cattell's research on American men of science has already been mentioned; Brimhall extended Cattell's data analysis by analyzing family resemblances (1923). Candolle (1885) had earlier done a historiometric study of the inheritance of mental traits among scientists. Odin (1895) and Clarke (1916) applied the method to the origins of great writers, and Woods (1906) used it to study intellectual and moral traits in royalty.

All these studies were relatively unsophisticated by today's standards of personality measurement, though keen observation abounds in them. Although fundamental dimensional analysis of personality began about 40 years ago, only recently have psychometrically established insights into the structure of personality found application in historiometry. An excellent example of this has been given us by a later Cattell, Raymond B., nephew of James McKeen Cattell; since it bears also upon the important topic of creativity in science and has its analogue in work by R. B. Cattell and others using psychological tests with living scientists its method and conclusions have special interest.

The first step in R. B. Cattell's method was recourse to biography. He reports that his extensive reading of biographies of great scientists was not intended at the time to serve the end to which he finally put it in this study: it was simply his hobby. The psychograms he eventually drew, depending on his memory of his reading, consisted of variables for whose existence there was no firm evidence during the time the reading actually occurred. His qualitative observations had found expression in an earlier paper, however, and there is a convincing degree of congruence between them and the final psychographic statement.

A summary of results of another study, this one of contemporary scientists, by Cattell and Drevdahl (1955), is shown in Table 1.10; from it the reader may acquaint himself with the psychograph Cattell employed in the historiometric study. In Table 1.10 the average psychograph of 140 eminent contemporary researchers in physics, biology, and psychology is shown in relation to a general population average, a set of data of interest in itself.

TABLE 1.10. PERSONALITY FACTOR SCORES OF EMINENT RESEARCHERS ($N = 140$)

| *Personality dimension label at minus pole* | *Direction of average* | *Personality dimension label at plus pole* |
|---|---|---|
| Schizothymia | — — | Cyclothymia |
| Low intelligence | + + | High intelligence |
| Low ego strength | + | High ego strength |
| Low dominance | + + | High dominance |
| Desurgency | — | Surgency |
| Low group superego | 0 | High group superego |
| Threctia | + | Parmia |
| Harmia | + + | Premsia |
| Low protension | + | High protension |
| Praxernia | + | Autia |
| Simplicity | + | Shrewdness |
| Low guilt proneness | 0 | High guilt proneness |
| Conservatism | + + | Radicalism |
| Low self-sufficiency | + + | High self-sufficiency |
| Low self-sentiment | + | High self-sentiment |
| Low ergic tension | 0 | High ergic tension |

The significant results of the biographical study, stated briefly, follow. Scientists are:

1. Decidedly schizothymic as opposed to cyclothymic (especially the physical scientists, such as Lord Cavendish, Dalton, Priestley, Lavoisier, Scheele, Avogadro, and J. J. Thomson)
2. Of very high intelligence
3. Of high ego strength
4. Very dominant (in a sense of dominance that includes self-assertiveness, independence, and a refusal to be bound by convention)
5. Desurgent (the desurgency factor loads highly on introspectiveness, restraint, brooding, and solemnity of manner)

Especially worth noting here are two unusual *combinations* of variables: high schizothymia with high ego strength, a finding in accord with IPAR results on other professional groups, and high dominance with high desurgency. A rather cold, introspective, solemn or even grim, strong-willed, unconventional, and highly intelligent person; this is the picture that Cattell gives us of the distinguished scientist, although he notes some striking exceptions. Humor, when present, may take a peculiar turn. Cattell recalls with relish the story that Cavendish, when dragged to a state function and about to meet some supposedly distinguished but pompous foreign scientists, broke away and ran down the corridor, squeaking like a bat. We are left in no doubt as to where Cattell stands, for he comments: "One wishes that this salutary response to pretension could be made more often."

## THE PRODUCTIVE SCIENTIST

The measures on contemporary scientists in the Cattell and Drevdahl study do support in almost every instance the findings from biographical research, although three additional factors which Cattell did not discuss can be seen as significant: emotional sensitivity (premsia), radicalism, and self-sufficiency. The premsia factor is not entirely clear, but it is believed to be an emotional sensitivity stemming from a protective parental environment.

The IPAR study of scientists employed quite different tests, but the results are consistent in many respects, particularly in terms of the California Psychological Inventory profiles for the 45 scientists studied by Gough (1961). The notable features of the group profile are summarized by Gough as follows:

> "The profile for these scientists is generally elevated, a favorable indication (for effective functioning), but patterning is also visible. The scores are above average on the first cluster of scales dealing with poise and self-assurance (Dominance, Capacity for Status, Social Presence, and Self-acceptance). Then there is something of a drop on the scales assessing . . . social conformity (Socialization, Self-control), followed by another rise on the achievement indices, particularly on Achievement via Independence. The highest point

on the profile occurs on the scale for psychological-mindedness, a measure of the degree to which one is interested in and responsive to the inner needs, motives, feelings, and experiences of others."

Gough's other findings showed that the scientists were of quite high intelligence (see Table 1.9), were psychiatrically stable and of high ego strength, and were unusually independent in judgment when, in the Crutchfield conformity experiment, they were put under pressure to agree with a false group consensus. In fact, as Crutchfield's data in a series of studies show, research scientists are the most outstanding in this regard among all groups studied (Table 1.11). As might be expected, on the Allport-Vernon-Lindzey Scale of Values, they are notably high in Theoretical and Aesthetic values and notably low in Religious, Social, and Economic values.

Perhaps the most intriguing and eventually most useful result of Gough's research is not the further support it lends to the findings of Ann Roe and of Cattell and Drevdahl in drawing a *general* picture of the scientist, but rather the unique contribution of a descriptive and statistical basis for discovering *styles of scientist behavior* in a modern laboratory setting. Together with Donald G. Woodworth (1960) he developed a Research Scientists' Q-sort Deck, consisting of 56 short assertions, each referring to a mode of approach to research. Examples are: "Indifferent to the practical implications of his own research"; "Is good at developing short cuts and approximation techniques"; "Likes to talk out his research ideas and get other people's reactions"; "Takes an esthetic view; is sensitive to matters of form and elegance in research problems."

Each of the 45 scientists was asked to sort these statements into 5 groups in such a manner as to give a description of his own mode of approach to research problems. This made it possible to correlate scientist with scientist and so to discover subgroups of scientists who were similar to one another but different from members of other subgroups. In other words, from the 45 x 45 matrix of correlation coefficients expressing resemblances among pairs of scientists, statistical components,

8 in all, were identified by factor analysis. These are, in short, types of approach to research problems, describable in terms of the original 56 assertions in the Research Scientist Q-sort Deck.

The 8 types were named as follows, on the basis both of Q-sort item content and other test correlates: the zealot, the initiator, the diagnostician, the scholar, the artificer, the esthetician, the methodologist, and the independent. Their qualities are sketched by Gough and Woodworth as follows:

*The zealot.* This man is dedicated to research activity; he sees himself as a driving, indefatigable researcher, with exceptional mathematical skills and a lively sense of curiosity. He is seen by others as tolerant, serious-minded, and conscientious, but as not getting along easily with others and as not being able to "fit in" readily with others.

*The initiator.* This man reacts quickly to research problems, and begins at once to generate ideas; he is stimulating to others and gives freely of his own time; he sees himself as being relatively free of doctrinaire bias—methodological or substantive—and as being a good "team" man. Observers describe him as ambitious, well-organized, industrious, a good leader, and efficient. They also characterize him as being relatively free of manifest anxiety, worry, and nervousness.

*The diagnostician.* This man sees himself as a good evaluator, able to diagnose strong and weak points in a program quickly and accurately, and as having a knack for improvising quick solutions in research trouble spots. He does not have strong methodological preferences and biases, and tends not to be harsh or disparaging towards others' mistakes and errors. Observers see him as forceful and self-assured in manner, and as unselfish and free from self-seeking and narcissistic striving.

*The scholar.* This man is blessed with an exceptional memory, and with an eye for detail and order. However, he is not a research perfectionist nor an endless seeker for ultimates. He does not hesitate to ask help when blocked in his work, and feels that he can adapt his own thinking to that of others. He is well-informed in his field, and is not given to bluffing. Observers describe him as conscientious and thorough, and as very dependable, but as lacking confidence and decisiveness of judgment.

*The artificer.* This man gives freely of his own time, and enjoys talking shop with other researchers. He is aware of his own limitations and does not attempt what he cannot do. He sees himself as having a special facility for taking inchoate or poorly formed ideas of others and fashioning them into workable and significant programs. Observers see him as honest and direct, getting along well with others, and as usually observant and perceptive and responsive to nuances and subtleties in others' behavior.

*The esthetician.* This man favors analytical over other modes of thinking, and prefers research problems which lend themselves to elegant and formal solutions. His interests are far-ranging, and he tends to become impatient if progress is slow or if emphasis must be put upon orderliness and systematic detail. His own view of experience is primarily an esthetic one. Observers see him as clever and spontaneous, but as undependable and immature, somewhat lacking in patience and industry and indifferent about duties and obligations.

*The methodologist.* This man is vitally interested in methodological issues, and in problems of mathematical analysis and conceptualization. He is open about his own research plans and enjoys talking about them with others. He has little competitive spirit and tends to take a tolerant view of research differences between himself and others. Observers characterize him as a considerate, charitable person, free from undue ambition; at the same time they report a certain moodiness and an occasional tendency toward complicated and difficult behavior.

*The independent.* This man eschews "team" efforts, and dislikes and avoids administrative details connected with research work. He is not a driving, energetic research man, although he does have a lively sense of intellectual curiosity. He prefers to think in reference to physical and structural models rather than in analytical and mathematical ways. Observers describe him as active and robust in manner and hard-headed and forthright in judgment. He appears relatively free from worry and self-doubt, but inclined to behave impolitely or abruptly.

This effort to delineate types is important because it gives explicit recognition to variety within a given professional grouping, even though the sample itself, like most of those that have been studied intensively, is too small to permit reliable comparisons among the subgroups thus discerned. But the point is that there are different styles of functioning and different ways of making a contribution in science, and unless we remember this fact we are liable to be misled by the consistencies we see when the method of group averages is relied upon exclusively.

The consistencies themselves are impressive, of course. They are especially so in view of the variety of techniques employed, which have ranged from clinical interviews and projective techniques through empirically developed biographical inventories to factor-based tests. The common core of agreement from study to study requires only slight accommodation of terminology from one theoretical viewpoint to another. If we take in combination the researches of A. Roe, C. W. Taylor, R. H. Knapp, R. B. Cattell, R. D. MacCurdy, D. C. McClelland, B. Eiduson, J. A. Chambers, and H. G. Gough, and list the traits found in one study after another, this unified picture of the productive scientist emerges.

1. High ego strength and emotional stability
2. A strong need for independence and autonomy; self-sufficiency; self-direction
3. A high degree of control of impulse
4. Superior general intelligence
5. A liking for abstract thinking and a drive towards comprehensiveness and elegance in explanation
6. High personal dominance and forcefulness of opinion, but a dislike of personally toned controversy

7. Rejection of conformity pressures in thinking (although not necessarily in social behavior)
8. A somewhat distant or detached attitude in interpersonal relations, though not without sensitivity or insight; a *preference* for dealing with things or abstractions rather than with people
9. A special interest in the kind of "wagering" which involves pitting oneself against the unknown, so long as one's own effort can be the deciding factor
10. A liking for order, method, exactness, together with an excited interest in the challenge presented by contradictions, exceptions, and apparent disorder

Taylor and Barron (1963) wrote as follows in fitting together certain research observations with the nature of the process of scientific discovery itself.

"The more highly regarded young scientists are: (1) of superior measured intelligence; (2) exceptionally independent in judgment and resistant to group-endorsed opinions; (3) marked by a strong need for order and for perceptual closure, combined with a resistance to premature closure and an interest in what may appear as disorder, contradiction, imbalance, or very complex balance whose ordering principle is not immediately apparent; (4) unusually appreciative of the intuitive and nonrational elements in their own nature; (5) distinguished by their profound commitment to the search for esthetic and philosophic meaning in all experience.

"How, now, do such personal characteristics bear upon the meaning of scientific creativity? Science in the abstract may be seen as a set of sentences expressing qualitative and quantitative relationships, and the history of the growth of this set of sentences may give the impression of a steady progressive differentiation and gradual enlargement of scope. As Kuhn has argued earlier, a comparison by decades of textbooks in the natural sciences would strongly support such a view. Certainly in every science there are long stretches of increasing convergence, consensus, and filling in of gaps. Thus viewed, scientific advance appears cumulative and steady.

"Such a view, however, would give only part of the picture. Scientific knowledge undergoes development as a living body in much the same way as human beings do: through alternating periods of crisis and of coalescence, diffusion and integration, revolution and consensus. The image of scientific advance as cumulative is not so apt as an image of it as 'development through periodic crisis which produces genuine divergence following periods of convergence.' It is precisely the point at which a strong and established consensus finds itself confronted with an unassimilable fact that the forces of revolution are set in motion. These forces, as in all revolutions, threaten the established order and turn the state, in this case the state of knowledge, in a radically new direction of development. Since the forces of the revolution must be embodied in persons, what kind of person may serve as the vehicle for the change in thinking which must come? We would argue here that a person possessing the traits just described is the one most likely to be called to the task.

"Briefly, let us consider the nature of those relationships.

1. The more highly developed a body of knowledge becomes, the more intelligence and capacity for discrimination and discipline is required for its mastery. The scentist who can respond creatively to crisis must therefore be of a high order of intellectual ability and must be orderly, thorough, and disciplined in his acquisition of current knowledge.

2. As discoveries occur which cannot be assimilated to current conceptions of orderliness in nature, increasing effort must be made to understand the unordered and to find a new principle which will restore order. The person who pays close attention to what appears discordant and contradictory and who is challenged by such irregularities is therefore likely to be in the front ranks of the revolutionaries.

3. If such a person then embarks on the risky business of seeking and putting forth new theories, he must be prepared to stand his ground against outcries from the proponents of the previous but, in his view, no longer tenable consensus. He must possess independence of judgment and hold to his own opinion in the face of a consensus which does not fit all the facts.

4. Such a creative person in science must be passionately committed to his own cosmology and must respect his private intuitions, even when they seem unreasonable to himself; he must be able to open himself to sources of information which others deny to themselves.

5. Through such persons, who are embodiments of the creative process in nature, science remains alive and open to novelty; a scientific enterprise or organized scientific activity which does not allow free play to its own creative possibilities will shortly become moribund."

## THE POETIC AND ARTISTIC IMAGINATION

It should be clear from this description of the creative scientist that imagination of a high order characterizes the scientific intellect, and in fact that creative scientists are similar to artists in the importance they give to esthetic qualities in their theories. On the Barron-Welsh Art Scale, the more original scientist differs from the less original one in preferring the complex asymmetrical figures that artists too prefer. Gough even found that the Art Scale was the single best predictor of his criterion ratings of scientific creativity, and that it had the highest weight in the best prediction equation he could derive.

It would be a mistake, then, to oppose the artistic imagination or the poetic imagination to the scientific imagination. Nevertheless, the impulse to create in the arts does seem to arise in rather different sorts of persons than does the impulse to create in scientific or mathematical theory. We may have recourse once again to the Terman data. In Volume II of *Genetic Studies of Genius* we find a classification of the 301 geniuses studied by Catherine Cox into 11 subgroups, and among them, in addition to Scientists, are such groups as Artists and Imaginative Writers (Poets, Novelists, and Dramatists). These groups were characterized in terms of personal and moral qualities (67 "good traits") as well as intellectual ones. It is interesting to see the difference between scientists and the groups of imaginative writers and artists.

The picture of scientists is not notably different from that revealed by recent research, though it is less complete. The average IQ is estimated as probably greater than 170. The scientific geniuses are disproportionately high, as compared with eminent individuals from all other subgroups, in "intellectual traits," "strength or force of character," "balance," and "activity." They are disproportionately low in "excitability," "sensitiveness to criticism," and various "social" traits. Cox in conclusion describes them as "a group of youths who are the *strongest* and *most forceful* and *best balanced* in the study."

Artists as a group are estimated to be of lower intelligence; one basis of estimate places the average IQ at 135, although the author estimates the true IQ to be nearer 160. They are below the average of eminent men as a whole in their "average goodness," but they are notably high in "esthetic feeling," "desire to excel," "belief in their own powers," "the degree to which they work with distant objects in view," and "originality of ideas."

Imaginative writers are judged to have an average IQ of 165, and they characteristically differ from other geniuses in certain ways. They are notably high in "imaginativeness and esthetic feeling," and in a quaintly worded variable known as "amount of work spent on pleasures." They are also higher than eminent men in general in "originality of ideas," "strength of memory," and "keenness of observation"; they are lower in "soundness of common sense" and "the degree to which action and thought are dependent on reason."

This latter observation is especially important to the understanding of creative writers. Reason seems often to be the enemy of poetic imagination, at least "common reason." Jacques Maritain sees as one of the principal steps in the evolution of modern art, especially poetry and painting, "liberation from and transformation of . . . rational language." He writes, in *Creative Intuition in Art and Poetry* (1955):

> "Rational language is not cut out to express the singular, it is burdened with social and utilitarian connotations, ready-made associations, and worn-out meanings, it is invaded by the inevitable insipidity which results from habit. So it does not only interfere with poetry, it perpetually sidetracks it and makes poetry say something other than what poetry wants to say. The same observation can be made with regard to that intelligible discursus—organizing together, according to the accustomed patterns of the pleasure of the eyes or the ears, the movements of the design or the sounds of the melody —which is the rational language of painting and music. Why should we be surprised by the fact that modern artists struggle to free themselves from rational language and its logical laws? Never did they pay more attention to words, never did they attach greater importance to words: but (they do so) in order to transfigure them, and to get clear of the language of discursive reason. . . . Be it a poem or a painting, the work speaks: it speaks no longer in terms of logical reason."

But this is "reason as prison" of which Maritain speaks, bonds the creative writer seeks to break. Aristotle's "creative reason" is another matter entirely, and even the modern artist's effort at escaping the limitations of the consensus is in the service finally of reason in this sense of a free, creating generative principle. We have been impressed, in seeking to relate the writer's work to his life, with the force of a special intellectual motive: the cosmological motive, a strong desire to create a private cosmos of meaning through work which is grounded in the individual artist's unique being.[1] The scientist as artist is animated by this same drive. This perhaps is the primary motive in creation and is most analogous to the creative process in an evolving universe as well as to the creative process in the sexual act. The relationship of masculinity to femininity in the creative process presents a fundamental problem. We have noted earlier that a certain femininity of interest pattern is found in creative men, even though they are of normal masculinity. Berdyaev, in *The Meaning of the Creative Act* (1954), argues that the figure of Christ is androgynous, and that all creators must be so if they are to conceive and bear greatly and whole.

Does this help us with a certain puzzle: the extraordinary preponderance of men in the ranks of the great creators in all the arts and sciences? Of the actual Adele Galton we know virtually nothing except as she appears in her brother's childhood. Virginia Woolf has written in earnest vein of an imaginary female Shakespeare (*A Room of One's Own*, 1935) who remains unknown to the world mainly for the reason that she was born a woman and not a man and was for that reason denied the opportunities her talent needed. She also wrote with high irony of the same problem in the brilliant *Orlando* (1928), who begins as a man but ends as a woman. Surely it is true that the opportunities provided by society for creative women have been severely limited; as that situation changes (and it is changing rapidly), we may discover whether some

[1] Of making many motives there is no end in modern psychology, and we offer this suggestion almost reluctantly. Yet our observations force us to accord motivational status to the system-making disposition.

deeper psychological (biological-spiritual) motive arising from the biological basis of sexuality may not be playing a part as well. Perhaps there are fundamental and virtually unalterable correspondences between biological functions in procreation and male and female differences in creativity in the psychic sphere.

## A STUDY OF POTENTIALLY CREATIVE YOUNG WOMEN

Actually this study began with a look backward rather than forward. At Vassar College in 1954, the Mellon Foundation, at that time under the direction of Nevitt Sanford, who was on leave from the Institute of Personality Assessment and Research, began a study of Vassar alumnae. Subjects from as far back as the class of 1904 were asked to take part, and did. Most of the work involved only a series of questionnaires by mail, but for alumnae of vintage 1929 a more intensive study by the living-in assessment method was bravely proposed. As matters worked out, some of the intended total of 50 alumnae had to be drawn from classes just before or after 1929. Mary McCarthy, Vassar '30, had not yet written *The Group*, but, as it happened, the subjects of the Mellon Foundation study could well have been characters in that novel (and perhaps some of them were).

Several members of the Institute staff journeyed to Poughkeepsie to take part in the study of what proved to be an unusually independent group of women, as Crutchfield's data showed (see Table 1.11). Among them was an unusual proportion of women who were quite creative as well. But also among them were some almost tragic figures of creative potential gone sour; for some, too, a crisis involving the use to which their creative intellectual abilities were to be put still lay ahead of them.

These women were highly intelligent, of course, and as a group they highly valued intellect and were aware of their own capacities. But most of them were good-looking as well, and some were sweet, and no one failed to be one of the three, so as common sense would lead us to expect, they were all marriageable. And almost all did marry, some more than once. The story of the marriage was almost always the story of the life, in a way that is conspicuously absent in the life histories

TABLE 1.11. Resistance to Conformity Pressures, Crutchfield Conformity Experiment

| *Group* | *Number of Ss* | *Average conformity in percent* | *Resistance or independence* |
|---|---|---|---|
| *Males:* | | | |
| 1. "More original" Research Scientists | 17 | 10 | 90 |
| 2. Research Scientists (total sample) | 45 | 14 | 86 |
| 3. "Less original" Research Scientists | 17 | 18 | 82 |
| 4. Engineering Honors Society (seniors) | 30 | 20 | 80 |
| 5. College sophomores, University of California | 52 | 26 | 74 |
| 6. Military officers | 50 | 33 | 67 |
| *Females:* | | | |
| 1. Vassar College alumnae (classes of 1929-1930) | 50 | 22 | 78 |
| 2. Mills College "creatives" (seniors) | 22 | 23 | 77 |
| 3. College sophomores, University of California | 80 | 38 | 62 |
| 4. Mills College "controls" | 29 | 41 | 59 |

of creative men; and the story of the marriage was also in large part the story of what fate befell the woman's creative potential.

The focus of research in the Vassar studies was not upon

creativity, and the questions about creativity that arose from it seemed to come almost incidentally, though all the more spontaneously. They were such questions as these:

How does she perceive herself in relation to her husband's life work and *his* creativity?

To what extent is being a mother an *intellectually* creative enterprise, and is it seen as such?

How much is her creative ability used outside the family? At what cost, if any?

Is creative activity outside the marriage a rejection of husband and family? Is it seen as such by them? By her? Does it arise from unhappiness within the family, or does it stem from a desire to grow and to bear fruit in all ways possible?

Were these considerations important in the decision to marry? Did the decision mean opting for or against her own creative potential?

What would she wish for her daughters?

Is she fulfilled? disappointed? still waiting? too busy to notice?

These are big questions to put to a woman of age 45, and for the most part they were not put to that group of Vassar alumnae. But these questions and questions like them could be framed as part of an inquiry that looked forward rather than backward, and so they have been, in a study carried on since 1957 at the Institute of Personality Assessment and Research under the direction of Ravenna Helson, who came to the Institute staff from a teaching career at Smith College. She chose the senior year in college, Mills College in Oakland, California in this case, as the starting point for her inquiry, and she has conducted 2 five-year follow-ups which bring most of her subjects past the point of marriage and 1 or 2 children and show them *in medias res* with lively options all about.

## DESIGN OF THE MILLS COLLEGE STUDY

Having obtained the blessing of the Mills College administration and the freely given consent of the senior class, who decided quite democratically and with ample debate at a class meeting that they were willing to take part in the research, the Institute sought from the faculty a set of names of senior women who in the faculty member's judgment had important creative potential. All members of the senior class were candidates for inclusion in this list, and all faculty members were asked to make nominations. The procedure was repeated with another senior class 2 years later, in part as a check on the early findings and in part to increase the number of cases for the continuing study of development of these women in the years after college.

The nominations from the faculty were solicited by letter. The letter emphasized originality and creativity as the traits under study and made plain that good grades, leadership, and good character alone should not qualify a student for nomination as creative; in fact, that they should be considered irrelevant. And creative *potential* was stressed; the faculty was asked to refrain as far as they could from injecting their own predictions as to whether the potential would be realized.

About 15 percent of the senior class in the first study received nominations. Their chosen majors in college work included art, music, dance, drama, education, writing, biology, mathematics, history and government, and psychology. Only those were finally included who received multiple nominations and who were rated on originality by the faculty significantly higher than any member of a "control" group comprised of women with the same departmental majors and comparable scholastic aptitude.

The "creatives" and the "controls" were now studied by the living-in assessment technique, and, as in the case of Helson's earlier study of women mathematicians, the assessment staff was kept in ignorance of whether any given subject was considered a "creative" or a "control." In all, 21 "creatives" were assessed and were compared with 30 "controls."

The intriguing developmental questions with which the study began must be left for future reports as Dr. Helson continues her observations of the lives of these women. In one of her completed reports, however, she provides data from the living-in assessment studies of the women as college seniors which make it quite clear that potentially creative young women are very similar indeed to creative men in the ways in which they differ from appropriately chosen comparison groups. And not only do they differ from less potentially creative women in these ways, but actually they strongly resemble creative men in the variables we have found important thus far. The results suggest that on the threshold of adult life, before career and marriage choices are made, there is little difference in the important personality traits between creative women and creative men. Let us look at these findings in brief.

First of all, creative young women are independent in judgment. Independence as shown in the Crutchfield experiment was significantly associated with "creative" status in the assessment sample. On the Barron Independence of Judgment Scale the average score of the "creatives" is 15, not significantly different from distinguished creative writers, and significantly higher than the Mills College "controls."

On both the Originality and the Complexity Scales, the Mills "creatives" again score as high as creative writers and architects, and significantly higher than their control group. On the Art Scale, their average score is 35.86 compared with a mean of 30.9 for the Mills control group; their average score places them just below creative architects and slightly above creative writers.

In terms of psychopathology and personal effectiveness, these potentially creative college women showed much the same pattern as we have observed in creative architects and writers. They differ from their classmates in having significantly higher scores on an MMPI index comprising such scales as Schizophrenia, Paranoia, Hypomania, and the *F* Scale, while at the same time they are higher on Ego-Strength. They produce a clear picture of effectiveness on the California Psychological Inventory, with high scores on Achievement through Independence, Flexibility, and Psychological-mindedness. Helson comments that blind interpretations of the Rorschachs of the "creatives" abound in unfavorable comments concerning their personal stability, yet a rating of Cognitive Flexibility from the Rorschach, given without knowledge of the criterion status of the subjects, correlated .78 with Potential Creativity as rated by the Mills College faculty.

The same sort of picture emerged from interviews. One interview question was, "When was the last time you cried?" Not only had the "creatives" as a group cried more recently, they also had cried *so* recently that the interviewers were sometimes startled. Four-fifths of the "creatives" as compared with one-third of the "controls" reported having experienced overwhelming feelings of emptiness, desolation, and aloneness. Preoccupation with thoughts of death and even of suicide were common in the creative group. Perhaps these findings simply reflect greater emotional intensity in these potentially creative women, but perhaps also they tell us something of the existential reality deeply experienced by young women who sense their own potential and yet despair at the prospect before them when they move out into a world which demands that they sacrifice either their femininity or their intellectual creativity.

## NURTURING CREATIVITY

While in some respects creativity seems to be a hardy plant and even to flourish in the midst of hardship and privation, a developing body of testimony from educators and from psychologists in the school system suggests that much potential creativity is made to wither by an unfavorable climate both in the classroom and in society at large.

We have already had a look at some of the data of the Getzels-Jackson study, in which especially creative but relatively less intelligent, though still quite bright, pupils were less popular with teachers, and less in line with both teacher and peer value systems, than pupils whose IQ's were relatively high as compared with their creativity. Although no evidence existed directly in the data, there was at least the implication that creativity was maintained at some cost to personal security, or that a special motive was required to sustain creativity in the face of its comparative devaluation by the immediately present representatives of society.

The Getzels-Jackson findings have been replicated in essential details by E. Paul Torrance and his associates at the University of Minnesota Bureau of Educational Research, in a series of studies at the University of Minnesota Laboratory Elementary School, a Minneapolis public high school, the University of Minnesota High School, and two graduate schools. They showed not only that creative thinking abilities contributed to academic achievement in a way that had not been properly appreciated, but that peer disapproval was just as potent a factor as teacher devaluation in driving divergent thinking underground.

It is interesting that the creative young women studied by Helson had themselves exhibited in childhood a tendency towards divergent thinking and a rejection of conventional feminine adjustment, although outright tomboyishness was only one of several possible creative patterns for them as girls (1961). On a Creative Activities Checklist, devised by Helson, the creative Mills College seniors, retrospecting on their childhood activities by way of the Helson 37-item list, differed significantly (at the .05 level or better) from the control group on the following listed activities: *writing poems and stories; painting, drawing, and working with clay; creating complex imag-*

*inary situations and acting in them;* and *reading*. They reported more frequently *putting on shows, hiking and exploring*, and *horseback riding*, although these differences did not quite reach significance. *Playing alone*, and *playing the piano or violin*, were included by Helson in addition to the first five items above in a "creative activities scale" which significantly differentiated the "creatives" from the control group and which also had significant correlations with the Independence of Judgment Scale, the C.P.I. Originality Scale, and the Complexity Scale. Helson generalized the findings as showing "complex unstereotyped symbolic activity" as the characteristic difference between creative and uncreative girls; the latter more commonly preferred social play.

The relative lack of reward in the school system, as expressed in that most transferrable of coinage, school grades, for creative intellectual ability was shown in another interesting study, this time of adolescents in a Michigan high school. Elizabeth Drews (1960) studied three groups who had been equated for intelligence: social leaders, studious achievers, and creative intellectuals, as revealed by interest and performance patterns in high school. The creative intellectuals received significantly lower teacher grades, and these were especially low in comparison with their actual scholastic achievement as evidenced in other accomplishments.

An impressive study in depth of the creative adolescent has been made by Emanuel Hammer, working with students of painting in the High School Scholarship Painting Workshop at New York University. The Workshop faculty, themselves painters of distinction, classified the students, 18 in all, into 3 categories: (1) merely facile and lacking in creativity and originality; (2) intermediate; and (3) truly creative, with a high degree of promise for serious painting. There were 5 students each in categories 1 and 3. While this is of course a very small number of cases, they were studied in such depth that the findings commend themselves to our attention as a serious preliminary exploration.

Hammer's findings, expressed in terms of the qualities of the genuinely creative young painters, are consistent at many points with the results both of the Institute's studies of creative adults and the studies of Torrance, Drews, Getzels and Jackson with creative children and adolescents. The genuinely creative as opposed to merely facile young painters showed greater depth of feeling, stronger determination and ambition, independence, rebelliousness, tolerance of discomfort, greater need for self-expression as well as range of emotion, self-awareness, and an integration of feminine and masculine components in their natures.

Torrance's studies of developmental patterns throughout the elementary grades have made him especially alert to the damping effect of the school system upon creativity. Creative children in the first three grades, especially boys, often have a reputation among the other children for having "silly ideas," or "naughty ideas," or are thought of as "wild" by their teachers. By the end of third grade they have usually learned to be evasive and to keep their thoughts to themselves, with a consequent loss of some of that precious spark of originality. The ninth and tenth years are a transitional period for most children, however, one of the several nodal points at which the child gets noticeably more "broken in" and learns to take the bit for society's sake, and hopefully for his own as well, of course.[2] The dynamics of freedom and discipline, integration and diffusion, order and disorder, expression and restraint, become apposite to creativity most vividly at these crisis points in development.

Torrance has a number of recommendations for the school counselor in his dealings with creative children, which make

[2] Naturally. We recall once in a street in Berkeley walking along behind a mother with a 5-year-old boy in tow. They met a slightly older boy, evidently a neighbor, unaccompanied, carrying a school book. The 5-year-old stopped and said, "Come and play with me tomorrow." The about-6 replied, "I can't tomorrow." 5-year-old: "Why?" 6-year-old: "I have to go to school." 5-year-old: "Why?" 6-year-old, eyes clouding, puzzled, in a lost voice: "I don't know."

sense for teachers and principals as well, and indeed can apply in a variety of situations in which a creative individual, child or adult, is experiencing difficulty. "Society is downright savage toward creative thinkers, especially when they are young," says Torrance, and recommends the following: (1) provide a refuge; (2) be a sponsor or patron if you possess power or prestige in the social subsystem that is exerting pressure; (3) help the creative individual *understand* his divergence and the good reason for it; (4) let him communicate his ideas by listening to him and helping him to get listened to by others; (5) make efforts to get his creative talent recognized and rewarded; and (6) help parents (superiors, the authorities, and so on) to understand him.

For the creative individual himself, Torrance also has some wise suggestions. The creative individual needs to recognize and esteem his own creativity; he needs to learn how to guard it from exploitation and abuse; he needs to know how to accept inevitable limitations in the environment while yet holding to his purposes and searching for opportunities for the expression of his talent. He needs also to learn how to cope with hardships and with failure, with anxieties and fears, and to avoid isolation and retreat; he perhaps needs to learn not to be more obnoxious than necessary. He must not in his own mind equate rebellion with delinquency, or be led from rebellion to senseless and categorical opposition to society; he must resist the idea that his divergence is a sign that he is mentally ill or a bad person; he must be able to integrate the masculine and the feminine in his nature and not sacrifice part of himself to the social stereotype of masculinity or femininity.

While this might seem a large order, it is clear from our own research findings that highly successful creative individuals have been able to do this, though mostly on their own. How many others of potential creativity have fallen by the wayside cannot be estimated as yet, but there seems little doubt that the loss is considerable. The remedy surely does not lie simply in school counseling, but in a change of spirit in the educational system and in society at large. As we shall see later, there are signs that change is in the offing.

One of the most important of the changes is occurring in the National Merit Scholarship Corporation, whose program of competitive scholarship awards has attracted much attention, quite out of proportion indeed to the amount of money involved in the 500 scholarships awarded each year. The establishment of a highly discriminating basis of selection has made the National Merit Scholarship a highly desirable one; it is a signal honor as well as a help to the struggling student. Recently, on the basis of research and recommendations by John Holland (1960), the National Merit Scholarship administrators decided to make 25 scholarships each year available to candidates who could not qualify on high school grades or on standard scholastic aptitude tests but who had manifested a high level of creative ability in the sciences or the arts. Holland devised rating scales in which the following sorts of behaviors were recognized as having importance quite apart from grades or test-measured achievement:

*Creative Science Scale*

1. Presenting an original paper at a scientific meeting sponsored by a professional society
2. Winning a prize or award in a scientific talent search
3. Constructing scientific apparatus on own initiative
4. Inventing a patentable device
5. Having a scientific paper published in a science journal

*Creative Arts Scale*

1. Winning one or more speech contests
2. Having poems, stories, or articles published in a public newspaper or magazine or in a state or national high school anthology
3. Winning a prize or an award in an art competition (sculpture, ceramics, painting, and so forth)

4. Receiving the highest rating in a state music contest
5. Receiving one of the highest ratings in a national music contest
6. Composing music that is performed at least once in public
7. Arranging music for a public performance
8. Having at least a minor role in plays (not high-school or church-sponsored)
9. Having leads in high-school or church-sponsored plays
10. Winning a literary award or prize for creative writing
11. Having a cartoon published in a public newspaper or magazine

Certainly the provision of social recognition and reward for creative endeavor is one effective way of endorsing it and increasing the valuation placed upon it by society. The late President Kennedy lent the prestige of his high office to this sort of social endorsement of creativeness, not only through the hospitality that he and Mrs. Kennedy extended at the White House to great creators in the arts and sciences, but also through the emphasis he gave to the selection of recipients for the Medal of Freedom and, in innumerable less public acts, to the encouragement of flexible and original thinking in all kinds of projects touching upon our national life.

## INCREASING INDIVIDUAL CREATIVITY THROUGH EDUCATION

But quite apart from nurturing and rewarding the creativity that has sprung up more or less on its own, can we do anything to increase it in ourselves and others by education, training, or selected unusual experiences? Since we are getting more and more information about the factors involved, can we begin to devise programs that will strengthen creative thinking abilities and reduce the effect of inhibiting circumstances?

Is our knowledge useful knowledge, in the sense that it leads to prediction and control?

Two of the earliest efforts at application were brainstorming and synectics, the former the idea of Alex Osborne, the latter a system of training devised by William J. J. Gordon for industrial inventors. Both have a slightly artificial flavor to them, although this first impression disappears when one examines them closely. The interpretation of them as gimmicks probably comes from the fact that they were packaged to sell to industry and sometimes were made to sound like a new mechanical device to step up the output from tired Research and Development brains. We choose them for discussion here simply as representatives of programs of training; throughout the country there are a number of programs with similar emphases.

Brainstorming in all seriousness has been taught in recent years most notably by Sidney J. Parnes, whose article "Do You Really Understand Brainstorming?" (1962) is refreshing and clarifying. He points out that brainstorming is essentially part of a total process; creative problem solving is the whole, brainstorming is an element that is usually present whether one sets it up deliberately or not. The basic property of the brainstorm is the outpouring of ideas *without evaluation while the storm is on.* The critical faculty tends to slow down the rate of production of ideas and to reduce them in quantity in a given space of time. It might be clearer, Parnes suggests, if one spoke simply of a *principle of deferred judgment* while ideas were allowed to spring freely to mind and combinatorial play was encouraged in order to increase quantity.

Thus understood, brainstorming is equally applicable to individual thinking as to the group technique that made the term and the method popular. The four rules of brainstorming in a group are : (1) adverse criticism is taboo; (2) freewheeling is welcomed; (3) quantity is wanted; and (4) combination and improvement are sought. Although there have been some studies (for example, Taylor, Berry, and Block, 1957) which call into question the claim that group brainstorming results in the production of more ideas per unit time than individual conventional problem-solving techniques, the majority of controlled investigations do show an increase in both quantity and quality. It must be remembered, however, that only certain kinds of problems can be approached through such a method, and that when the problem itself requires a high level of integral intellect applied to a vast range of details in a search for a resolving explanation, the *whole* process of creative problem solving is called into play.

A recognition of this integrating quality in the creative act gives to "synectics" some depth as a method. The word means "the joining together of different and apparently irrelevant elements." It too began as a group method, its intention being to integrate diverse individuals into a problem-stating and problem-solving group; like brainstorming, however, its fundamental rules or principles of operation are equally applicable to problem-solving by an individual. Its aim is to increase awareness of the mechanisms through which novel solutions are arrived at; one goal, therefore, is to gain insight into the underlying process itself as it occurs, either in the group or the individual, and then to arrange the most suitable circumstances for the emergence of novelty.

Synectics in operation depends heavily on two mechanisms: making the strange familiar, and making the familiar strange. The first of these is the search for similarity; confronted with a new problem, we ask ourselves whether it is not an old problem, had we but the wit to see it. Seeing even partial resemblances may lead to the application of familiar methods in solving the new problem.

Making the familiar strange is a way of shedding preconceptions and perceptual habits. Innocence of vision, a certain naïveté, and ingenuousness, characterize the creative individual; if these qualities can be cultivated, the novelty of invention and problem solution should be increased. Problem stating especially is dependent on this sort of naïveté; one of the worst effects of habit is to blind us even to the fact that a problem exists. (We are so habituated to the idea of death, for instance, that medicine hardly asks the question, "Can death be prevented?," but asks only, "How can life be prolonged?" One might reasonably expect such a problem to be insoluble even if stated, but a priori improbability of solution may not be the reason for its not being stated.)

To attain these goals of making the familiar strange and the strange familiar, synectics employs four main methods: personal analogy, direct analogy, symbolic analogy, and fantasy. Examples of personal analogy given by Gordon (1961) are: Faraday "looked into the very heart of the electrolyte endeavoring to render the play of its atom visible to his mental eyes"; Kekule identified himself with a snake swallowing its tail, and saw thereby an analogy to the benzene molecule as possibly a ring rather than a chain of carbon atoms. Personal analogy there merges into direct analogy. As an example of direct analogy: Alexander Graham Bell writes of his invention of the telephone, ". . . it struck me that the bones of the human ear were very massive, indeed, as compared with the delicate thin membranes that operated them, and the thought occurred that if a membrane so delicate could move bones relatively so massive, why should not a thicker and stouter piece of membrane move my piece of steel . . . and the telephone was conceived."

*Symbolic analogy*, as Gordon describes it, is usually a visual image, disembarrassed of words yet immediate and poetic. It is especially valuable to the inventor because a complex visual resolution fitting a number of requirements is the inventor's product. An example from Gordon is: "How to invent a jacking mechanism to fit a box not bigger than four by four inches yet extend out and up three feet and support four tons?" The solution began to develop when a group member suggested the Indian rope trick as a symbolic analogy "The rope is soft when the guy starts with it . . . the magic is how he makes it hard so he can climb up on it . . ." A few intermediate symbolic analogies led onward to the solution: the hydraulic principle of erection of the penis, and analogy then to a steel tape measure, then to a bicycle chain with flexible links that stiffened as they were driven out of the jacking mechanism.

Biological analogies, frequently including the sexual, were found most useful by the synectics group in the development of new products. Many mechanical devices are direct analogies to the form and function of the human body, of course; the machine is an extension of human might built on the human model.

Fantasy is used in synectics as a way of freeing the imagination from the bounds of the given world. Specific physical laws are imagined not to hold—what would be the consequences? The procedure is very much like the Guilford *Consequences Test* itself, which in turn was based upon Bennett's *Productive Thinking Test*. The latter was used at the Institute of Personality Assessment and Research in 1950 in our first study of originality in graduate students, and when scored for "cosmicality" and "originality" it proved to be an excellent predictor of faculty ratings of Originality. The reader is referred again to "An Odd Fellow" for some examples of original and more or less cosmic responses in that type of test situation.

We have ourselves found Gordon's techniques quite useful in a just-completed, year-long training and research program with teachers and principals in the Goleta, California, public schools. The immediate goal of the program was to increase creative thinking in the teachers and principals themselves; the long-term goal of course was to enhance creative thinking in the students by changing the entire school climate through changes in the teachers and the administration. The program was under the general direction of George I. Brown, of the School of Education at the Santa Barbara campus, University of California; the present writer participated both by conducting living-in assessments of the teachers and principals and by lectures on creative problem solving during frequent week-end training sessions throughout the school year. The assessment test battery was administered at the beginning and at the end of the year. Dr. Brown met weekly with the teachers in small groups for experimentation with the analogical approaches of synectics. The influence of physical environment, especially light, colors, music, and textures, was the object of one set of experiments; brainstorming in the classroom was another. An "open system" as opposed to a "closed system" in the classroom was demonstrated and given much emphasis as a desirable approach. Brown also employed a theoretical approach he had earlier used successfully in teacher training at the undergraduate level, involving identification of a "subself" with a fictionalized symbol of creativity. (An especially effective children's story book used in this project is *The Very Nice Things* by J. Merrill and R. Solbert. It tells the story of William Elephant and Wise Old Owl, who find "some very nice things" washed up on a desert island they are inhabiting; the very nice things are a shirt, pants, gloves, and a hat. William Elephant proceeds to put the things to unusual uses, making a trunk-warmer out of one of the gloves, for example, and a sail for a home-made boat out of the shirt. Elephant's ideas are scorned by Wise Old Owl, who acts for all the world like the peer groups in Torrance's studies who discourage creativity. Children, and teachers as well for that matter, can be taught to adopt Elephant's frame of mind and reject Owl's, with a consequent increase in originality. In fact, in two studies with teacher candidates, Brown found significant increases in both the Barron-Welsh Art Scale and the Complexity Scale when *S*'s were asked to take the tests as though they were William Elephant.

Covington and Crutchfield (1965) have attacked the problem of training by constructing a special curriculum in creative problem solving, using an autoinstructional program. To assess it they gave tests of creativity to an experimental group (those who had experienced the special training) and a matched control group of elementary school students who experienced simply the standard curriculum. They found that the special training did in fact result in an increase in creativity. Some earlier experiments in training for originality (Maltzman *et al.*, 1960; Parnes, 1959; and Mednick, 1961) likewise showed increases in the originality of response in groups receiving such training. A special virtue of the Crutchfield and Covington demonstration is that it was made within the school system itself and resulted in the development of techniques that can be incorporated into existing curricula.

In view of what has been said about the integral quality of creative intellect, one may wonder whether such experiments and such training programs with teachers and students produce lasting change. In Brown's experiments as well as in those of Covington and Crutchfield, only a short time had elapsed between the training program and the appraisal of changes.

It would be easy enough to dismiss such results as superficial changes, but there may be more to the matter than that. The year-long program with adult teachers and principals was considered by all concerned to have resulted in important changes in the classroom and also, in many cases, in the daily living of the teachers themselves. A deep-seated personal process of opening-up was encouraged from the beginning. The results of the initial living-in assessment were communicated in detail to each teacher in intensive interviews in which the actual test scores were revealed and their meaning considered. Strengths and weakness of each teacher were discussed with them in these interviews, and the relationship of their individual test results to the research findings of the Institute's entire program came under scrutiny. It is too early to offer definite evidence or an evaluation as yet, since the program will be continuing through the 1964-1965 school year with emphasis primarily on effects in the classroom, and with objective test evaluation of the effects on the students of these teachers as compared with a control group. The Crutchfield program too is continuing, and within two or three years an evaluation of students who took part in the training course should result in a sound basis for appraising the duration of the effects.

This question of depth or superficiality is a question that runs through all efforts to appraise behavior change, whether or not the theory itself claims depth of understanding, as psychoanalysis does, as well as depth of intervention. Synectics is explicit in aiming at the preconscious in an effort to stimulate the rate and complexity of combinations there through the use of metaphor, symbol, and fantasy. Psychoanalysis in a sense also seeks to broaden the sphere of influence of the preconscious, specifically by intervention in the unconscious with the goal both of freeing content in the unconscious and freeing energy that is being used uneconomically in the neurosis to keep ideational representations of tabooed and repressed drives "bound" in the unconscious. Kubie (1958) has argued that the creative process is interfered with, and distorted by, neurotic complexes and conflicts, and in this sense of the unconscious he is right.

But when artists speak of the unconscious as the source or wellspring of creativity, as many have convincingly done, they mean by unconscious a potentiality that is hardly personal at all, and certainly is not the "personal repressed." D. H. Lawrence, in his short monograph *Psychoanalysis and the Unconscious* (1961), puts the matter as clearly as it has been put analytically; Maritain says much the same thing as Lawrence, though more poetically as well as analytically, in *Creative Intuition in Art and Poetry:*

"Reason does not only consist of its conscious logical tools and manifestations, nor does the will consist only of its deliberate conscious determinations. Far beneath the sunlit surface thronged with explicit concepts and judgments, words and expressed resolutions or movements of the will, are the sources of knowledge and creativity, of love and suprasensuous desires, hidden in the primordial translucid night of the intimate vitality of the soul. Thus it is that we must recognize the existence of an unconscious or preconscious which pertains to the spiritual powers of the human soul and to the inner abyss of personal freedom, and of the personal thirst and striving for knowing and seeing, grasping and expressing: a spiritual or musical unconscious which is specifically different from the automatic or deaf unconscious.

"When man seeking for his own inner universe takes the wrong road, he enters the internal world of the deaf unconscious, while believing he enters the internal world of the spirit, and he thus finds himself wandering in a false kind of self-interiority, where wildness and automatism mimic freedom."

Maritain also says:

"My contention, then, is that everything depends, in the issue we are discussing, on the recognition of the existence of a spiritual unconscious, or rather, preconscious, of which Plato and the ancient wise men were well aware, and the disregard of which in favor of the Freudian unconscious alone is a sign of the dullness of our times. There are two kinds of unconscious, two great domains of psychological activity screened from the grasp of consciousness: the preconscious of the spirit in its living springs, and the unconscious of blood and flesh, instincts, tendencies, complexes, repressed images and desires, traumatic memories, as constituting a closed or automatic dynamic whole. I would like to designate the first kind of unconscious by the name of *spiritual* or, for the sake of Plato, *musical unconscious* or preconscious; and the second by the name of automatic unconscious or *deaf unconscious*—deaf to the intellect, and structured into a world of its own apart from the intellect; we might also say, in quite a general sense, leaving aside any particular theory, *Freudian unconscious*.

"These two kinds of unconscious life are at work at the same time; in concrete existence their respective impacts on conscious activity ordinarily interfere or intermingle in a greater or less degree; and, I think, never—except in some rare instance of supreme spiritual purification—does the spiritual unconscious operate without the other being involved, be it to a very small extent. But they are essentially distinct and thoroughly different in nature."

This idea of a *musical unconscious* squares well with accounts both of creative transport and of mystical experience, although, as Maritain notes, only rarely, if ever, is any human experience utterly free of influences from the personal-historical or Freudian unconscious. Perhaps this fact accounts for some of the puzzlement we are left with when we try to understand either creative genius or rare religious experience.

Freud tackled Dostoevski with the tools of psychoanalysis (*Dostoevski and Parricide*, 1952), and indeed made some progress in relating the themes of crime and punishment, or imagined parricide and self-sought expiation of guilt, in Dostoevski's personal life as well as in his greatest novels; yet Freud confessed before he offered us the results of his speculation that "before the problem of the creative artist analysis must, alas, lay down its arms." The more credit to Freud for doing so, however, and, if we do adopt the designation "Freudian unconscious" for the sphere of mental influence that he investigated so brilliantly, we should do so as one names a new land in honor of its discoverer and explorer, or perhaps as one names a disease in honor of the physician who described its workings and helped conquer it.

Berdyaev has taken quite a different approach to Dostoevski, one that pays heed precisely to the musical unconscious before which Freud lay down his arms. To read the two works together is to see immediately, in the light of three geniuses, these two very different sorts of unconscious mental life. And for some further light reading, nothing could be better than two of Balzac's last works, *Louis Lambert* and *Seraphita* (1907), the first of which shows us Balzac's own tortured inquiry into the two sorts of unconscious as they bear upon the renunciation of sexuality, and the second of which tells of the final embodiment, in both male and female form, of a spirit on the very edge of "supreme purification." Balzac gives us for good measure in the latter story an interior essay on Emanuel Swedenborg, himself one of the great psychological puzzles in whom the Freudian unconscious and the musical or spiritual unconscious are almost inextricably mixed.

Inquiries into the creative unconscious have been proceeding apace with the measurement-based sort of research to which we have devoted most attention in this chapter. Because the methods of inquiry have emphasized the unique value of direct, subjective experience and have tended to scorn the relatively pedestrian sorts of enumeration and crudely drawn comparisons by which we have chosen to proceed in assessment-type studies, the results are not to be stated as scientific knowledge-claims. To say so, however, is neither to impugn their value nor to accept this limitation as necessary or inevitable or desirable.

The methods to which we refer are methods of inducing an altered state of consciousness in which aspects of reality to which one usually does not have access suddenly become prominent because of changes in the very mode of experiencing. The methods themselves, or prototypes of them, are described concisely in two books by Aldous Huxley (1964), *The Doors of Perception* and *Heaven and Hell* (the latter an allusion perhaps to Swedenborg's monumental work, in reply to which William Blake had written *The Marriage of Heaven and Hell* (1926), one of the germinal contributions to a theory of the creative process). The main methods, some of which may sound modern but all of which in basic idea are ancient, are these: (1) breathing of carbon dioxide in a specially prepared mixture consisting of 7 parts of oxygen to 3 parts of carbon dioxide; (2) exposure with eyes open to the rhythmic flashing of a stroboscopic lamp; (3) fasting (either general fasting or abstention from specific foods); (4) bodily mortification, such as self-flagellation; (5) ingestion of naturally occurring substances whose active chemical ingredients produce changes in consciousness, such as the peyote cactus.

The ancients, without scientific knowledge of physiological causation, used practices that are equivalent to some of these, such as Yogic breathing exercises which by way of prolonged suspension of breathing produce high carbon dioxide concentrations in the blood. Hypoxia will produce the same effects, and perhaps some of the mystical qualities attributed to an ascent to mountain heights for meditation are due actually to a decreased proportion of oxygen in the air and hence via decreased oxygen intake to an increase in carbon dioxide concentration. Prolonged rhythmic shouting, singing, and dancing may also produce this effect, and perhaps these have something in common as well with the methods that depend on rhythmic alternations in neural stimulation. Fasting may produce vitamin deficiencies; such disorders as scurvy and pellagra have long been known to generate negative affects of a quasi-mystical sort. Adrenalin metabolism and low blood sugar have also been implicated in accounts of unusual psychic states. And the peyote cactus, of course, is the source of mescaline, one of the more potent hallucinogenic drugs along with psilocybin and LSD-25.

The mediating mechanism in purely psychological terms may be simply a common mode of action physiologically, producing as the most noticeable effect an alteration of perceptual constancies. These are manifestations at the perceptual level of the principle of homeostasis. The central nervous system acts in an adaptive fashion not only by the production of relevant behaviors which help maintain the organism's integrity against environmental dangers, but also in an eliminative fashion by restricting the possible input to consciousness from the great variety of stimuli which are either irrelevant to our efficient functioning or potentially harmful to it.

Both the human organism's capacity to integrate stimuli, and the individual human being's personal history of "learning to see," are involved in the eliminative or selective function in the service of homeostasis. Seeing in the adult is in large part a process of recognizing those signs in the environment which have been proved in his individual experience to be important in maintaining his biological and psychological being in integral form. In brief, we learn to identify, in the very process of receiving stimulation, those aspects of the sensory process that correspond to important aspects of the inner and outer environments. When our "education" is more or less complete, we bring to the act of seeing a large assortment of selective perceptual schemata, most of them of proven adaptive value. The hallucinogenic drugs in particular appear to act centrally upon the faculty of conscious attention in such fashion as to render these perceptual schemata, or constancies—in sum, the normalizing and adaptive apparatus of the ego—temporarily inoperative or at least substantially abrogated.

Because the hallucinogenic drugs are both convenient and powerful and sometimes produce effects that are virtually identical with the mystical experience, they have quite driven out of the market the older methods that take a lot of time and require suffering and spiritual discipline as a prelude to "the supreme purification." It would be easy to be skeptical of them for this reason, and some wag has dubbed them "instant Zen" in appreciation of their meeting the popular American demand for quick results. But if the cortex is the repository of potentialities which we as individuals have had little or nothing to do with, why should we need to suffer individually to gain access to a potential nature that is our evolutionary legacy and for which we ourselves as individuals provide a vehicle for man's journey into the future? Further, who is to measure suffering in terms of time, and how do we know that the drugs are a shortcut? Perhaps one can gain from them only what one can suffer in the brief span of their action . . . perhaps they enable us to suffer more . . . to "die unto ourself" . . . so might the reply run.

That they can also lead into a wild ride in the deaf unconscious, the automatic jig of horrors that may simulate freedom but is actually automatism, as Maritain states it, is incontrovertible. Unmistakably psychotic states have occurred as a result of ingestion of the hallucinogenic drugs, and in some cases these psychoses have proved long-lasting and resistant to treatment. The hallucinogens are unquestionably dangerous, as almost anything so powerful can be. In a certain percentage of cases, perhaps 1 in 100, given unfavorable predisposing circumstances in the individual or in the surrounding circumstances at the time the drug is taken, the hallucinogenic drugs may lead to unconstructive mental imbalance and actual breakdown of ego functions rather than temporary abrogation of them. Control based on understanding is the key to their constructive use, as it is to the use of other energy sources, such as fire or nuclear energy or the rush and pressure of water. (See Barron *et al.*, 1964.)

When the hallucinogens *are* used carefully and with understanding, what are the effects that have led some investigators to think they may be useful in increasing creativity? The following list of reported effects is drawn from numerous subjective reports in writing by individuals who have taken mescaline, LSD-25, or psilocybin. The whole range of effects does not occur on every occasion, but those given here are reported repeatedly and even though not invariant may be considered typical.

1. *Intensification of esthetic sensibility*. Colors become more vivid and glowing; the play of light on objects is enchanting; surface details become sharply defined; sensual harmonies, of sound, light, color become marked. There are beautiful synesthesias, in which patterns of association usually confined to a single sense modality may cross over to others: music is "heard" as colored light, for example.

In some cases, ugliness will become intensified. A garish light may seem horrible, an unmusical sound unbearable; a false tone in a human voice may seem like a shriek; a false expression on a face may make it into a grotesque mask.

Both beauty and ugliness in objects thus are more than usually important and the esthetic qualities of the perceived world take on much greater value.

2. *Unusual associational patterns are much more frequent.* Much as in the synectics technique when it works, the familiar can become quite strange. One may look at a familiar object as though seeing it for the first time. Perceptual habits drop away; hidden essences seem to reveal themselves. Analogical and symbolic properties of persons, events, and objects come into the foreground and combine to produce meaning and pattern where none was seen before.

3. *Intuition in relation to other people is increased.* Other people, whether they themselves are under the influence of the drug or not, are "seen through," though not necessarily in a negative sense. One subject wrote: "The faces of other people became clear and beautiful and open. . . . I could look at them without fear or shyness. . . . People looked naked, shed of a fog of dissimulations, anxieties, hypocrisies. Everyone was true to his own self and no one was ashamed."

Again, however, there can be a negative aspect to this. Intuition is a risky way of understanding others; it can result in brilliant successes or in almost incredible misapprehensions. It proceeds by seizing upon striking details at the expense of other details and making a sort of theory on very limited evidence on the basis simply of "fit." Fictional amateur detectives in the Sherlock Holmes tradition made intuition their stock in trade, and of course they were always right. But when the intuitive approach fails, it can be spectacularly wrong.[3] So far as the hallucinogenic drugs are concerned, we can say with assurance that they increase the use of intuition and so increase one factor in creativity; but sober judgment is the final arbiter of the validity of the intuitive leap.

4. *Higher purposes and the motivation to make one's life philosophically meaningful become very important.* Trivial motives, pretences, social "games" are seen as distractions from the true business of life. One's own life and meaning may be

[3] In an anonymous novel, *The Smiling Corpse,* a master of detective fiction turned the tables on such colleagues as G. K. Chesterton, Sax Rohmer, Dashiell Hammett, and S. S. Van Dyne by imagining them at a literary tea during the course of which the host is found murdered. The authors proceed in the fashion of their fictional detective heroes to solve the murder, each quite ingeniously by mutually contradictory theories, all of which of course are wrong. Sax Rohmer, for instance, knowing that there is an Ancient Order of the Purple Toes in Japan, and finding (by ingenious means) that the Japanese houseboy's toes are painted purple, proceeds to accumulate much circumstantial evidence that implicates the houseboy, who proves embarrassingly enough to have athlete's foot which he is treating with potassium permanganate. And so on . . .

meditated upon, and a new appraisal "sub specie aeternitatis" may be made. Thus, profound motivational change in the direction of dedicating one's life to a higher purpose may come about. The ordinary round of life will no longer do.

This too may have troublesome consequences, it need hardly be added. For one thing, it upsets other people, who can no longer count upon one's more mundane motives. Changes of this sort in motivational structure may result in ruptures in personal relations, work relations, financial arrangements, as well as general social behavior. If in this new cosmic scale of things one's life seems intolerably empty and too far gone to change, there may be impulses toward self-destruction or cessation of the known self. (For a profound discussion of the desire for cessation, see Edwin Shneidman's essay (1963) in *The Study of Lives.*)

5. *A mystical experience of absolute freedom may occur.* This is perhaps not so frequent a phenomenon as to deserve to be called typical, but it occurs often enough in persons under the influence of hallucinogenic drugs to warrant remark; and as a source of motivational change it is by all odds the most powerful of all. In it, the personal ego seems utterly dissolved, and the individual has his existence in the grounds of being itself. The experience is of "the void"; that is, the "abyss" of which philosophers have spoken. Without entering into the metaphysics of the matter, we can say as psychologists that the individual who has had this experience emerges from it with a sense of inner freedom and power, although as usual there may be a negative as well as a positive aspect to this. In the negative case, the freedom seems based on a sense of non-being, on identification with a final nothingness. Heidigger (1929) has expressed this interpretation of freedom as having its ground in Non-being most vividly, perhaps, in his *Beyond Metaphysics;* and it may be no accident that he was a supporter of Nazism. The writings of Jakob Boehme offer a more inclusive formulation in which both the positive and the negative mystical experience of freedom are comprehended. Berdyaev,

again, gives trenchant statement in religio-mystical terms to the positive and creative meaning of freedom.[4]

> "The creative act is a free and independent force, immanently inherent only in a person, a personality. Only something arising in original substance and possessing the power to increase power in the world can be true creativity. . . . Creativity . . . is an original act of personalities in the world."

Berdyaev further describes the nature of freedom:[5]

> ". . . only the free man creates. The determinism which is so compulsively forced upon us is false because freedom of personality does exist, creatively breaking the chains of necessity. We cannot understand the creative secret of being in a passive way, in an atmosphere of obedience to the world's heavy materialism. It can be understood only actively, in the atmosphere of the creative act itself."

Such elevated motives may carry their own penalty, in the form of a loss of contact with ordinary human feeling and an unrealistic inflation of one's own self-estimate. The Grounds of Being may be only a step from the grounds of melodrama. William James remarks somewhere on the reaction of German philosophers to the idea of the transcendental Ego: "at the mention of the term they act as though a balloon is about to go up." Certainly more melodrama than research has resulted from many of the explorations with the hallucinogenic drugs in contexts which emphasize the transcendental nature of the experience. Perhaps this is only to be expected in the early stages of exploration; still, at present it is fair to say that there is no evidence of a scientific nature supporting the reasonable hope that the hallucinogens may be effective in increasing creativity. This is true also of most of the special training programs for increasing creativity; the step of objective evaluation of change is all too often omitted. There is considerable basis in subjective report for believing that such change is possible, but

[4] *The Meaning of the Creative Act,* p. 135.

[5] Ibid., p. 155.

hard evidence is lacking. In the case of the hallucinogens, it should be possible to use a procedure like living-in assessment to provide a set of baseline measures prior to the drug-centered regimen itself, and even, with the careful preparation of subjects and one or two familiarization sessions, to administer during experimental drug sessions certain assessment measures relevant to associational and ideational fluency, originality, esthetic discrimination and expression, and so on. Then, further living-in assessments several months after the creativity training could provide evidence as to the durability of effects.

Thus we come round again to the two themes with which we began. Creativity is intimately bound up with the religious interpretation of experience, yet it is open to study in a thoroughly naturalistic and scientific way. Perhaps in the end it is through a scientific approach that it will be best understood. And it is peculiarly a problem of our own times, for the interest in expressing to the full one's own potentiality for creativity has never before been so widespread. The technological revolution is underlining what the release of nuclear energy foreshadowed: we are in a period in which the power of intellect, and particularly its capacity for innovation and creativeness, is reaching an entirely new level of capacity to decide the milieu in which human nature shall evolve further, and perhaps the very form of that evolution. Individual psychic creativity is thus brought into a new sort of relationship to the creative process throughout nature, and the emergence of novelty in human thought and action is a phenomenon which for psychology as a scientific discipline provides a point of entry into a problem that surely will be central to the unity of science.

# REFERENCES

Allport, G. W. *Personality*. New York: Holt, Rinehart and Winston, 1937.

Anderson, H. H. *Creativity and its cultivation.* New York: Harper & Row, 1959.

Andrews, E. Development of imagination in pre-school children. University of Iowa Studies in Character, 1930, 3, 4.

Arnheim, L. Perceptual abstraction and art. *Psychol. Rev.*, 1947, *54*, 66-82.

Asch, S. E. *Social psychology*. Englewood Cliffs, N. J.: Prentice-Hall, 1952.

Balint, M. The three areas of the mind. *Int. J. psychol. Analysis*, 1958, *39*, 328-340.

Balkan, E. R., and J. H. Masserman. Language of phantasy, III. *J. psychol.*, 1940, *10*, 75-86.

Balzac, de, H. *Louis Lambert* and *Seraphita.* In Vol. 17 *Oeuvres*, 24 vols. Paris: Société d'éditions littéraires et artistiques, 1907.

Barron, F. Complexity-simplicity as a personality dimension. *J. abnorm. soc. Psychol.*, 1953, *68*, 163-172.

Barron, F. Creativity. In A. Deutsch (Ed.), *The encyclopedia of mental health*, Vol. II. New York: F. Watts, 1963.

Barron, F. *Creativity and psychological health.* Princeton, N. J.: Van Nostrand, 1963.

Barron, F. Integration, diffusion, and enduring attention as aspects of the creative process. In R. W. White (Ed.), *The study of lives: essays on personality in honor of Henry A. Murray*. New York: Atherton Press, 1963.

Barron, F. Inventory of personal philosophy. Berkeley: University of California, 1952.

Barron, F. Originality in relation to personality and intellect. *J. Personal.*, 1957, *25*, 730-742.

Barron, F. Personality style and perceptual choice. *J. Personal.*, 1952, *20*, 385-401.

Barron, F. Some personality correlates of independence of judgment. *J. Personal.*, 1953, *21*, 289-297.

Barron, F. The disposition toward originality. *J. abnorm. soc. Psychol.*, 1955, *51*, 478-485.

Barron, F. The needs for order and disorder as motives in creative activity. In C. W. Taylor and F. Barron (Eds.), *Scientific creativity*. New York: Wiley, 1963.

Barron, F. The psychology of creativity. *Encyclopaedia Britannica*, 1963, *6*, 711-712. New York: Encyclopaedia Britannica, Inc.

Barron, F. The psychology of imagination. *Sci. Amer.*, 1958, *199*, 151-166.

Barron, F. The word rearrangement test. Maxwell Air Force Base, Alabama: Officer Education Research Laboratory, May 1955. (*Technical Memorandum OERL-TM-55-11.*)

Barron, F. Threshold for the perception of human movement in inkblots. *J. consult. Psychol.*, 1955, *19*, 33-38.

Barron, F., J. P. Guilford, P. R. Christensen, R. M. Berger, and N. W. Kettner. Interrelations of various measures of creative traits. *Technical Memorandum AF18(600)-8*. Berkeley, California: Institute of Personality Assessment and Research, 1957.

Barron, F., M. Jarvik, and S. Bunnell. The hallucinogenic drugs. *Sci. Amer.*, April, 1964.

Barron, F., and G. S. Welsh. Artistic perception as a possible factor in personality style: its measurement by figure preference test. *J. Psychol.*, 1952, *33*, 199-203.

Bartlett, F. C. Types of imagination. *J. Phil. Studies*, 1928, *3*, 78-85.

Bellak, L. Creativity, some random notes to a systematic consideration. *J. proj. Tech.*, 1958, 22, 363-380.

Bennett, G. K. *A test of productive thinking*. New York: Psychological Corporation, 1947.

Berdyaev, N. *Dostoevski: an interpretation.* (Trans. by Donald Attwatter.) New York: Sheed and Ward, 1934.

Berdyaev, N. *The meaning of the creative act.* (Trans. by D. A. Laurie.) New York: Harper & Row, 1954.

Beres, D. Perception, imagination and reality. *Int. J. Psychoanal.*, 1960, *41*, 327-334.

Beres, D. The psychoanalytic psychology of imagination. *J. Amer. Psychoanal. Assoc.*, 1960, *8*, 252-269.

Berger, R. M., J. P. Guilford, and P. R. Christensen. A factor-analytical study of planning abilities. *Psychol. Monogr.*, 1957, *71* (Whole No. 435).

Bergson, H. *The creative mind.* New York: Philosophical Library, 1946.

Bischler, W. Intelligence and the higher mental functions. (Trans. by P. Winner.) *Psych. Quart.*, 1937, 277-307.

Blake, W. "The marriage of heaven and hell." In D. J. Sloss and J. P. R. Wallis (Eds.), *The prophetic writings of William Blake,* Vol. 1. Oxford: Clarendon Press, 1926.

Blatt, S. J., and M. T. Stein. Some personality, value and cognitive characteristics of the creative person. *Amer. J. Psychol.*, 1957, *12*, 406.

Bowerman, W. G. *Studies in genius.* New York: Philosophical Library, 1947.

Brimhall, D. R. Family resemblances among American men of science. *American Naturalist*, 1923.

Brittain, H. L. A study of imagination. *Ped. Sem.*, 1907, *14*, 137-207.

Brittain, W., and K. Beittal. Analyses of levels of creative performance. *J. Aesth. Art. Crit.*, 1960, *19*, 83-90.

Buell, W. D. Validity of behavioral rating scale items for assessment of individual creativity. *J. appl. Psychol.*, 1960, *44*, 407-412.

Burchard, E. The use of projective techniques in the analysis of creativity. *J. Prof. Tech.*, 1952, *16*, 412-427.

Burkhart, R. The relation of intelligence to artistic ability. *J. Aesth. Art. Crit.*, 1958, *12*, 230-241.

Burt, C. The structure of the mind: a review of the results of factor analysis. *Brit. J. educ. Psychol.*, 1949, *19*, 100-111, 176-199.

Campbell, D. T. Blind variation and selective retentions in creative thought as in other human knowledge processes. *Psychol. Rev.*, 1960, *67*, 380-400.

Candolle, de, A. *Histoire des sciences et des savants depuis deux siècles*. Geneve: Georg, 1885.

Carroll, J. B. A factor analysis of verbal abilities. *Psychometrika*, 1941, *6*, 279-307.

Cattell, J. McK. A statistical study of eminent men. *Popular Science Monthly*, February 1903, 359-377.

Cattell, R. B. The personality and motivation of the researcher from measurements of contemporaries and from biography. In C. W. Taylor and F. Barron (Eds.), *Scientific creativity*. New York: Wiley, 1963.

Cattell, R. B., and J. E. Drevdahl. A comparison of the personality profile of eminent researchers with that of eminent teachers and administrators and that of the general population. *Brit. J. Psychol.*, 1955, *46*, 248-261.

Chambers, J. A. Relating personality and biographical factors to scientific creativity. *Psychol. Monogr.*, 78, 7, 1964.

Christensen, P. R., and J. P. Guilford. An experimental study of verbal fluency factors. *Brit. J. stat. Psychol.*, 1963, *16*, 1-26.

Clarke, E. L. *American men of letters, their nature and nurture*. New York: Columbia University Press, 1916.

Covington, M. V., and R. S. Crutchfield. Experiments in the use of programed instruction for the facilitation of creative problem solving. *Programed Instruction*, January 1965.

Cox, C. The early mental traits of 300 geniuses. *Genetic Studies of Genius*, Vol. II. Stanford: Stanford University Press, 1926.

Crawford, P. R. *Techniques of creative thinking*. New York: Hawthorn, 1954.

Crutchfield, R. S. Assessment of persons through a quasi-group-interaction technique. *J. abnorm. soc. Psychol.*, 1951, *4*, 577-588.

Crutchfield, R. S. Conformity and character. *Amer. Psychol.*, 1955, *10*, 191-198.

Crutchfield, R. S. Conformity and creative thinking. In H. E. Gruber, G. Terrell, and M. Wertheimer (Eds.), *Contemporary approaches to creative thinking*. New York: Atherton Press, 1962.

Crutchfield, R. S., and M. V. Covington. Programed instruction in creativity. *Programed Instruction*, January 1965.

Crutchfield, R. S. Independent thought in a conformist world. In S. M. Farber and R. H. L. Wilson (Eds.), *Conflict and creativity*. New York: McGraw-Hill, 1963.

Davenport, C. B. *Naval officers: their heredity and development*. Washington: Carnegie Institute, 1919.

Davis, P. C. A factor analysis of the Wechsler-Bellevue scale. *Educ. psychol. Measmt.*, 1956, *14*, 127-146.

Dearborn, G. V. A study of imagination. *Amer. J. Psychol.*, 1898, *5* (9), 183.

Drevdahl, J. E. Factors of importance for creativity. *J. clin. Psychol.*, 1956, *12*, 21-26.

Drevdahl, J. E., and R. B. Cattell. Personality and creativity in artists and writers. *J. clin. Psychol.*, 1958, *14*, 107-111.

Drews, E. Freedom to grow. *N. E. A. Journal*, September 1960, *49* (6), 20-22.

Eiduson, B. L. Artist and non-artist: a comparative study. *J. Personnel*, 1958, *26*, 13-28.

Ellis, Havelock. *A study of British genius*. London: Hurst and Blackett, 1904.

Eysenck, H. J. *Dimensions of personality*. London: Routledge, 1947.

Eysenck, H. J. *The structure of personality*. New York: Wiley, 1953.

Flanagan, J. Definition and measurement of ingenuity. In C. W. Taylor and F. Barron (Eds.), *Scientific creativity*. New York: Wiley, 1963.

Fleming, E. S., and S. Weintraub. Additional rigidity as a measure of creativity in gifted children. *J. educ. Psychol.*, 1962, *53*, 81-85.

Freud, S. Dostoevski and parricide. (Trans. by D. F. Tait.) In *Collected papers,* Vol. V., 222-242. London: Hogarth, 1952.

Frick, J. W., J. P. Guilford, P. R. Christensen, and P. R. Merrifield. A factor analytic study of creative thinking. *Educ. psychol. Measmt.*, 1959, *19*, 469-496.

Galton, F. *English men of science: their nature and nurture.* London: Macmillan, 1874.

Galton, F. *Hereditary genius.* London: Macmillan, 1925.

Galton, F. *Inquiries into human faculty.* London: Macmillan, 1883.

Gardner, J. *Self-renewal.* New York: Harper & Row, 1963.

Getzels, J. W., and P. O. Jackson. *Creativity and intelligence.* New York: Wiley, 1962.

Getzels, J. W., and P. O. Jackson. Occupational choice and cognitive functions. Career aspirations of the highly intelligent and the highly creative adolescent. *J. abnorm. soc. Psychol.*, 1960, *61*, 119-123.

Ghiselin, B. *The creative process.* Berkeley: University of California Press, 1952.

Giovacchini, P. L. On scientific creativity. *J. Amer. psychoanal. Assoc.*, 1960, *8*, 407-476.

Glass, S. I. Creative thinking can be released and applied. *Person. J.*, 1960, *39*, 176, 177.

Goertzel, V., and M. G. Goertzel, *Cradles of eminence.* Boston: Little, Brown, 1962.

Gordon, W. J. J. *Synectics: the development of creative capacity.* New York: Harper & Row, 1961.

Gough, H. G. *Manual for the California Psychological Inventory.* Palo Alto, California: Consulting Psychologists Press, 1957.

Gough, H. G. *Manual for the Adjective Checklist.* Palo Alto, California: Consulting Psychologists Press, 1965.

Gough, H. G. Techniques for identifying the creative research scientist. In D. W. MacKinnon (Ed.), *The creative person.* Berkeley: University of California Extension, 1961.

Gough, H. G. The Adjective Check List as a personality assessment research technique. *Psychol. Rep., Monogr. Suppl.;* 1960, *6*, 107-122.

Gough, H. G., and D. G. Woodworth. Stylistic variations among professional research scientists. *J. Psychol.*, 1960, *49*, 87-98.

Greenacre, P. The childhood of the artist. Libidinal phase development and greatness. *The Psychoanalytic Study of the Child*, Vol. XII. New York: International Universities Press, 1957. Pp. 47-72.

Griffin, D. P. Movement responses and creativity. *J. consult. Psychol.*, 1958, *22*, 134-136.

Guilford, J. P. Basic conceptual problems in the psychology of thinking. *Ann. New York Acad. Sci.*, 1960, *91*, 6-21.(a)

Guilford, J. P. Creative abilities in the arts. *Psychol. Rev.*, 1957, *64*, 110-118.

Guilford, J. P. Creativity. *Amer. Psychologist*, 1950, *5*, 444-454.

Guilford, J. P. Factorial angles to psychology. *Psychol. Rev.*, 1961, 68, 1-20.

Guilford, J. P. Factor analysis in a test-development program. *Psychol. Rev.*, 1948, *55*, 79-94.

Guilford, J. P. Frontiers in thinking teachers should know about. *Reading Teacher*, 1960, 176-182.(c)

Guilford, J. P. *Personality*. New York: McGraw-Hill, 1959, 382, 383.

Guilford, J. P. Progress in the discovery of intellectual factors. In C. W. Taylor (Ed.), *Widening horizons in creativity*. New York: McGraw-Hill, 1964.(a)

Guilford, J. P. Structure of intellect. *Psychol. Bull.*, 1956, *53*, 267-293(b)

Guilford, J. P. Three faces of intellect. *Amer. Psychologist*, 1959, *14*, 469-479.(b)

Guilford, J. P. Zero correlations among tests of intellectual abilities. *Psychol. Bull.*, 1964, 61,(c).

Gutman, H. Biological roots of creativity. *Genet. psychol. Monol.*, 1961, *64*, 417-458.

Halbeck, C. R. The creative personality. *Amer. J. Psychoanal.*, 1945, *5*, 49-58.

Hall, W. B. The development of a technique for assessing aesthetic predisposition and its application to a sample of research scientists. Paper read at Western Psych. Assoc., Monterey, California, April 1958. Berkeley: Institute of Personality Assessment and Research, University of California.

Hammer, E. F. *Creativity*. New York: Random House, 1961.

Harms, E. A test for types of formal creativity. *Psychol. Bull.*, 1939, *36*, 526, 527.

Harris, D. Development and validity of test of creativity in engineering. *J. appl. Psychol.*, 1960, *44*, 254-257.

Hathaway, S. R., and J. C. McKinley. *Manual for the Minnesota Multiphasic Personality Inventory*. Minneapolis: University of Minnesota Press, 1943.

Heidigger, M. *What is metaphysics?* Bonn: F. Cohen, 1929.

Helson, Ravenna. Creativity, sex, and mathematics. In D. W. MacKinnon (Ed.), *The Creative Person*. Berkeley: University of California Extension, 1961.

Henry, W. E. *The analysis of fantasy*. New York: Wiley, 1956.

Hilgard, E. R. Creativity and problem solving. In H. H. Anderson (Ed.), *Creativity and its cultivation*, 1959. Pp. 162-180.

Holland, J. L., and L. Kent. The concentration of scholarship funds and its implications for education. *College and University*, Summer 1960, *35* (4), 471-483.

Hutchinson, E. D. Materials for the study of creative thinking. *Psychol. Bull.*, 1931, *28*, 392-410.

Hutton, E., and M. Basset. The effect of leucotomy on the creative personality. *J. ment. Sci.*, 1948, *94*, 333-380.

Huxley, A. *The doors of perception* and *Heaven and hell.* New York: Harper & Row, 1964.

Johnson, S. R., and E. E. Glaze. A critical analysis of psychological treatments of children's drawings and paintings. *J. Aesth. Art. Crit.*, 1958, *17*, 242-250.

Jung, C. G. *Psychological types.* New York: Harcourt, 1924.

Kettner, N. W., J. P. Guilford, and P. R. Christensen. A factor-analytic study across the domains of reasoning, creativity, and evaluation. *Psychol. Monogr.*, 1959, 73 (Whole No. 479).

Knapp, R. H., and H. B. Goodrich. *Origins of American scientists.* Chicago: University of Chicago Press, 1952.

Kris, E. *Psychoanalytic exploration in art.* New York: International Universities Press, 1952.

Kubie, L. S. *Neurotic distortion of the creative process.* Lawrence, Kansas: University of Kansas Press, 1958.

Lawrence, D. H. *Psychoanalysis and the unconscious* and *Fantasia of the unconscious.* Melbourne: W. Heinemann, 1961.

Lehman, H. C. *Age and achievement.* Princeton, N. J.: Princeton University Press, 1953.

Levy, N. Notes on the creative process and the creative person. *Psychiat. Quart.*, 1961, *35*, 66-77.

MacKinnon, D. W. Fact and fancy in personality research. *Amer. Psychologist*, 1953, *8*, 138-146.

MacKinnon, D. W. Fostering creativity in students of engineering. *J. engng. Educ.*, 1961, *52*, 129-142.

MacKinnon, D. W. Genus architectus creator varietas Americanus. *Amer. Inst. Architects J.*, September, 1960, 31-35.

MacKinnon, D. W. The nature and nurture of creative talent. *Amer. Psychologist*, 1962, 484-495.

MacKinnon, D. W., *et al. Proceedings of the Conference on "The Creative Person," University of California Alumni Center, Lake Tahoe, California.* Berkeley: University of California Extension, 1961.

Maltzman, I., S. Simon, D. Raskin, and L. Licht. Experimental studies in the training of originality. *Psychol. Monogr.*, 1960, *74*, no. 6, 1-23.

Mandell, M. M., and S. Adams. Measuring originality in physical scientists. *Educ. psychol. Measmt.*, 1948, *8*, 515-582.

Maritain, J. *Creative intuition in art and poetry*. New York: Meridian, 1955.

Markey, F. V. Imagination. *Psychol. Bull.*, 1935, *32*, 212-236.

Maslow, A. H. Creativity in self-actualizing people. In H. H. Anderson (Ed.), *Creativity and its cultivation*, 1959, Chap. 7.

Maslow, A. H. Defense and growth. *Merrill-Palmer Quart.*, 1956, *3*, 37, 38.

May, R. The nature of creativity. In H. H. Anderson (Ed.), *Creativity and its cultivation*. New York: Harper & Row, 1959.

McCarthy, M. *The group*. New York: Harcourt, 1963.

McCloy, W., and N. C. Meier. Re-creative imagination. *Psychol. Monogr.*, 1931, *51* (5), 108-116.

McGeoch, J. A. Relationship between three tests for imagination and their correlation with intelligence. *J. appl. Psychol.*, 1924, *8*, 443-459.

Mednick, S. The associative basis of the creative process. *Psychol. Rev.*, 1962, *69*, 220-232.

Mednick, S., and M. Mednick. Experiments in the associational process. In press.

Meer, B., and M. I. Stein. Measures of intelligence and creativity. *J. Psychol.*, 1955, *39*, 117-126.

Mooney, R. L. A conceptual model for integrating four approaches to the identification of creative talent. In C. W. Taylor and F. Barron (Eds.), *Scientific creativity*. New York: Wiley, 1963.

Mosing, L. W. Development of a multi-media creativity test. *Dist. Abstract*, 1959, *19*, 2137.

Mueller, R. E. *Inventivity*. New York: John Day, 1963.

Mullins, C. J. Selection of creative personnel. *Person. J.*, 1960, *39*, 12, 13.

Munsterberg, E., and P. H. Mussen. Personality structure of art students. *J. Personal.*, 1953, *21*, 457-466.

Murphy, G. Creativeness. *Menn. Quart.*, 1957, 1-6.

Murray, H. A. *Explorations in personality.* New York: Oxford, 1938.

Murray, H. A., and P. R. Christensen. *The Thematic Apperception Test Manual.* Cambridge, Mass.: Harvard University Press, 1943.

Murray, H. A., D. W. MacKinnon, J. G. Miller, D. W. Fiske, and E. Hanfmann. *Assessment of Men.* Reissue. New York: Holt, Rinehart and Winston, 1963.

Myers, Isabel B. *Some findings with regard to type and manual for Myers-Briggs Type Indicator, Form E.* Swarthmore, Pa.: Author, 1958.

Nisbet, R. A., and D. Blisten. The creative context: a preface. *Autonomous Groups Bull.*, 1957, *12*, 1-3.

Odin, A. Genèse des grands hommes. *Gens des Lettres Français Modernes*, Paris, 1895.

Orowan, E. Our universities and scientific creativity. *Bull. Atom. Sci.*, 1959, *6*, 2369.

Osborn, A. F. *Applied imagination.* New York: Scribner, 1957.

Ostwald, W. *Grosse Manner.* Liepzig: Akademische Verlagsgesellschaft, 1909.

Owens, W. A., C. F. Schumacher, and J. B. Clark. The measurement of creativity in machine design. *J. appl. Psychol.*, 1957, *41*, 297-302.

Parnes, S. J. Do you really understand brainstorming? In S. J. Parnes and H. F. Harding (Eds.), *A source book for creative thinking.* New York: Scribner, 1962.

Parnes, S. J. Effects of brain-storming instructions on creative problem-solving. *J. educ. Psychol.*, 1959, *50*, 171-176.

Parnes, S. J., and A. Meadow. Evaluation of persistence of effects produced by a creative problem-solving course. *Psychol. Rep.*, 1960, 7, 357-361.

Peterson, R. O. *Creativity and conformity: a problem of or-*

*ganization.* Foundation for research on human behavior. Ann Arbor, Michigan, 1958. 46 pp.

Phratol, P. Experimental study of creativity and intelligence and school achievement. *Psych. Studies, Mysore,* 1962, 7, 1-9.

Piaget, P. *The psychology of intelligence.* New York: Harcourt, 1950.

Piers, G. V., and J. M. Daniels. The identification of creativity in adolescence. *J. educ. Psychol.,* 1960, *51,* 346-357.

Pine, F. Thematic drive content and creativity. *J. Personal.,* 1959, *27,* 136-151.

Pine, F., and R. Hoh. Creativity and the primary process: a study of adaptive regression. *J. abnorm. Psychol.,* 1960, *61,* 370-379.

Portnoy, J. Is the creative process similar in the arts? *J. Aesth. Art. Crit.,* 1960, *19,* 191-195.

Rees, M. E., and M. Goldman. Some relationships between creativity and personality. *J. genet. Psychol.,* 1961, *65,* 145-161.

Rexroth, K. The vivisection of a poet. *The Nation,* 1958.

Rhodes, J. M. The dynamics of creativity: an interpretation of literature on creativity with a proposed procedure for objective research. *Diss. Abst.,* 1957, *17,* 96.

Rivlin, L. G. Creativity and the self-attitudes and socialization of high school students. *J. Educ. Psychol.,* 1959, *60,* 147-152.

Roberts, W. Normal and abnormal depersonalization. *J. ment. Sci.,* 1960, *106,* 478-493.

Roe, Anne. A psychological examination of eminent biologists. *J. consult. Psychol.,* 1949, *13,* 225-246.

Roe, Anne. A psychological study of eminent biologists. *Psychol. Monogr.,* 1951, *54* (14), 68 pp.

Roe, Anne. A psychological study of eminent psychologists and anthropologists, and a comparison with biologists and physical scientists. *Psychol. Monogr.,* 1953, *57* (2), 55 pp.

Roe, Anne. Artists and their work. *J. Pers.,* 1946, *15,* 1-40.

Roe, Anne. A study of imagery in research scientists. *J. Pers.*, 1951, *19*, 459-470.

Roe, Anne. Painting and personality. *Rorschach Research Exchange*, 1946, *10*, 81-100.

Roe, Anne. Psychological tests of research scientists. *J. consult. Psychol.*, 1951, *15*, 491-495.

Roe, Anne. *The making of a scientist.* New York: Dodd, Mead, 1952.

Roe, Anne. The personality of artists. *Educ. Psychol.*, 1946, *6*, 401-408.

Rorschach, H. *Psychodiagnostics.* Bern: Huber (Grune & Stratton, New York, distributors), 1942.

Rosen, V. H. Some aspects of the role of imagination in psychoanalysis. *J. Amer. Psychoanalysis Association*, 1960, *8*, 229-251.

Rutherford, J. M. Personality correlates of creativity. *Diss. Abst.*, 1960, *20*, 4434.

Schachtel, E. G. *Metamorphosis: on the development of affect, perception, attention and memory.* New York: Basic Books, 1959.

Schiner, J. Free association and ego formation in creativity. *Am. Imag.*, 1960, *17*, 61-74.

Schneidman, E. S. Orientations toward death. In R. W. White (Ed.), *The study of lives.* New York: Atherton, 1963.

Simons, J. H. Scientific research in universities. *Amer. Sci.*, 1960, *48*, 80-90.

Simpson, R. M. Creative imagination. *Amer. J. Psychol.*, 1922, *33*, 23-35.

Spoerl, D. T. Personality and drawing in retarded children. *Charact. and Pers.*, 1940, *8*, 227-239.

Sprecher, T. B. An investigation of criteria for creativity in engineers. *Diss. Abst.*, 1958, *18*, 1101, 1102.

Stein, M. I. Creativity and culture. *J. Psychol.*, 1953, *36*, 311-322.

Stein, M. I., and S. J. Heinze. *Creativity and the individual.* New York: Free Press, 1960.

Stein, M. I., and B. Meer. Perceptual organization in a study of creativity. *J. Psychol.*, 1954, *37*, 39-43.

Stern, W. Cloud pictures. A new method for testing imagination. *Charact. & Pers.*, 1937, *6*, 132-146.

Strong, E. K., Jr. *The Vocational Interests of Men and Women.* Stanford: Stanford University Press, 1943.

Swedenborg, E. *Heaven and hell.* London: The Swedenborg Society, 1850.

Taylor, C. W. The identification of creative scientific talent. *Amer. Psychologist*, 1959, *14*, 100-102.

Taylor, C. W., and F. Barron. *Scientific creativity: its recognition and development.* New York: Wiley, 1963.

Taylor, C. W., P. C. Berry, and C. H. Block. Does group participation when using brainstorming facilitate or inhibit creative thinking? ONR Technical Memorandum, Psychology Department, Yale University, 1957.

Taylor, I. A. The nature of the creative process. In P. Smith (Ed.), *Creativity*. New York: Hastings, 1959. Pp. 51-82.

Terman, L. M. The intelligence quotient of Francis Galton in childhood. *Amer. J. Psychol.*, 1917, *28*, 204-215.

Terman, L. M., and M. H. Odin. *The gifted child grows up.* Vol. 4 of Genetic Studies of Genius. Stanford, California: Stanford University Press, 1947.

Thurstone, L. L. Creative talent. In L. L. Thurstone (Ed.), *Applications of psychology*. New York: Harper & Row, 1952.

Thurstone, L. L. Primary mental abilities. *Psychometric Monogr.*, No. 1, 1938.

Torrance, E. P. Current research on creativity. *J. consult. Psychol.*, 1959, *6*, 309-316.

Torrance, E. P. Explorations in creative thinking. *Educat.*, 1960, *81*, 216-220.

Torrance, E. P. *Guiding creative talent.* Englewood, N. J.: Prentice-Hall, 1962.

Torrance, E. P. Problems of the highly gifted child. *Gifted Child Quart.*, 1961, *5*, 31-34.

True, G. H. Creativity as a function of ideational fluency, practicability and specific training. *Diss. Abst.*, 1957, *17*, 402.

Vernon, P. E. *The structure of human abilities.* New York: Wiley, 1950.

Vinacke, W. E. Creative thinking. In W. E. Vinacke (Ed.), *The psychology of thinking.* New York: McGraw-Hill, 1952. Pp. 238-261.

Visher, S. S. *Scientists starred in American men of science, 1903-1943.* Baltimore: The Johns Hopkins Press, 1947.

Wallas, G. *The art of thought.* New York: Harcourt, 1926.

Weisberg, P. S., and K. Springer. Environmental factors in creative functioning of gifted children. *Arch. Gen-Psych.*, 1961, *5*, 554-564.

Weissman, P. Development and creativity in actor and playwright. *Psychoanal. Quart.*, 1961, *30*, 638-643.

Welch, L. Recombination of ideas in creative thinking. *J. appl. Psychol.*, 1946, *30*, 638-643.

Wenkart, A. Modern art and human development. *Amer. J. Psychoanal.*, 1960, *20*, 174-179.

Wertheimer, M. *Productive thinking.* New York: Harper & Row, 1954.

White, R. W. *The study of lives.* New York: Atherton, 1963.

Whiting, C. S. *Creative thinking.* New York: Holt, Rinehart and Winston, 1958.

Wilson, R. N. Poetic creativity, process and personality. *Psychiat.*, 1954, *17*, 163-176.

Wilson, R. C., J. P. Guilford, and P. R. Christensen. The measurement of individual differences in originality. *Psychol. Bull.*, 1953, *50*, 362-370.

Woods, F. A. *Mental and moral heredity in royalty.* New York: Holt, Rinehart and Winston 1906.

Woolf, Virginia. *A room of one's own.* London: Hogarth, 1935.

Woolf, Virginia. *Orlando.* New York: Harcourt, 1928.

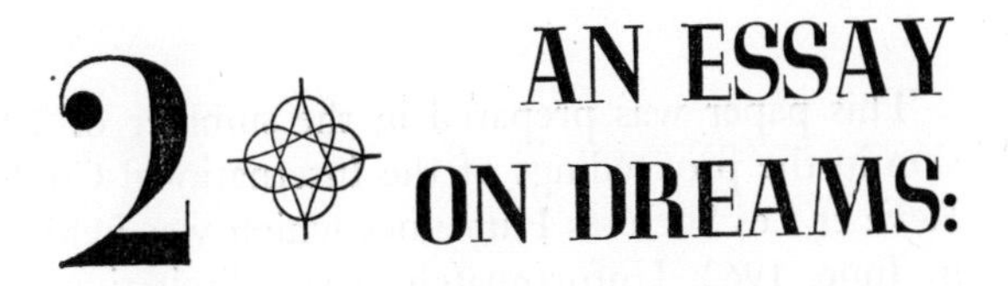

# 2 AN ESSAY ON DREAMS:

## THE ROLE OF PHYSIOLOGY IN UNDERSTANDING THEIR NATURE

WILLIAM C. DEMENT
STANFORD UNIVERSITY

This paper was prepared in the summer of 1962 for inclusion in the proceedings of the International Conference on Le Reve et Les Sociétés Humaines which was held at Royaumont in June, 1962. Unfortunately, space limitations prevented the publication of such a lengthy review. A few months ago, the interest of the editors of *New Directions* saved the manuscript from being consigned to the wastebasket, but there was not enough time to bring it entirely up-to-date and yet meet the publication deadline. However, although there has been a great deal of work done in this area in the past one and one-half years, nothing has taken place that would contradict or radically alter any of the material in this review. Therefore, I have been content merely to add a few of the more important of the very recent findings. Many of the ideas expressed herein have grown out of collaborative efforts with various colleagues, although I must claim final responsibility for any overly high speculative flight. I especially acknowledge my association with Nathaniel Kleitman, Professor Emeritus, Department of Physiology, at the University of Chicago. Investigations carried out by the author were supported by a Postdoctoral Public Health Service Research Fellowship from the National Institute of Neurological Diseases and Blindness, a Foundations' Fund for Research in Psychiatry Training Fellowship, and Research Grants MY-3267 and MH 08185-01 from the National Institute of Mental Health.

# INTRODUCTION

## SOME DIFFICULTIES IN THE STUDY OF DREAMS

Dreams have been a source of wonder and fascination for man since time immemorial. With primitive peoples, it was as if they enjoyed a curious privilege of citizenship in two worlds, each with its own logic and its own limitations, and there was no obvious reason for thinking one of them was more significant than the other. The waking world had certain advantages of solidity and continuity, whereas the dream world offered the chance of intercourse, however fugitive, with distant friends, dead relatives, and even gods and demons. Thus, the dream world was accorded a validity equal, in some cases, to that of waking life, though different in kind.

Modern man, on the other hand, has confined the attribute of reality to only one of his two worlds, and has dismissed the other as pure illusion, or more precisely as the characteristic mental activity of the organism during sleep. For some, this means that the dream is trivial and unimportant, a shoddy facsimile of the activity of the waking mind in which critical judgment is suspended and all manner of chance stimuli are completely misinterpreted; for others, it simply means a different set of rules and perhaps a different purpose in which the aim is to express certain aspects of the dreamer's inner life;

and a few others, unconcerned with rendering opinions, continue to welcome the dream as the sole experience in which they can escape the offensive and incomprehensible bondage of time and space.

Yet, in spite of their inherent fascination, their possible clinical usefulness, and their ubiquity, it is only recently that more than one or two branches of the scientific community have accepted dreams as a topic worthy of investigation. There are undoubtedly many reasons for this, but perhaps the most important is the status of the dream as a "private" event to which the dreamer is the sole witness. Although we may tell each other our dreams at every opportunity, there is no certainty that we are all talking about the same thing.

This state of affairs is reflected in the fact that exactly what is meant by the word "dream" has never been adequately defined. Indeed, as was mentioned above, the very nature of the phenomenon renders it inaccessible to the close and detailed scrutiny that would make such a definition possible. Even so, any discussion that seeks to adorn itself with the mantle of scientific respectability should be obliged to formulate a clear statement of the nature and limitations of its subject matter; and yet, in nearly all "scientific" papers on dreams and more than a few books, we find that this is simply taken for granted. The possibility that everyone does *not* know what is meant by a dream, or that we may be applying the label to more than one basic phenomenon is rarely, if ever, given serious consideration.

One of the reasons for this lack is, of course, that experimental dream research has not been in existence long enough for the rules of scientific inquiry to have been rigidly enforced, but perhaps more important is that we have been misled by the degree of similarity among many dream reports and by our assumption that they all arise from the same condition. In other words, we associate dreams with sleep and we conceive of sleep as a single uniform state possessing at the most some variation in "depth." Many details of what we have regarded as a valid and comprehensive picture of sleep, however, were spuriously derived from observations confined to an overly small fragment of the sleep period. Thus, we find that more recent studies with observations covering the entire night have established that there are at least two distinct kinds of sleep with contrasting neurophysiological characteristics and apparently mediated by different neuroanatomical systems (Jouvet, 1962; Dement, 1964). If conscious mental activity occurs in both kinds of sleep, it obviously follows that there may be two kinds of dreaming, or at least two distinct psychic phenomena to which the label "dream" has been applied. If such a possibility were verified, we could no longer make general statements about all dreams until we had tested their validity when applied separately to each of the two kinds. What may be even more pertinent, finally, is that if there are several basic types of dreams, they might also be differentially accessible, depending upon the method of study. This would mean that we should hesitate in attempting to construct a general picture from the pooled data of several disciplines, or that we should at least recognize the possible pitfalls in such an undertaking.

The easiest way of getting around these difficulties is to construct a definition of the dream that is sufficiently vague and general as to encompass all possibilities. For example, *Funk and Wagnall's New Practical Standard Dictionary* (1954 edition) defines a dream as "a train of thoughts or images passing through the mind in sleep." Since thoughts and images in their varying complexity include just about everything ordinarily relegated to the mental sphere, this is tantamount to saying that *any* mental activity occurring in sleep is a dream, except for implying that a *single* thought or image for some reason should not be included. Calvin Hall (1953) gives us a somewhat more exclusive definition, stating that "a dream is a succession of images, predominantly visual in quality, which are experienced during sleep." The trouble with this definition is that until it can be established that imageless thought does not occur in sleep, excluding it from the definition is completely arbitrary.

Nearly all definitions include two points: (a) that a dream is mental and by implication "conscious" and accessible to recall, and (b) that a dream occurs during sleep. Of course, there is no assurance that sleep is a necessary condition for the mechanism or mechanisms producing dreams to function. The identical mechanisms might also be responsible for such waking state phenomena as hallucinations, images, visions, daydreams, and so forth. In addition, there is extreme difficulty in establishing that dreams actually do occur during sleep. As Malcolm (1959) has pointed out, the "dream" must always be a description given in the waking state of an event that has already taken place. The dreamer accordingly has no way of localizing the experience in time except for his impression that it *did* occur in the past and that sometime in the remote or immediate past he *was* asleep. Even his statement that he was asleep needs outside verification to be absolutely reliable, but at least, in contrast to dreaming, the presence of sleep *can* be verified as it is occurring.

Even if we assume that dreams *do* occur during sleep, the sole witness is the dreamer himself and we have no way of knowing if his report is an accurate account of the actual experience. From a psychoanalytic point of view, Masserman (1944) has suggested that "no dream as such has ever been analyzed—or ever will be analyzed—until we develop a technique of reproducing the dream sequence itself on a television screen while the patient is asleep. All we can do at present is to note carefully the patient's verbal and other behavior patterns while he is talking 'about' his hypothetical 'dream' during some later analytic hour, remembering all the while that his hypnagogic imagery has inevitably been repressed and distorted in recollection, that it is described in words and symbols colored by his experiences not only before but since the 'dream,' and that in the very process of verbalization his 'description' and 'associations' are further dependent on his unconscious motivations in telling the dream at all, his transference situation, his current 'ego defenses,' his physiologic status and the many other complex and interpenetrating factors of the fleeting moment." Thus, it is obvious that any description of a dream experience, in analysis or out, may be highly distorted by faulty recall and the many factors which influence memory, or may even be a deliberate falsehood.

Most people who attempt to deal with dreams simply ignore these difficulties and accept as dreams all descriptions of experiences said to have occurred in sleep. Since any statement, accurate or not, is still a creation of the dreamer and may reveal something about his personality, it is clear that this definition is very useful for the practicing psychotherapist. But whatever arbitrary definition we may choose, somewhere in the back of our minds we must continue to maintain a distinction between the report and the "real" dream. Unfortunately, the principle is often forgotten, and we find in the literature an unqualified acceptance of a wide variety of questionable dream experiences such as "blank" dreams (Lewin, 1946), "reconstruction" dreams (Levin, 1939), dreams limited to a single nonvisual perceptual mode (Ramsey, 1953), "thought" dreams (Foulkes, 1962) and so on, which may actually tell us more about the process of remembering a dream than about its true nature. An interesting example of such an unusual dream experience is Freud's famous "autodidasker" dream of which he says, "The first piece was the word 'autodidasker,' which I recall vividly." There were no sensory elements involved. As an imageless thought with its content limited to a single word, this would seem to be the smallest amount of experience that could be called a dream. Any further reduction would bring us to the usually unchallenged reports of "dreamless sleep," which as possible products of faulty recall have no more likelihood of accuracy than any other report.

At this point we would seem to be impaled on the horns of a dilemma. In order to be consistent, if we accept *any* dream report, we must accept *all* dream reports, since we have no way of selecting only the accurate ones; in which case, we may be building up an entirely illusory picture of the actual phenomenon. If we do *not* accept them, we shall be getting no picture at all.

Occasionally, the narration of a single dream "adventure" runs to several closely spaced typewritten pages when transcribed, and is replete with a variety of imagery and detail almost as if it had happened in real life. Is it possible that the true dream experience is always like this, and that the wide variation in the complexity of our reports only represents a greater or lesser degree of decimation by faulty recall? Or, if the various reports are accurate portrayals (at least some of the time), should they all qualify equally for the status of a dream? Should the concept of a dream be limited to experiences containing sensory imagery?—to experiences that possess some kind of movement or progression of events? What is to stop us from distinguishing a thousand types of dreams in the face of the bewildering variation in quality, complexity, vividness, mode, and so on, that exists in our reports?

It should be apparent that the penetrating analysis of *any* subjective phenomenon will lead inevitably to the brink of epistemological nihilism. This is true of the activities we attribute to the mind in the waking state as well as in the sleeping state. Yet, in our waking life we do not ordinarily concern ourselves with the validity of sensations, perceptions, thoughts, and so forth, or their ultimate reality. We accept all verbalizations concerning these concepts without qualification because long experience has shown over and over that they *do* correlate with observable events in the real world. Their function is to bridge the gap between sensory input and motor output; to help order the intervening processes that govern human behavior. As elaborated in the philosophy of Hans Vaihinger (1924), they belong to the multitude of "useful fictions" that "facilitate action" and serve to "make the interconnection between sensory and motor nerves richer and easier, more delicate and more serviceable." The sole justification for the existence of the concept of mind is that it is useful, which in turn is based entirely on the fact that the reports of its presumed activities bear a consistent relationship to the real world. A burning torch is brought close to a human observer. The observer says, "I feel heat." The sensation of heat correlates with the approach of the burning torch. From this example, we can envisage a two-fold process of enrichment. By repeatedly confirming that the burning torch and the report of feeling heat are inextricably linked, we reinforce our *faith* in the concept of the intervening sensation of heat, and by implication, in the general consistency of the psyche. The sensation of heat may then be used to order other events in the physical world. Thus, although the ultimate reality of the sensation cannot be verified, the concept is important and useful—a useful fiction.

But let us see how all this applies to the problems that confront us in the dream world. The main stumbling block has been that the sleeping organism, for all practical purposes, has ceased to interact with its environment. In contrast to the waking state where a multiplicity of real events (external stimuli, motor patterns, for instance) can be observed to interconnect logically with sensations and thoughts, the sleep state has seemed to offer for examination only the monotonous regularity or relative cessation of its own isolated functioning. Thus, in view of the complexity of dreams and the presumed simplicity of sleep, we have denied the possibility of looking at dream events in relation to a series of interconnecting real events, and we have tended to regard the dream as a phenomenon completely isolated from its physical background.

Fortunately the truth of the matter is that the sleeping organism is much more than a pulsating blob of protoplasm. Although it requires considerable work and technological resource to demonstrate, the complexity of its functioning, particularly with reference to the central nervous system, may not be very much less than when it is awake. There are a myriad of observable physiological events that we may be able to correlate with dream reports if we are willing to make the effort. Thus, what is needed is a more extensive and penetrating study of physiological activities and their variations throughout sleep together with a repeated testing of their possible relations to the psychic events that make up the dream. The nature and degree of these relationships will allow us, in turn, to make inferences about the role of memory and the possible multiplicity of basic types of dreams.

In this presentation I would like to describe the beginning that has been made in this ambitious undertaking. While not absolutely infallible, the combined study of physiological and psychological data throughout the entire night of sleep has enabled us to verify certain aspects of the dream experience, and perhaps more important, has stimulated a recent upsurge of scientific interest in sleep in *all* its various manifestations and attributes.

Although the two phases of the work, (a) physiological description and (b) psychological correlation, have been proceeding apace, for the purposes of clarity we will describe them separately. The material describing the physiology of the sleeping organism will be reviewed first, with emphasis on studies done over the entire sleep period. This will be followed by a consideration of the relationships between psychological and physiological activities. We may then be in a better position to answer some of the questions that were raised earlier and to achieve a better understanding of the basic processes underlying the verbal and written reports that have heretofore been our only access to the world of dreams.

# PHYSIOLOGICAL VARIATIONS DURING SLEEP

It has recently been shown that during a typical night of sleep in the human a number of physiological variables fluctuate in a fairly orderly and parallel or interrelated fashion. Taken together, these fluctuations describe a basic sleep cycle.

## THE ELECTROENCEPHALOGRAM

Perhaps the most definitive of the variables is the electroencephalogram (EEG) which, in a continuous all-night recording, clearly shows a regular cyclic alternation of its various stages. Actually, any small sample of brain wave patterns contains a highly complex mixture of amplitudes and frequencies, but certain ones usually predominate and may serve to characterize the sample. Thus, it has been possible to divide the continuum of change through wakefulness and sleep into several easily recognized stages. Interestingly enough, the widest range of variation occurs in sleep. Our system of classification, which is quite similar to others that have been proposed (for example, Loomis *et al.*, 1937), is as follows (see also Dement and Kleitman, 1957b).

*Awake.* A low voltage record with a mixture of frequencies above 8 cycles per second. It is often dominated by continuous sinusoidal fluctuations of 8 to 13 cycles per second, called Alpha Rhythm, which is most prominent in the occipital region.

*Stage 1.* A low voltage record with a wide mixture of both slow (less than 8 cycles per second) and fast frequencies. Alpha Rhythm is often present but takes up much less of the record than in the Awake stage. The most important characteristic is an absolute lack of *sleep spindles* which are generally present in other sleep stages. Thus, any EEG pattern between full wakefulness and the appearance of sleep spindles is included in Stage 1.

*Stage 2.* Characterized by the presence of sleep spindles (waxing-waning bursts of regular waves of 12 to 14 cycles per second) with a low voltage background.

*Stage 3.* An intermediate stage characterized by the appearance of moderate amounts of large amplitude waves of 1 to 2 cycles per second or slower. Sleep spindles are generally present.

*Stage 4.* The record is dominated by large amplitude, slow waves.

These definitions are illustrated in Figure 2.1 They are strictly valid only for the human adult. In younger age groups the over-all frequency spectrum of the EEG is shifted toward the slow side and classifications must be altered to take this into account.

Figure 2.2 illustrates the typical changes of the EEG during the course of the night. The individual cycles are essentially determined by the appearance and reappearance of periods of Stage 1 EEG, and for purposes of definition, this stage represents the final phase of each cycle. It may be seen that the periods of Stage 1 tend to increase in length as the night wears on. Most of the Stage 4 patterns occur early in the night while later the change is mainly limited to an alternation between Stages 1 and 2. It has long been assumed, without much evidence, that the EEG is an adequate measure of that elusive quality, "depth of sleep." The gradual development of high amplitude, low frequency brain waves is assumed to be paralleled by a reduction in nervous activity and responsiveness while a change in the opposite direction (Stage 4 to Stage 1) is associated with an increase in activity and responsiveness. According to this formulation, Stage 4 represents "deep sleep" and Stage 1, "light sleep." While this may be tentatively acceptable for EEG Stages 2, 3, and 4, and the brief interval of Stage 1 at the sleep onset, the periods of Stage 1 at the end of

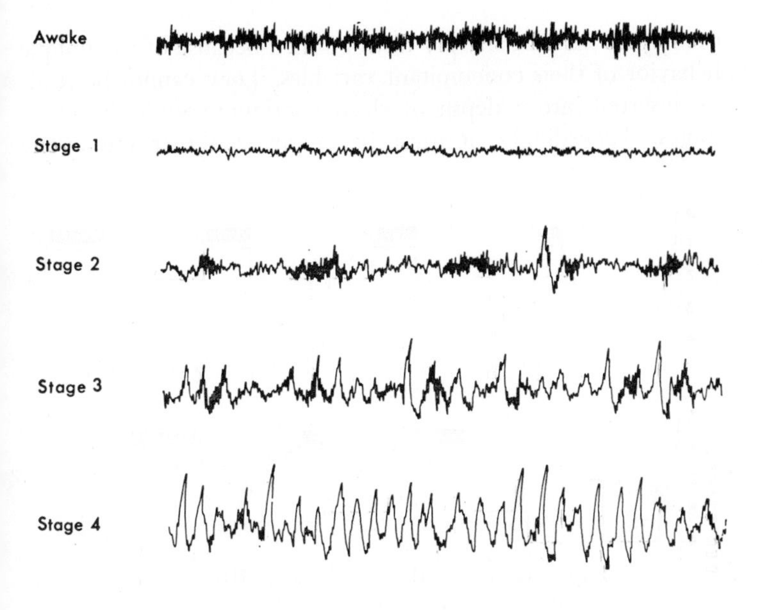


*Figure 2.1.* Examples of the recorded tracings of EEG stages of sleep for the same subject over a period of a single night. The recording paper was moving under the pens at ⅓ the standard speed, which means that the waves are somewhat pushed together. However, this also means that only ⅓ as much paper is needed during the night, a considerable saving in 8 hours of continuous recording.

The top line shows the 10 per second alpha waves characteristic of the "Awake" EEG. Their mean amplitude, for comparison with the sleep patterns, is about 50 microvolts. The second line (Stage 1) shows a mixture of low voltage, irregular, relatively fast waves. The sample of Stage 2 in the third tracing shows the characteristic waxing-waning bursts of regular waves (*sleep spindles*) lasting 1 to 2 seconds. The frequency of the spindle waves is about 12-14 per second, which causes them to be somewhat blurred at this paper speed. Nonetheless, they stand out sharply from the low voltage, irregular background rhythms. A moderate amount of high voltage, slow activity is seen in the Stage 3 tracing. Stage 4, shown in the bottom line, is charatcerized by continuous high voltage, slow activity. The frequency is about 1 per second.

each cycle must be sharply distinguished because of the unique behavior of their concomitant variables. They cannot be readily inserted into a depth of sleep continuum with the other stages. Accordingly, it must be emphasized that the cyclic

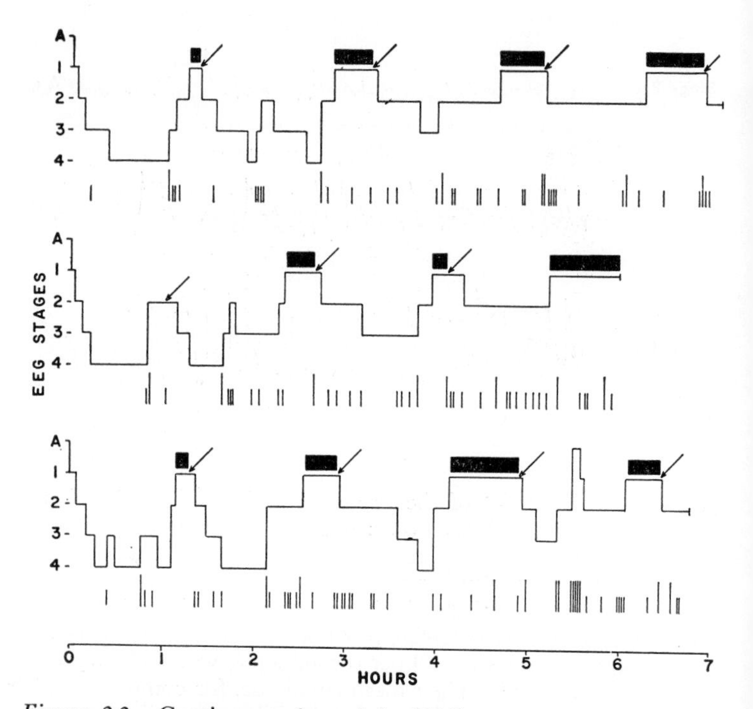


*Figure 2.2.* Continuous plots of the EEG stages during three representative nights. The thick bars immediately above the EEG lines indicate periods during which rapid eye movements were seen. The vertical lines below stand for body movements. The longer lines indicate large movements, changes in position of the whole body; and the shorter lines represent smaller movements. The arrows indicate both the end of one EEG cycle and the beginning of the next. (Reprinted, by permission, from Dement, W., and N. Kleitman, Cyclic variations in EEG during sleep and their relation to eye movements, body motility, and dreaming, *EEG Clin. Neurophysiol.*, 1957, *9*, 673-690.)

variation illustrated in Figure 2.2 is not a "depth of sleep" curve.

## OCULOMOTOR ACTIVITY

The final phases of each cycle (periods of Stage 1 EEG) have been designated "rapid eye movement periods" (REMPs) because their most prominent and exclusive feature is an asso-

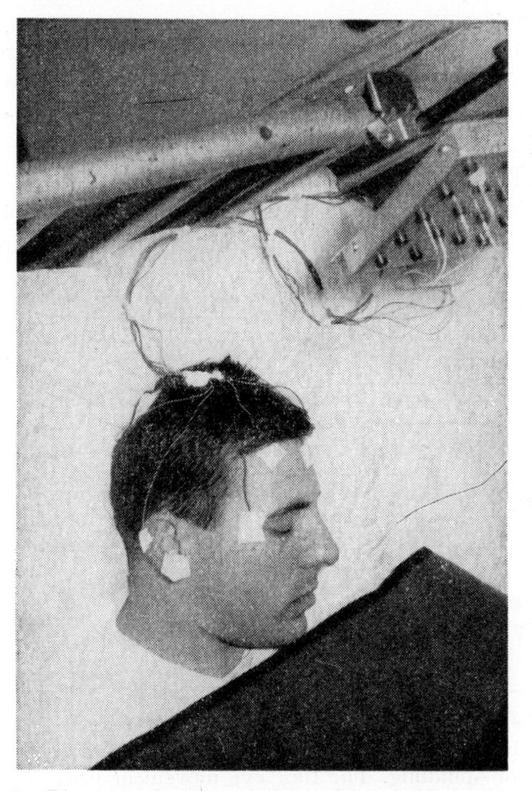

*Figure 2.3.* Photograph of a sleeping subject with brain wave and eye movement electrodes attached. All the recording apparatus is in another room to which the electrode lead wires run. A similar photograph is included in Kleitman's recent article (1960).

ciation with the occurrence of rapid, conjugate, eye movement. Eye movements during wakefulness or sleep may be easily recorded without disturbance by placing small electrodes around the orbits and continuously monitoring the transorbital potential differences generated by displacement of the eyeballs (Kris, 1960). In Figure 2.3 we can see that the attachment of electrodes does not prevent a subject from sleeping, and ordinarily does not interfere with movement or disturb sleep in any way.

The rapid eye movements (REMs) of sleep are quite similar to the purposeful movements associated with visual perception in the waking state. They are binocularly synchronous; individual deviations show wide variability in direction and size of arc. Their velocity approximates that of fixation shifts in the waking state, although it is probably more variable. Some of these properties are illustrated in a typical recording (Figure 2.4).

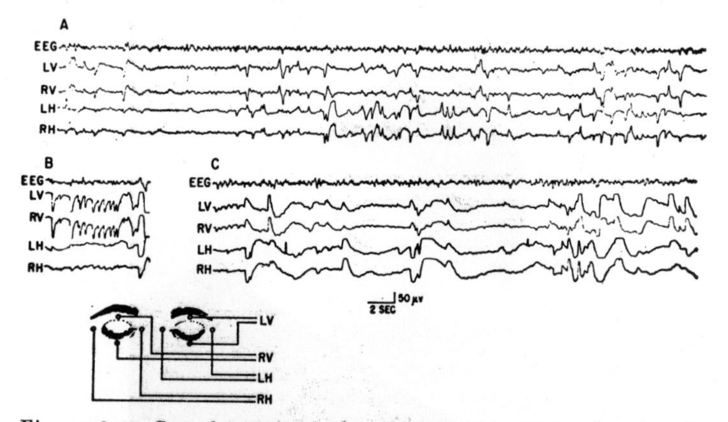


*Figure 2.4.* Sample tracings of rapid eye movements showing that they are binocularly synchronous. The concomitant EEG is low voltage, non-spindling. The four eye movement pens give the left and right vertical and horizontal derivations as shown in the diagram. (Reprinted, by permission, from Dement, W., Eye movements during sleep. In M. Bender, (Ed.), *The Oculomotor System*, New York: Hoeber, 1964.)

Even though the eyelids are closed, the REMs may be easily seen on direct observation and several investigators have documented their occurrence with motion pictures. Using Oswald's (1960) technique of taping the eyelids, Rechtschaffen has observed REMs with the eyes open. He states (personal communication to the author) that, although the subjects were unquestionably asleep as determined by their EEG's, they gave the uncanny appearance of being wide awake and looking about.

Rapid eye movements occur *only* during the Stage 1 phase of the sleep cycle and are generally present throughout the entirety of the period, although the amount varies widely from moment to moment. By tabulating their presence or absence in successive 2-second intervals of the Stage 1 phases, we have found that they are present in anywhere from 15 to 40 percent of all such intervals and that the percentage tends to be an individual characteristic.

One of the most consistent attributes of sleep in both man and animals is constriction of the pupils or miosis (Kleitman, 1939). The degree of the miosis may be somewhat variable and it has been suggested that it is related to depth of sleep. If the periodic abundance of oculomotor activity described above is indicative of "light" or "disturbed" sleep, the degree of miosis at these times ought to be relatively small. However, by gently lifting the eyelids with fine threads, Roffwarg and the author were able to observe the pupils during REMPs without disturbing the subjects and found that the pupilloconstriction was usually maximal. Rechtschaffen confirmed this finding in his subjects who slept with their eyelids taped open.

Although the occurrence of rapid eye movement is entirely limited to the emergent[1] periods of Stage 1 EEG and does not

[1] The term, "emergent," has been applied by Kleitman (1960) to all periods of Stage 1 preceded by other stages of sleep, in order to distinguish them from the brief period of Stage 1 at the onset of sleep which is associated with completely different physiological characteristics, although the EEG patterns are similar.

even appear during the brief period of Stage 1 at the onset of sleep, the eyes are not absolutely quiescent at other times. At frequent intervals throughout the night, slow swings of the eyeballs that are mainly horizontal and often asynchronous may be observed. They are most prominent at the sleep onset, at which time their pendular quality results in a recording that resembles a sine wave with a period of 2 to 4 seconds.

The rapid eye movements of sleep were first described in human subjects by Aserinsky and Kleitman in 1953, and their relationship to the EEG sleep cycle was elucidated shortly thereafter (Dement and Kleitman, 1955; 1957b). Since then, analogous EEG variations during sleep with REMs related to the appropriate phase have been described in a number of other species, such as the cat (Dement, 1958), the monkey (Weitzman, 1961), the dog (Shimazono *et al.*, 1960), and the rat (Swisher, 1962). In nearly all instances where identical variables have been measured, the phenomena of the sleep cycle have behaved similarly across species. Furthermore, a great deal of unique information has been accumulated from subhuman species because of their greater accessibility to experimental and operative manipulation. Accordingly, the ensuing description of other physiological variations in the human will be supplemented by animal data, particularly when such data are not available from human studies.

In addition to the phylogenetic homogeneity of the sleep cycle, it has been found that REMPs and associated EEG changes are present at all age levels in the human from birth to senescence (Roffwarg *et al.*, 1964). It is to be expected that ontogenetic studies will eventually be carried out on a wide variety of subhuman species, but the presence of REMPs has thus far been verified only in the kitten (Jouvet *et al.*, 1961).

## OTHER PHYSIOLOGICAL VARIATIONS

Many aspects of human physiology have been examined during sleep, but often with the sole objective of making a simple comparison with the waking state. A common procedure was to take a measurement in the waking state, allow the subject to fall asleep for a few minutes, and repeat the measurement. As was pointed out earlier, the limited scope of such endeavors tended to reinforce the characterization of sleep as a single, uniform state. In recent years, however, research interest has shifted to focus upon variability *within* the sleep period. The most dramatic result of this shift of interest has been the elucidation of the contrast between the physiology of the rapid eye movement period and the remainder of sleep.

*Respiration.* Although sleep is generally thought to be associated with quiet, deep respiration, all-night recordings have shown that during REMPs the quality of breathing undergoes

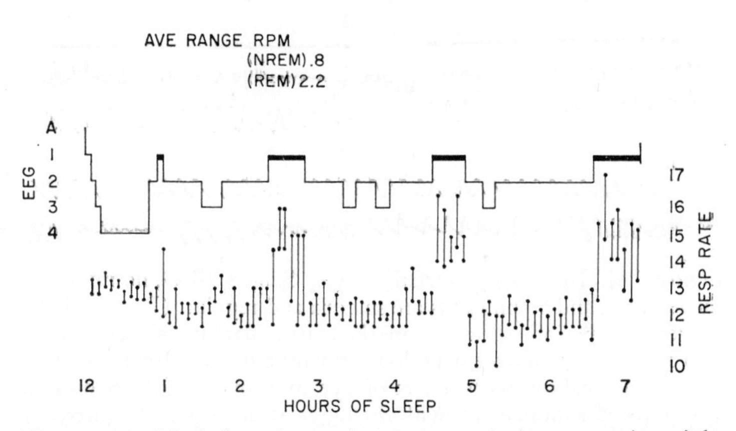


*Figure 2.5.* Variations in respiratory rate during an entire night of sleep. The top line is a continuous plotting of the EEG in terms of the four stages, and the dark bars indicate the eye movement periods. The number of respirations in each successive minute were counted and each vertical line represents the range of minute counts for each successive five minute period. It can be seen that during rapid eye movement periods, there is an over-all increase in both range and rate. (Reprinted, by permission, from Dement, W., Eye movements during sleep. In M. Bender (Ed.), *The Oculomotor System*, New York: Hoeber, 1964.)

considerable change. There is a marked increase in breath-to-breath variability and an over-all acceleration of respiratory rate. Figure 2.5 is a plot of respiratory changes throughout an entire night of sleep. Figure 2.6 illustrates how striking some of

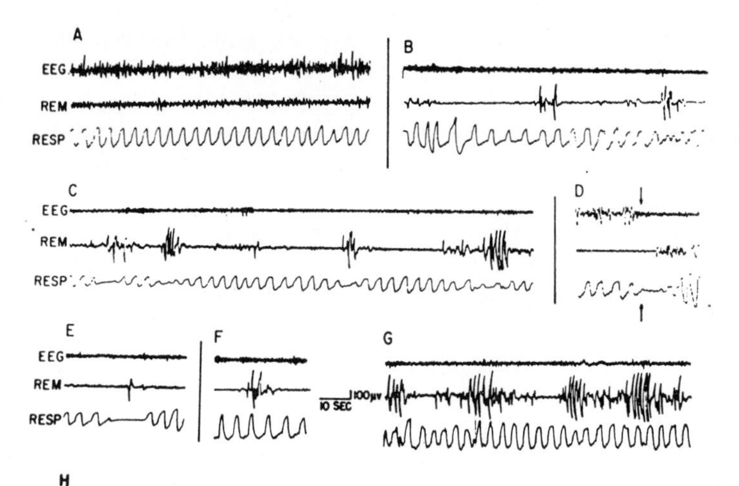


*Figure 2.6.* Respiratory variations. (A) Stage 4 EEG, no rapid eye movements, and respirations are smooth and regular. (B) Rapid eye movement period showing marked irregularity of respiration. (C) Rapid eye movement period showing tendency for respiration to become shallow with bursts of eye movements. (D) Shows an apneic pause simultaneous with the onset of Stage 1 EEG (arrows) and rapid eye movements. (E) An apneic pause of more than 10 seconds is associated with a small burst of eye movement, while in (F) no change in respiration is seen in association with another burst. (G) A large amount of eye movement may be associated with relatively little change in respiration. (H) Respiratory records from Stage 2 and rapid eye movement periods are placed side by side for closer comparison. Respiration recorded by means of a pneumograph around the chest coupled with a strain gauge. (Reprinted, by permission from Dement, W., Eye movements during sleep. In M. Bender (Ed.), *The Oculomotor System,* New York: Hoeber, 1964.)

these changes are from moment to moment. Very few data are available from REMPs for some of the more basic indices of respiratory function such as blood oxygen saturation, alveolar carbon dioxide, pulmonary ventilation, and so on. Bulow (1963) has observed a few subjects and reports that the level of the alveolar carbon dioxide tension during REMPs is about the same as the level during sleep onset Stage 1. This would probably represent an increase with reference to the waking state and a decrease with reference to the adjacent sleep periods. The marked irregularity of respiration makes this kind of observation very difficult.

*Cardiovascular changes.* During the sleep onset and EEG Stages 2, 3, and 4, the heart rate is fairly regular with an over-all trend of continued reduction that reaches a minimum around the seventh hour of the night. This trend is interrupted during REMPs by a transient acceleration and increased variability.

Blood pressure is generally somewhat reduced during sleep in the human. Shapiro (1962) failed to find any significant change during REMPs using the finger cuff method, except for one isolated instance in which a dramatic rise of 60 mm Hg occurred. On the other hand, Snyder *et al.* (1963) measured the pressure in the leg and found small but consistent elevations associated with REM sleep. Subjects with normal blood pressure were used in both studies. In view of the not uncommon occurrence of cerebral vascular accidents during sleep, it would be of great clinical interest to test the possibility that exaggerated elevations of blood pressure occur during REM sleep in patients with hypertension.

Finger pulse volume, which is a measure of peripheral vasoconstriction, is often decreased in the presence of REMs, while it is characteristically dilated during relaxation and sleep in general (Williams *et al.*, 1964).

The cardiovascular system represents one of the few areas in which the human and the cat show opposite changes during REM sleep. Jouvet (1962) has reported that the heart rate is typically decreased during REMPs in the cat. Measuring the blood pressure directly by means of a small cannula inserted into an artery, Candia *et al.* (1962) observed a marked and consistent reduction whenever REMs appeared.

A technique for the measurement of cerebral cortical blood flow in the freely moving cat has recently been devised by Kanzow and his collaborators. Their findings with this technique deserve special attention (Kanzow, 1961; Kanzow *et al.*, 1962). First, they made observations during a wide variety of waking activities which included feeding, introducing a mouse into the cage, "listening" to special noises, and a sudden arousal from sleep or relaxation; from which they concluded, "It is especially the psychic process of the direction of attention and of the transition to a state of higher consciousness which is accompanied by a dilatation of cortical blood vessels. The motor behavior and the electrical activity of the cortex (EEG) seem to be correlated to the cortical blood flow only if they are connected to these psychic processes and reactions." In other words, merely changing from the sleeping state to the waking state was not accompanied by an increase in cortical blood flow. The animals had to engage in some meaningful perceptual activity for a rise to occur.

Then, they made a comprehensive study of sleep phases and found that REMPs were invariably accompanied by a rise in the cortical blood supply amounting to a 30 to 50 percent increase over that of the adjacent periods of sleep. They reasoned that the increase in blood supply had to be accomplished by vasodilatation, since it occurred in spite of the decrease in systemic blood pressure. Further experiments will be necessary to determine the exact mechanisms underlying the vasodilatation, but it is interesting to speculate that they may be analogous to those producing dilatation of cortical vessels in the waking state, which implies that psychic processes may play a role.

*Muscular activity.* The biological essence of being awake lies in executing the infinite variety of movements that serve to bring the organism into an adaptive relationship with its environment. By contrast, the most characteristic feature of sleep is immobility; however, this immobility is far from absolute. In addition to the aforementioned oculomotor activity, a night of sleep generally includes from 20 to 60 gross body movements.

Surprisingly, the occurrence of large numbers of REMs is not paralleled by a maximal incidence of gross body movements (Dement and Kleitman, 1957b). In fact, the incidence of body movement shows a peak just prior to the REMP, subsides during its course, and rebounds at its termination. However, while gross body movement is relatively infrequent during REMPs, close observation reveals the presence of large numbers of fine finger movements. These latter may be somewhat analogous to the frequent twitches of limbs, tail, and vibrissae that have been observed to accompany REMs in the cat (Dement, 1958) and the dog (Shimazono *et al.*, 1960).

In an electromyographic study of sleep, Wolpert (1960) observed a significant increase in isolated bursts of potentials from the wrist muscles during REMPs. However, wrist potentials occurring in combination with activity in other muscle groups were equally distributed throughout the entire sleep period.

Observations of great theoretical importance have been made on *tonic* muscular activity in the cat by Jouvet and his collaborators (1959). Using electromyographic techniques, they found that while tonic activity in most muscle groups disappeared during sleep, it was maintained in the posterior neck muscles. At the onset of REMPs, however, even the neck muscles became atonic. The suppression of nuchal tone continued until the phase was terminated, at which time tonicity abruptly returned. In other words, Jouvet found a greater degree of muscular relaxation during REM sleep than at any other time. Even in cerebellectomized animals, where extensor rigidity of the trunk and forelegs persisted into sleep, complete atony occurred in association with the eye movement phase. From these results, Jouvet has postulated that the complete loss of muscle tone involves an *active* and fairly powerful inhibitory mechanism rather than a passive reduction in motor outflow. That a profound degree of skeletal muscular relaxation might actually involve heightened activity within the central nervous system is a concept with far-reaching implications, some of which will be considered in a later section. A dramatic confirmation of this hypothesis was recently provided by Pompeiano (1963) who found that both extensor and stretch reflexes were profoundly suppressed during REM sleep in the cat, while they were easily elicited during other periods of sleep. Experiments involving partial and total transection of the spinal cord indicated that the abolition of muscle reflexes during REM sleep was due to an active inhibitory influence descending from the brain to the spinal cord rather than a decrease in facilitatory processes.

The possibility of a similar mechanism existing in the human has also been demonstrated. Berger (1961) found a small amount of tonic activity in the suprahyoid muscles (just below the chin) during Stages 2, 3, and 4, which invariably disappeared during the "emergent" Stage 1. This is illustrated in Figure 2.7.

On the other hand, Fischgold and Schwartz (1960) have expressed doubt that generalized inhibition of muscle tone occurs in the human on the basis of their finding that snoring, which implies relaxation of the nasopharynx, does *not* take place during REMPs although it is often heard at other times. However, this may be a special case since the embryology of the pharyngeal muscles is quite different from that of the skeletal muscles.

Finally, Hodes and Dement were able to study the reflex behavior of the calf muscles in response to electrical stimulation of peripheral nerve during sleep in human subjects. Reflex contractions occurred all during Stages 2, 3, and 4, but were abolished or markedly reduced throughout the periods of REM sleep.

*Neuronal physiology.* While the empirical relationships

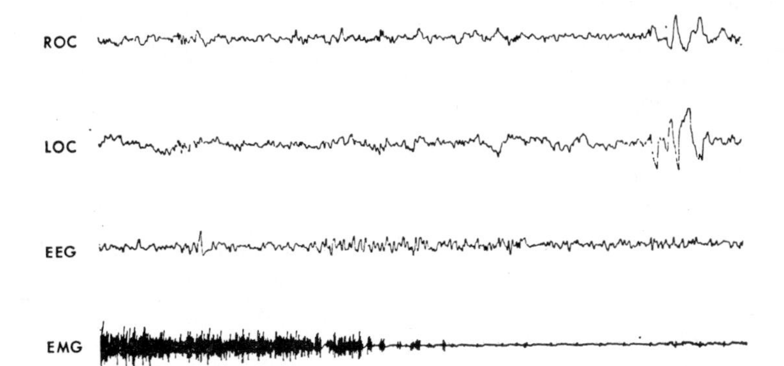


*Figure 2.7.* The onset of REM sleep. Electrode placements; ROC, right outer canthus referred to ears; LOC, left outer canthus referred to ears; EEG, left parietal electrode referred to left occipital electrode; EMG, bipolar electrodes placed on anterior neck muscles. Note that the tonic EMG potentials that were present all during NREM sleep disappear rather abruptly. A few seconds later, the first rapid eye movement potentials appear (at the left of the figure in ROC and LOC). Although it is not obvious in this brief segment of record, the EEG has changed to Stage 1.

of the electroencephalogram have been of immense value in the study of sleep and of many aspects of wakefulness as well, there is a growing doubt that EEG studies alone will lead to an understanding of the intimate and precise nature of the processes involved in higher nervous functions (compare Chow, 1961; Morrell, 1961). Many workers are turning toward more specific methods of analysis, foremost of which is the microelectrode technique for measuring the electrical activity of individual nerve cells within the central nervous system (CNS). Although the technique has only recently been applied to the study of spontaneous neuronal activity during sleep, and is limited to animal experimentation, it has already uncovered findings of great interest.

One of the first surprises resulting from its use was that the transition from wakefulness to sleep was not necessarily accompanied by a reduction of spontaneous discharge in neuron populations (Strumwasser, 1958; Hubel, 1959). In the cat, there appears to be no significant difference in the over-all mean rate of impulses per second between slow wave sleep (analogous to Stages 2, 3, and 4) and quiet wakefulness (Evarts, 1960).

Huttenlocher (1961) recorded the activity of brain stem neurons during several different states. He found that the neuron population was most active during sleep, specifically during REMPs. The next highest degree of activity was during what he called "strong arousal" elicited by stimulating an awake cat with a puff of air on its nose. Slow wave sleep and "quiet wakefulness" showed the least activity and were almost identical, except that there was more variation in the latter state.

Similar observations were made on neurons in the visual cortex by Evarts (1962a; 1962b). The over-all activity was about 70 percent higher during rapid eye movement periods as compared to slow wave sleep. In the waking state, when visual inspection (looking at a mouse) occurred, neuronal discharge rates were comparable to those seen during REMPs, while at other times when the cat was awake but not doing anything, they approached the level of slow wave sleep.

Pyramidal tract discharge has been monitored during wakefulness and the two phases of sleep in the cat by Arduini *et al.* (1963). Again, the highest level of activity occurred during REMPs, slightly less during wakefulness, and least during the slow wave phase. Recalling the observations on muscle tone, here is another example of the disparity between central and peripheral indices of activity during sleep—a high level of discharge in the primary motor pathway of the brain is associated with profound muscular relaxation.

*Gastrointestinal activity*. Gastric activity has not been studied in association with EEG and eye movement recordings. Many years ago, however, Luckhardt (1915) described the inhibition of gastric motility during periods of sleep in the dog that were characterized by twitching movements of the limbs. These twitching movements are now known to occur during

REMPs. He also observed an inhibition of gastric motility in the waking state when the dogs were "emotionally upset" and suggested that the inhibition during sleep was likewise due to emotional upheaval since the twitching movements "might indicate the presence of dreaming."

*The skin.* Falling asleep is consistently associated with an increase in basal skin resistance. Additional variations are thought to reflect changes in the level of sleep with increases signaling greater depth. During REMPs, however, the basal skin resistance has been reported to increase (Hawkins *et al.*, 1962) or to show no significant change (Kamiya, 1961). In addition, there is some suggestion that galvanic skin responses, both spontaneous and evoked, are reduced during REMPs.

## SYNTHESIS

The foregoing has been a fairly detailed review of physiological data harvested from studies that have covered the entire sleep period rather than just one small fraction. The material emphasizes the physiology of the "rapid eye movement period" as contrasted with the remainder of sleep. What emerges with striking clarity is that two entirely distinct states of being are subsumed under the general heading of "sleep." One of these two states is, of course, the final phase of the sleep cycle—the rapid eye movement period—and the other is all the sleep that precedes it. Physiological variations within the two states are essentially quantitative and generally do not exhibit sufficient magnitude or persistence to warrant further subdivision.

In view of this formulation, the description of four EEG stages becomes somewhat redundant. While only one EEG stage is present during REMPs, four EEG stages may be present in the interspersed intervals without, however, showing any significant covariance with other physiological measurements. The data plotted in Figure 2.5 may be used as an example to clarify this point. A glance at this figure reveals that the increases in both rate and variability of respiration during REMPs stand out sharply against a rather stable respiratory background. In the first EEG cycle, there is a complete swing from the Stage 1 at the sleep onset, through Stages 2 and 3 to Stage 4, and back to Stage 2. However, almost no change in respiration is associated with this wide variation in EEG. The same is true for succeeding cycles, although this cannot be accorded equal significance, since the EEG changes are less marked.

Looking at Figure 2.5, it would be only a very slight exaggeration to say that all EEG phases outside of REMPs are associated with a uniform rate and regularity of respiration. We have additional evidence suggesting that heart rate, muscle tone, and body temperature similarly do not covary with the EEG. This is not to say that EEG shifts between Stages 2 and 4 are entirely without significance as will be seen when we take up the question of depth of sleep. Any related changes, though, are generally quantitative and relatively minute when compared to the changes that mark the onset of REMPs. We must conclude that an apparent wide shift in EEG activity can be somewhat illusory and does not necessarily reflect wide variations in underlying activity. Thus, in the absence of any compelling reason to do otherwise, EEG Stages 2, 3, and 4 will be considered to comprise a single uniform state of sleep.

In summary, there are two kinds of sleep. All intervals *outside* of REMPs constitute one kind; rapid eye movement periods the other. For ease of description, we will refer to the former as "nonrapid eye movement" sleep, abbreviated NREM.

Most subhuman species have no problem with regard to EEG redundancy. Except for very brief transitional phases, the sleep cycle in the cat, dog, and rat consists of only two EEG stages which alternate rhythmically. A low voltage, fast EEG is associated with REMs, while an unvarying mixture of slow waves and spindles is present at all other times. In some of the prior discussion of subhuman data, this latter or NREM phase was referred to as "slow wave sleep."

In all mammalian species thus far studied, a basic sleep cycle exists which is characterized by a regular alternation of two distinct phases (REM and NREM), each described by a unique cluster of physiological attributes. Both phases account for substantial portions of the entire sleep period, but the larger share usually belongs to the NREM phase.

*Nonrapid eye movement sleep.* All things considered, probably the most characteristic feature of NREM sleep is regularity. This extends through the hierarchy of measurement from the minimum variance in spontaneous neuronal activity demonstrated by microelectrode recordings to the regularity seen in the peripheral registrations of respiration and heart rate.

A second important feature of NREM sleep is its over-all *low* level of activity. Since most of our older notions about sleep as a whole are based almost exclusively on the physiology of the NREM phase, it is this low level that is responsible for the idea that the essential difference between wakefulness and sleep *is* the level of activity. While this is unquestionably true when comparing NREM sleep to wakefulness as a whole, it fails to take into account the tremendous repertoire of the waking state. The main reason that we think of sleep as a slowing down, a resting or idling state—or to be more literary, a short death—is that we generally compare it with the *active* waking state. The fact is that most of the changes thought to be characteristic of falling alseep are actually a result of recumbency and relaxation and can be easily achieved while still awake (Kleitman, 1939). If a subject lies down in a quiet room, closes his eyes, and relaxes both physically and mentally, nearly every physiological measurement will show a decline in activity. The cardiac and respiratory rates will slow down, blood pressure will fall, body temperature will drop, metabolic activity will decrease, and so forth. If recumbency and relaxation are maintained long enough, when sleep finally intervenes there may be no further change in any of these measurements. Thus, the essential difference between wakefulness and NREM sleep may not lie in the level of activity. Rather, it may lie in the less easily quantifiable change in attentiveness and responsiveness to the outside world. The fact that levels of activity in the waking state are usually higher than in NREM sleep is because the former state is ordinarily a time of interacting with the environment. When this interaction with the environment is being *voluntarily* suspended, we may achieve a low level of activity but are still awake. When the suspension is *involuntary*, we are asleep.

For all practical purposes, however, an over-all low level of activity will still serve to distinguish NREM sleep from wakefulness on the one hand and REM sleep on the other.

The only time the monotonous quietude of NREM sleep is disrupted is when a gross body movement occurs. Considering the over-all length of the NREM phase, the total sum of these brief moments of upheaval constitutes a very small fraction. Nevertheless, it is worthwhile to question whether they should be considered part of the phase or momentary departures from it. Certainly, while a body movement is being executed, physiological activity is anything but regular and slow. Actually, once they begin, the movements themselves seem to have an arousing effect on the sleeper, probably via the barrage of proprioceptive stimuli, and one often observes a few seconds of waking patterns in the EEG before the organism sinks back to its prior NREM state. We cannot be sure whether gross body movements are a manifestation of spontaneous changes in CNS excitability or are elicited periodically by the building-up of stimulation from the pressure ischemia in our weight-bearing surfaces. It would be instructive to see if as much body movement would occur if the sleeper were suspended in water or floating in a free-falling space ship. For the present, the author thinks that gross body movements in any phase should be regarded as brief departures from sleep analogous to the similar brief arousals that are occasionally evoked by the random noise of the environment.

*Rapid eye movement sleep.* Although there is little sign of it on the surface, at periodic intervals during sleep a remarkable change takes place. With dramatic suddenness, muscle tone disappears, heart and respiratory rates increase and fluctuate widely, the eyes begin to dart about, and inside the nervous system there is a neuronic crescendo accompanied by an inpouring of additional blood supply.

Viewed from within, the brain would almost appear to be awake. Even from the outside, there are a few signs that would attest to this. As Rechtschaffen has said, if it were not for the closed eyelids, the subject would appear to be awake and *looking about.* The EEG reaches its closest approximation to the patterns of wakefulness and, in fact, in subhuman species the EEG during REM sleep is virtually indistinguishable from that of the waking state.

Indeed, we are compelled to wonder what it is that holds the organism to its resting place in the face of this inner turmoil. The apparent answer is that the brain is blocking the peripheral manifestations of its own activity. The tonic and reflex background of muscular activity is suppressed, possibly by direct inhibition of alpha motor neurons and, without this tonic background, there cannot be sustained movement. Thus, although pyramidal tract activity is greatly increased, the best it can achieve is an occasional phasic discharge (twitches, and so on); this is not sufficient to disturb the organism or displace it against the force of gravity.

Although he is outwardly very relaxed, the sleeper is certainly not complying with our older notions about sleep. This is no state of minimal function; quite the contrary, its level of function approaches that of a highly active waking state. What could be the purpose of such a sleep? Why should there be two kinds of sleep? We have as yet no good answers to these questions, but this should not be discouraging, since a few years ago we did not know enough even to ask them. There is still a great deal to say about these two contrasting phases of sleep, as we shall see when we take up their subjective aspects.

## NEUROANATOMICAL MECHANISMS

A detailed consideration of the neuroanatomical mechanisms that underlie the various aspects of sleep would greatly overextend this essay, but a brief outline at this point is appropriate in order to emphasize further the contrast between REM and NREM sleep.

The most common conceptualization of sleep in the past (as we have repeatedly pointed out) was as a period of minimal functioning of the organism that ostensibly fulfilled a need for rest and restoration. The main problem was how this low level of function was achieved. One of the most popular of early theories attributed it to an active inhibition of nervous activity, mainly at the cortical level. However, Kleitman (1929; 1939) emphasized that sleep could also be thought of as a passive state requiring no special mechanisms for its onset, and that the real problem was to explain the initiation and maintenance of wakefulness. He marshaled a great deal of evidence to support the hypothesis that the nervous system is maintained in a state of waking activity by the constant bombardment of afferent impulses and that the immediate cause of sleep is a reduction of the afferent inflow below some critical level necessary for the waking state. The classical experiment supporting this hypothesis was done by Bremer (1935), who showed that transection of the brain stem at the mid-collicular level, thereby depriving the forebrain of all but optic and olfactory input, immediately resulted in an uninterrupted condition of sleep as judged by the cortical EEG and miosis of the pupils. Human preparations for sleep imitate the effect of brain-stem transection. By retiring to a quiet room, switching off the lights and radio, removing constricting clothing, lying down, closing our eyes, we bring about a drastic reduction in afferent stimulation. In the absence of an afferent bombardment, the activity of the nervous system *passively* falls below some critical level and sleep ensues.

Further understanding of the process came with the experiments of Moruzzi and Magoun (1949) and of many others who subsequently found that a crucial structure was interposed between the forebrain and the afferent input, which seemed to be capable of modulating or amplifying the influence of the latter. This structure was the reticular formation of the brain stem, particularly its mesencephalic portion, which was found to receive collaterals from all the afferent pathways, together with centrifugal fibers from a variety of important forebrain structures (Magoun, 1958). By adding its own intrinsic activity to this multiple innervation, it is possible for the reticular formation to control changes in waking-sleeping behavior to a large extent independent of the immediate environmental input. Nevertheless, the essential factor producing sleep remains a passive one, except that instead of occurring as a consequence of a reduction in direct afferent stimulation, it is the reduced number of impulses relayed by the reticular formation that allows the activity of forebrain structures to fall below the waking level. In other words, the brain-stem reticular formation contains a center or system whose activity induces and maintains wakefulness and whose inactivity leads to sleep. The possible existence of accessory or secondary hypnogenic systems does not affect this formulation in a fundamental manner.

Although this hypothesis is still serviceable as an explanation of NREM sleep, it is obvious that it cannot explain REM sleep and its characteristically high level of nervous activity. A different mechanism must and does exist. Its neuroanatomical substrate has recently been elucidated in a series of brilliantly conceived experiments by Michel Jouvet and his collaborators at the University of Lyon, which have been summarized by Jouvet in a classic contribution to the physiology of sleep

(Jouvet, 1962). Jouvet showed that the REM phase is triggered by an area in the caudal brain stem, specifically in the medial portion of the pons, and that when this relatively small area is electrolytically destroyed, all manifestations of REM sleep are eliminated. There is no significant abnormality in the waking behavior of such a preparation, and sleep ensues quite normally, although it is limited to the NREM phase. The activation of forebrain structures characteristic of the REM period was found to involve the so-called, limbic-midbrain circuit (Nauta, 1958) or closely adjacent pathways. Lesions of the mesencephalic reticular formation which seriously impaired all the central and peripheral manifestations of wakefulness in no way hampered the occurrence of REM sleep. Furthermore, the peripheral effect on motor outflow seemed to be a direct function of the pontine area rather than, for example, an indirect effect of the above-mentioned forebrain activation, since brain-stem transections just above the pons did not interfere with the periodic complete suppression of muscle tone. Nor did the virtual isolation of the pons by transection either above or below it markedly interfere with the duration and periodicity of the remaining manifestations of the REM phase.

In summary, attempts to elucidate the neuroanatomical mechanisms of sleep and wakefulness have demonstrated the existence of two crucial systems, both of which act to produce an increase in activity of the forebrain. The system or structure which resides in the mesencephalic reticular formation produces its effect mainly by responding to afferent stimulation, and since it either enhances or at least does not interfere with motor output, the net effect is to produce waking behavior. The intrinsic rhythmicity of the pontine system is apparently the sole determinant of its periodic effect on forebrain activity. It only comes into play during NREM sleep and, because it actively inhibits motor output in addition to stimulating the forebrain, its effect is to maintain sleep. In the absence of adequate activity in either structure, the manifestations of NREM sleep may occur in an essentially passive manner.

# SUBJECTIVE EXPERIENCE DURING SLEEP: PHYSIOLOGICAL CORRELATES OF DREAM ACTIVITY

Although the title of this presentation may have held some promise for readers interested in the topic of dreams, the immediately preceding section was probably a little disappointing inasmuch as it dealt only with the physiology of sleep. Nonetheless, sleep seems to be a necessary condition for the occurrence of dreaming, and since this condition is far from being a constant one, as we have seen, we need to know something about its physiological vicissitudes before we can adequately discuss its subjective aspects. Accordingly, an attempt was made in the preceding section to outline some of the recent work on the physiology of sleep with emphasis on the newly elucidated REM state and its striking contrast to NREM sleep.

In the following pages we will begin our consideration of the psychological side of sleep. Although there has been a great interest in mental activity during REM sleep, many studies have emphasized its contrast to the NREM phase, and we will find that considerable light has thus been shed upon the subjective aspects of *both* phases.

The starting point for most of the work discussed in this paper was unquestionably Aserinsky and Kleitman's discovery of the occurrence of REMs which they first reported in 1953. As if this were not enough, they had the brilliant insight that the REMs might be related to dreaming and proceeded to test the possibility. They awakened ten subjects a total of 27 times when REMs were occurring and asked if they were dreaming. As a control, the subjects were awakened 23 times when their eyes were not moving. Twenty instances of vivid dream recall were elicited in the former condition, and in the latter, only four. This was the first time that a statistically significant correlation between an objectively measurable sleep variable and dream recall had ever been achieved.

Further studies of this relationship, in one way or another, usually dealt with two related problems: (a) *did dreaming actually occur during the REMP?* (b) *was the REMP the only time of dreaming, and if not, how much and what kind of dream activity occurred at other times?* Although the decision is somewhat arbitrary, the discussion will be organized rather strictly in terms of these two questions, both for the sake of clarity and because it essentially amounts to a consideration of psychic activity, first during REM sleep and then during NREM sleep, which is in keeping with the physiological emphasis. In the beginning, the term "dream" will of necessity be used rather loosely because that is the way it was used in the studies about to be described. In general, it was taken to mean an "adventure" or series of connected events with a variety of sensory imagery that seemed to be real at the time of occurrence.

## DREAMING DURING REM SLEEP

*Dream recall.* One method of establishing a relationship between REMs and dreaming was essentially a repetition of Aserinsky and Kleitman's study of awakening subjects during different phases of sleep with the addition of a variety of controls and precautions to minimize false positive dream reports and other possible sources of contamination. There are fifteen reports in the literature which contain data relating to the responses elicited from REM awakenings (Aserinsky and Kleitman, 1953; Berger and Oswald, 1962; Dement, 1955; Dement and Kleitman, 1957a; Foulkes, 1962; Goodenough *et al.*, 1959; Jouvet *et al.*, 1960; Kahn *et al.*, 1962; Kamiya, 1961; Roffwarg *et al.*, 1962; Snyder, 1960; Stoyva, 1961; Whitman *et al.*, 1962; Wolpert, 1960; Wolpert and Trosman, 1958). If we pool the results, we find that these studies utilized a total of 214 subjects and contained a large enough proportion of females so that the data may be validly applied to both sexes. A major weakness, however, is that nearly all the subjects were young adults. This is unfortunate, but it reflects not so much a methodological oversight as a very real limitation in the availability of subjects who are willing to sleep away from their homes at night in a laboratory setting for a relatively small fee. For all practical purposes, subjects in these experiments had to be drawn from a group who needed outside income rather urgently and who had no immediate family responsibilities. Most commonly, it was the university student who fulfilled these requirements.

At any rate, eye movements and brain waves were recorded from these subjects throughout a total of 885 subject-nights of sleep, or about 4 nights per subject. On 2240 occasions distributed among the 885 nights, sleep was interrupted during the REM phase to elicit 1864 instances of what was usually described as "vivid dream recall." This is a recall rate of 83.3 percent which, when compared to the over-all NREM results to be discussed later, unquestionably establishes the REMP as the time when the probability of being able to recall a dream is maximal. However, it does not provide crucial evidence that the dream experience is actually ongoing during REM sleep. It could be that there is something about the nature of this period which allows whole dream episodes to be conjured up with great ease in the moment of arousal.

Whenever the dreams actually do occur, these results indicate that dream memories are not as highly evanescent as is commonly thought, particularly if recall is elicited at the optimal time. On the other hand, the memories of dream experiences are clearly not as permanent as those of waking events, since only a small fraction of the apparently possible recall is obtained on the morning after *undistubed* sleep (Andress, 1911; Kleitman *et al.*, 1937).

*Dream duration and length of REMP.* A second demonstration of the correspondence between REMPs and dreaming was to show that the subjective duration of the dream experience is proportional to the length of the REMP prior to the awakening to elicit dream recall (Dement and Kleitman, 1957a). In one series of trials, subjects were awakened either 5 minutes or 15 minutes after the onset of REMs and were asked to choose the correct interval on the basis of the apparent duration of whatever dream material they recalled. A correct choice was made in 92 out of 111 instances. In another series, high correlation coefficients were obtained between the number of words in the dream narratives and the number of minutes of REMP preceding the awakenings. Finally, using the method of introducing an external subawakening stimulus into the ongoing dream (Dement and Wolpert, 1958a), a precise amount of dream content between the appearance of the stimulus and the awakening could be delimited and later compared to the actual duration of the corresponding segment of REMP. When the delimited portion of the dream story was acted out, the time required was almost exactly the same as the duration of the objective record (that is, the time between the introduction of the stimulus and the subsequent awakening which terminated the REMP). These data, of course, demolish any notion that dreams occur instantaneously, as was suggested by Maury (1861) to explain his famous guillotine dream.[2]

[2] In this dream, Maury found himself in Paris during the Reign of Terror. After witnessing a number of frightful scenes of murder, he was finally himself brought before the revolutionary tribunal. There he saw Robespierre, Marat, and other prominent figures of those terrible days. He was questioned, condemned, and led to the place of execution surrounded by an immense mob. He climbed onto the scaffold and was bound to the plank by the executioner. The blade of the guillotine fell. He felt his head being separated from his body, woke up in extreme anxiety—and found that the top of the bed had fallen down and had struck

*REM patterns and dream imagery.* To my mind, the most conclusive evidence that dreaming takes place during the REM period, and further, that it is an ongoing phenomenon, is the demonstrable correspondence between the specific directional patterns of the REMs and the spatial orientation of events in the dream. In other words, the sleeping human moves his eyes to watch or scan the hallucinatory dream images more or less as he would if he were really seeing them in the waking state. The first data supporting this relationship consisted of a number of anecdotal instances in which recall from awakenings preceded either by bursts of exclusively vertical REMs or by bursts of exclusively horizontal REMs corresponded exactly to the plane of action in the dream narrative (Dement and Kleitman, 1957a; Dement and Wolpert, 1958a). For example, a dream associated with several minutes of vertical movements was about watching leaflets flutter to the earth from a blimp hovering overhead. A statistical study by Dement and Wolpert (1958a) clearly showed that REMPs containing many individual movements were associated with active dreams (running, searching, fighting, and so on), while eye movement periods in which individual movements were relatively sparse were associated with inactive dreams (staring at a distant object, watching television, and so on). A confirmatory study was carried out by Berger and Oswald (1962) with nearly identical results.

---

his cervical vertebrae in just the way in which the blade of the guillotine would actually have struck. Since the lengthy events of the dream were so appropriate to the awakening stimulus (being struck by the top of the bed), Maury reasoned that the stimulus must have initiated the dream and that all the dream imagery was compressed into the short interval between the initial perception of the stimulus and the awakening. However, Ellis (1922) has pointed out that Maury did not record the dream until ten years after it had been dreamed and he may have embellished it considerably. The best explanation is that Maury was already dreaming about the French Revolution when the bed fell, and that *only* the final specifically appropriate images occurred after the perception of the stimulus.

A much more detailed analysis of the relationship was recently accomplished by Roffwarg *et al.* (1962). In this study, two experimenters were always present. One experimenter monitored the recording apparatus and awakened the subjects by sounding a buzzer immediately after some kind of distinct sequence of eye movements appeared in the electro-oculogram (EOG). A second experimenter (the interrogator) was stationed in another room where he would have no information about the eye movement recordings. When he heard the buzzer, he would enter the sleeping room, also separated from the apparatus room, listen to the subject report the dream, and ask clarifying questions. The subjects were previously instructed to concentrate on the portion of the dream just prior to the awakening. After he had obtained all the pertinent information from the subject, the interrogator wrote down *his own* judgment of the eye movement sequence preceding the awakening. In essence, he attempted to infer from the dream events and their spatial relationships, just how the dreamer must have moved his eyes to watch them. In addition to a description of the direction (up, down, right, left) of each movement, his judgment included a notation of lengthy fixational pauses (no movement in the record) to account for portions of the dreams in which the dreamer was, for example, staring at an unmoving object. It should be pointed out that this was one of the first studies in which the person who obtained and dealt with the dream material had no prior knowledge of the EEG stage or eye movement patterns. In most previous studies, the EEG-REM monitor and the dream interrogator were the same individual.

Twelve subjects participated in the study of Roffwarg and his collaborators. After 121 instances of dream recall were obtained, the interrogator's judgments and their associated eye movement recordings or electro-oculograms were compared and the degree of correspondence between them was rated as follows: *good,* if the judgment were an exact or near-exact description of the EOG with regard to direction, timing, and sequence of movements; *fair*, if there were a general correspondence but some components of the EOG were not described in the judgment or vice versa; and *poor*, if there were only fragmentary or no correspondence between the judgment and the EOG.

The following examples will serve to illustrate the procedure and results:

*Dream 1*

| | |
|---|---|
| Subject: | "Right near the end of the dream I was walking up the back stairs of an old house. I was holding a cat in my arms." |
| Interrogator: | "Were you looking at the cat?" |
| Subject: | "No, I was being followed up the steps by the Spanish dancer, Escudero. I was annoyed at him and refused to look back at him or talk to him. I walked up, as a dancer would, holding my head high, and I glanced up at every step I took." |
| Interrogator: | "How many steps were there?" |
| Subject: | "Five or six." |
| Interrogator: | "Then what happened?" |
| Subject: | "I reached the head of the stairs and I walked straight over to a group of people about to begin a circle dance." |
| Interrogator: | "Did you look around at the people?" |
| Subject: | "I don't believe so. I looked straight ahead at the person across from me. Then I woke up." |
| Interrogator: | "How long was it from the time you reached the top of the stairs to the end of the dream?" |
| Subject: | "Just a few seconds." |

*Interrogator's judgment.* "There should be a series of 5 equally spaced vertical upward movements as she holds her head high and walks up the steps. Then there should be a few seconds with only some very small horizontal movement just before the awakening."

*Comment.* The electro-oculogram associated with this dream is shown in Figure 2.8. It can be seen that the judgment

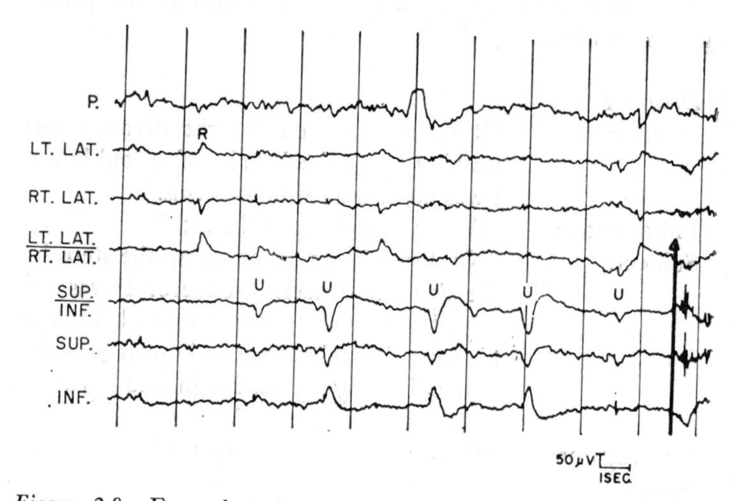


*Figure 2.8.* Example 1. An a.c. electro-oculogram showing the eye movements during the last 20 seconds before the awakening (arrow). Electrode positions: P, parietal (EEG); Lt. Lat., left lateral canthus; Rt. Lat., right lateral canthus; Lt. Lat./Rt. Lat., same leads in bipolar arrangement; Sup., supraorbital; Inf., infraorbital; Sup./Inf., same leads in bipolar arrangement. REMs: R, right; U, up. Note the 5 distinct upward deflections recorded in the vertical leads corresponding to the interrogator's prediction of 5 upward movements. The EEG pattern throughout the record was low-voltage, fast and non-spindling (Stage 1 sleep). (Reprinted, by permission, from Roffwarg, H., W. Dement, J. Muzio, and C. Fisher, Dream imagery: relationship to rapid eye movements of sleep, *Arch. Gen. Psychiat.*, 1962, 7, 235-258.)

almost exactly describes the temporal sequence and direction of the eye movement potentials. The correspondence between this judgment and its associated EOG would be rated *good*. It also illustrates how the interrogator by judicious questioning obtained additional information that enabled him to make an accurate reconstruction of the events.

*Dream 2*

| | |
|---|---|
| Subject: | "This was an unusual dream. Toward the end, I was in bed but I was listening to some people talking out in the hall. I was fascinated by what they were saying. I was lying on my back and for quite some time I just lay there looking at the wall and trying to hear their conversation. The man was telling about a friend of his who had just deserted his wife. It was almost as if he were hinting he might do the same thing and she was objecting. Then the buzzer (awakening stimulus) sounded and she was coming into the room. I looked toward the doorway. Then I was awake." |
| Interrogator: | "Where was the door?" |
| Subject: | "It was down at the foot of the bed." |
| Interrogator: | "Was the wall on your right or left side?" |
| Subject: | "It was on my right as I was lying on my back." |

*Interrogator's judgment.* "There should be a long interval of ocular quiescence as the dreamer stares at the wall listening to the people in the hall. Just at the awakening there should be a *downward* movement with some *leftward* component."

*Comment.* Again, there is a good correspondence between the judgment and the EOG (Figure 2.9). This example illustrates the very important point that the *lack* of eye movements for varying amounts of time within the REM period proper is just as much a part of the visual activity as the REMs themselves. Thus, as predicted, if the dreamer were staring at the

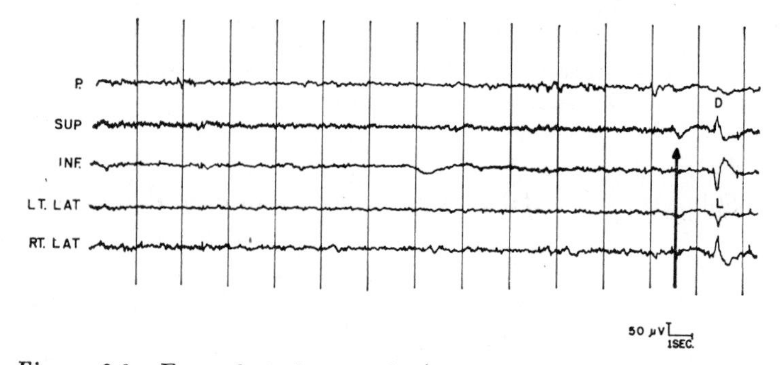


*Figure 2.9.* Example 2. An a.c. electro-oculogram showing 25 seconds of a recording before the awakening buzzer was sounded and 4 seconds after it was sounded. Electrode positions: P, parietal (EEG); Sup., supraorbital; Inf., infraorbital; Lt. Lat., left lateral canthus; Rt. Lat., right lateral canthus. REMs: D, down; L, left. Note that the buzzer did not abruptly awaken the subject. The P lead shows a continuation of Stage 1 after the buzzer. REMs may take place after the buzzer while the subject remains asleep. In these instances, the buzzer is often incorporated into the dream as in this example (see transcript). The subject awakened during the next 1-2 seconds. (Reprinted, by permission, from Roffwarg, H., W. Dement, J. Muzio, and C. Fisher, Dream imagery: relationship to rapid eye movements of sleep. *Arch. Gen. Psychiat.*, 1962, *7*, 235-258.

wall he would not be moving his eyes. It is also a good example of a fragment of the dream continuing beyond the awakening stimulus. In this case, the sound of the awakening buzzer apparently suggested that the door was opening, and so the dreamer looked toward it. Because of his position in bed with reference to the wall and the door, he had to look down and to the left to see the door. This movement is seen in the EOG immediately after the onset of the awakening buzzer.

The over-all results of the 121 instances are presented in Figure 2.10. At each awakening the dreamer was asked to rate the clarity of his recall on a 1+ to 3+ scale. Of the 121 dreams, 77 were rated as 3+ by the subjects and in 80.7

percent of these, the correspondence between judgment and EOG was *good*. As the subjects' rating of the clarity of their recall decreased, it can be seen that the ability of the interro-

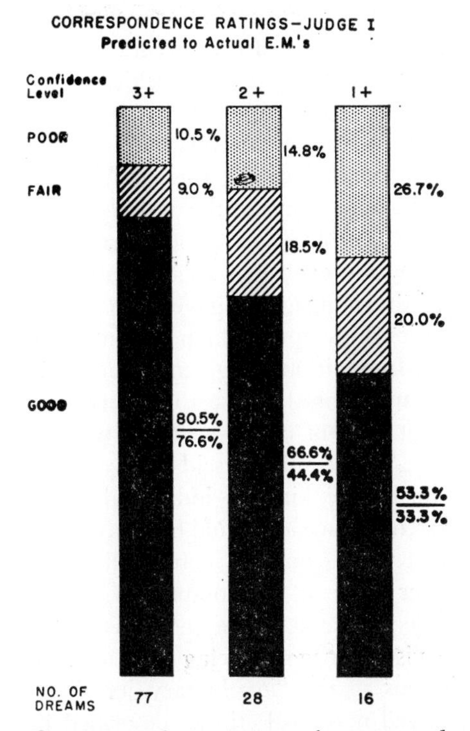


*Figure 2.10.* Summary of the degree of correspondence between EOG recordings and independent judgments based only on the associated dream content for 121 instances. The ratings are explained in the text. A good correspondence was obtained in about ⅔ of all the cases. As the graph shows, the best correspondence was obtained when the subjects' confidence in their recall was high. The percentage figures below the lines in the lower portion indicate the frequency of correspondences that were virtually perfect. (Reprinted, by permission, from Roffwarg, H., W. Dement, J. Muzio, and C. Fisher, Dream imagery: relationship to rapid eye movements of sleep, *Arch. Gen. Psychiat.*, 1962, 7, 235-258.)

gator to make an accurate judgment of the EOG sequence also fell off. This strongly suggests that poor correspondences were due to imperfections in the subjects' recall which introduced errors into the interrogator's inferences.

The conclusion that rapid eye movements are meaningfully related to the hallucinatory dream events as opposed to being a random motor discharge is inescapable. Roffwarg and his collaborators tentatively concluded that the results warranted hypothesizing a one-to-one correlation between eye movements and dream events just as if the dreamer were seeing and doing exactly the same thing in the waking state. If this were true, the failure to obtain a good correspondence in all cases would be readily explained by assuming that the dreamer forgot a crucial dream image, or gave an inaccurate account of the spatial relationships upon which the interrogators's inference was based. In addition, judgments were difficult to make for certain dream events because the interrogator could not be sure just what kind of eye movements would be appropriate. For example, if the subject said, "I was talking to someone," would he be the kind of individual who would stare fixedly at his listener's face, or would he be the so-called "shifty-eyed" individual who would be continually glancing around but would never stare at his companion's face? Along this line, it is possible that some of the movement was entirely unrelated to the visual imagery, being instead an expression of emotion analogous to the "involuntary jerks" in response to emotionally loaded nonvisual stimuli described by Asher and Ort (1951).

A final point to emphasize is that negative results in the above experiment would have meant little. The nature of the task is such that anyone could obtain negative results. In other words, a small degree of ineptitude in asking questions and making inferences, or a poor subject-interrogator relationship could easily introduce sufficient error to obscure the correspondence.

It is of historical interest that the oculomotor involvement in dreaming was predicted more than 70 years ago by Ladd (1892) in a series of reflections on the psychology of visual dreams. "But I am inclined also to believe that, in somewhat vivid visual dreams, the eyeballs move gently in their sockets, taking various positions induced by the retinal phantasms as they control the dream. As we look down the street of a strange city, for example, in a dream we probably focus our eyes somewhat as we should do in making the same observations when awake . . ."

*Dreams and REMs in the blind.* It has often been suggested that a crucial test of the hypothesis that REMs are not a random motor discharge, but are intimately related to dream imagery, would be to study congenitally blind subjects. It is well known that congenitally blind individuals do not describe visual components of sensation in their dreams, but rather experience dream imagery in other sensory modalities (Blank, 1958; Ramsey, 1953). Accordingly, their dream periods should be signaled by the presence of an "emergent" Stage 1 EEG *without* REMs. In order for such a study to be conclusive, it should be determined that the oculomotor system is intact, and that the resting potential of the eyeball is unimpaired so that movements could be recorded. The former could be assumed if the congenitally blind subjects showed normal vestibular responses and were able to execute voluntary eye movements in the waking state.

Offenkrantz and Wolpert (1963) have reported a study of one congenitally blind subject. This subject could move his eyes in a somewhat limited fashion while awake, and there was apparently a satisfactory resting potential since the movements could be recorded electrically. In 5 of 6 "emergent" Stage 1 EEG periods from which dreams were elicited, no REMs were seen. During the sixth period, a few bursts of rapid movement, resembling the kind the subject could execute when awake, were seen. Studies in 5 blind subjects are described by Berger, Olley, and Oswald (1962). No REMs were seen during sleep in 3 congenitally blind subjects. They nevertheless showed a periodic occurrence of Stage 1 EEG periods and nonvisual dream recall was elicited from such periods. REMs during sleep appeared in 2 subjects who were blinded later in life. These subjects reported dreams that contained visual imagery.

*Other correlations with dream imagery.* We may consider the possibility that some of the seemingly capricious fluctuations in autonomic variables during REMPs also represent changes appropriate to what is going on in the dream. For example, the respiratory pauses that are intermittently associated with bursts of eye movement may represent a sort of startle response or an interference with respiration by mechanisms related to vocalization. The emotional tone of the dream may determine whether the heart rate rises or remains relatively steady. Unfortunately, no one has as yet studied these problems and they await the efforts of future research.

Wolpert's (1960) electromyographic study represents the only attempt that has been made to relate a variable other than REM activity to dream imagery. He found that there was a significant correlation between the amount of EMG activity in the limb muscles and the reported activity in the dream. There was also a good fit between the presence of specific EMG findings and specific manifest dream activities. For example, a burst of muscle potentials from the leg might occur with a dream of kicking.

We have recently made some preliminary observations in our laboratory with multiple simultaneous electromyographic records from arm and leg flexors and extensors both above and below the knee and elbow. For all practical purposes, except for gross body movements, the REMP was characterized by EMG silence. Although there were rare bursts, we were convinced that the vast bulk of body movement in the dream does *not* find expression in phasic skeletal muscular discharge.

*Discussion.* The evidence cited above strongly supports the conclusion that dreaming occurs throughout the REM phases of sleep. It suggests that the experiential events of the dream are on-going or "progressively flowing," and that they have a temporal dimension which approximately corresponds to that of events in the real world. It would border on the ridiculous to argue that a complicated series of eye movements is executed with no experiential component whatsoever, and then, in the instant of arousal, a dream is composed which exactly corresponds to those previously executed eye movements. The only reasonable interpretation is that the dream images are appearing smoothly and progressively *during sleep* and the dreamer is looking at them. For some reason, the oculomotor apparatus actively participates in this looking. We should emphasize again that the varying durations of ocular quiescence between individual movements within the REMP should be considered as part of the over-all oculomotor activity, since they appear to represent fixational pauses; the eyes are being held stationary while the dreamer stares at some object.

The assumption that dreaming takes place as a progressive flow of experience throughout REM phases does not, however, mean that this flow need be coherent. There may be abrupt changes of scene or spatial orientation, or huge gaps in a progressive sequence of events, none of which could occur in real life. An example will clarify this point. A dream was reported to us in which the dreamer was ascending some steps into a building. The next thing he knew he was standing at the door of the check room taking off his coat. Since he recognized the building from real life, he knew that in order to get from the entering stairs to the check room, he had to go down a hall and make several turns. However, in the dream he remembered only ascending the steps and getting his coat off. The eye movement record verified the accuracy of his memory. A series of vertical movements compatible with mounting the steps was immediately followed by a burst of movements appropriate to taking off his coat. The activity of walking down the hall and turning corners, which would have been necessary in real life, was simply left out of the dream.

In conclusion, we may remark that the validity of at least the visual aspect of the dream experience has been established for REMPs by showing that the dream events interconnect in a logical fashion with observable real events (REMs). As was previously suggested, this is the best that can be done in establishing the validity of *any* subjective experience.

We will take up some additional details and implications of REM dreaming later. At this point we must consider the second part of the problem: does dreaming occur at other times?

## MENTAL ACTIVITY DURING NREM SLEEP

Someone recently asked why there seemed to be so many confirmatory studies of the relationship between REM sleep and dream recall, implying perhaps that the relationship must be somewhat tenuous and difficult to establish. As a matter of fact, most of the studies cited in the previous section were not designed for the express purpose of confirming the relationship, but rather to illuminate some further aspect of it. Nonetheless, an aura of skepticism has continued to surround this area of investigation, as if the relationship and its easy repeatability were simply "too good to be true." In the face of this natural pessimism, one can only point to the evidence and reaffirm with as much authority as can be mustered that REM sleep does exist, that it is supremely easy to monitor with EEG and eye movement recordings, that it never fails to appear during normal sleep, and that awakenings from it almost invariably result in vivid dream recall. Furthermore, these reports are generally so dramatic and detailed as to preclude any quibbling about what constitutes a dream report and what does not.

All this is by way of contrast to the situation that confronts us when we turn our attention to NREM sleep. Its possible associations with mental activity are not so straightforward and plausible, and we will have to devote what may seem an excessive amount of discussion to an adequate consideration of the problem, and ask the reader to bear with us in the following pages.

*Labeling dreams.* As we examine the possibility of dream activity during NREM sleep, we will find the definition of dreams becoming a progressively more important consideration. It might be helpful, therefore, to say a few words about the presumed development of individual concepts of dreaming before passing on to the experimental results.

Let us begin by assuming that in infancy or early childhood, no distinction is made between subjective experiences occurring during wakefulness and subjective experiences occurring during sleep. Insofar as they remember them or are motivated to speak of them, young children probably describe their sleep experiences merely as events that took place in the past, perhaps vaguely related to the previous evening or to their bedrooms. It is possible that children talk a great deal about their sleep experiences and no one notices, either because they are too commonplace to attract attention or may be thought to be imaginary. Sooner or later, though, the child is awakened from sleep by a nightmare or recounts a sufficiently unusual experience; and he is told, "that was a dream." Depending somewhat on the parents' interest, and on how often the sequence of events is repeated, children gradually learn that dreams are things that happen at night after they have gone to bed. A charming definition may be found in the children's book by Krauss (1952): "A dream is to look at the night and see things."

Children may also learn that dream experiences are not smoothly continuous from night to night the way waking experiences are from day to day. As the limitations of the real world are better understood, dreams begin to involve "impossible" events. The author's daughter, age 3, reported one morning, "Mommy likes to ride on the roller coaster at night." This was noteworthy to her since, despite her pleading, "Mommy" would never take her on the roller coaster during the day.

Probably one of the most important occurrences in learning to label dream experiences is that of suddenly waking up *from* a dream and realizing one is not in some strange place, but actually in one's very own familiar bed. In this way, dreams are firmly associated not only with the night but with sleep.

Most of our learning emphasizes *when* dreams occur. In general, we are not told *what* dreams are before the fact. Rather, we produce memories that may or may not be identified as dreams by our parents. Thus, it is obvious that what we learn to call a dream depends entirely upon the kind of subjective experience we have while asleep. If the nature of this subjective experience is more or less universal, then the word, "dream," is likely to mean the same thing to everyone. If the nature of the sleep experience is highly variable from person to person, then the word, "dream," can have no communicative function at all.

In addition, some of our sleep experiences may not be considered dreams because they are never labeled as such. Suppose a child says, "Last night I remembered where I lost my water pistol." This may have occurred in sleep but certainly will not be labeled as a dream by the parents.

Finally, no sleep experience can be labeled as a dream unless it is remembered and communicated. Thus, individual variations may depend on differences in the persistence of the memory traces.

In spite of all this, there is a great deal of similarity in what different persons report as dreams. At the same time, it is also apparent that there is considerable opportunity for the word to acquire highly individualized meanings. Accordingly, to ask a group of subjects about their "dreams" can hardly be considered a standardized scientific procedure. It is somewhat startling, in view of all this, that no one has thought to ask a group of volunteers to define a dream or to question them about what they would call a dream before using them as subjects.

*Recall from NREM awakenings.* As we have reported,

when subjects are awakened during REMPs, there is an excellent probability that they will recall an experience that they are willing to call a dream. The results from the individual studies from which data were pooled were remarkably uniform with regard to REM awakenings. The lowest recall rate was 60 percent and the highest was 93 percent. If we exclude five reports for the following reasons: too few subjects (Jouvet *et al.*, 1960), part of subject population selected because they *never* recalled dreams at home (Goodenough *et al.*, 1959), hypnotic relationship between subjects and experimenter (Stoyva, 1961), awakening criteria not fully established (Aserinsky and Kleitman, 1953), and a portion of the awakenings done after gross body movements (Wolpert and Trosman, 1958), the remaining 10 studies, which include 1764 of the original 2253 pooled awakenings, vary only from 79.6 to 88.2 percent.

In contrast, the dream recall rate varied from zero percent (Dement, 1955; Wolpert and Trosman, 1958) to 54 (Foulkes, 1962) and 57 (Kamiya, 1961) percent in the 10 studies that included awakenings during NREM periods. This would suggest, depending on which reports are considered, that (a) dreaming occurs only during REMPs, or (b) substantial dreaming occurs in all phases of sleep. Although the physiological contrast between the REM and NREM phases would favor the first possibility, the recall studies favoring the second possibility are among the most carefully designed and cannot be ignored.

It is difficult to attribute the wide variations in NREM recall to differences in method since all the investigators obtained uniformly high recall from REM awakenings. However, there is no other reasonable possibility, so, the question boils down to why the effects of these methodological differences were limited to NREM awakenings.

Two factors account for the largest share of the methodological variation. (a) There were significant differences in the criteria used in evaluating the responses of the subjects as to whether or not they were classified as dream recall. (b) There were implicit and explicit differences in the recall task, that is, the question posed to the subjects upon awakening.

In the study of Dement and Kleitman (1957a) which is representative of the earlier works, awakenings were done *during* REMPs and at varying increments of time *after* the cessation of REMs (NREM awakenings). The task imposed upon the subjects was to state, immediately upon being awakened, whether or not they had been dreaming, and if they answered in the affirmative, "to describe the content of the dream." It was assumed that the subjects knew what a dream consisted of and accordingly would be able to answer the question, "Were you dreaming just then?" without undue ambiguity. As one of the perpetrators of this study, the author admits that an exact definition of dreaming was not given, either for the subjects or for ensuing readers. In judging the responses, our published criteria were that subjects "were considered to have been dreaming only if they could relate a coherent, fairly detailed description of dream content. Assertions that they had dreamed without recall of content, or vague, fragmentary impression of content were considered negative." In spite of the inadequate precision and detail in these criteria, at the time they seemed very easy to apply to the responses of the subjects: 191 REM awakenings elicited 152 affirmative replies (80 percent) followed by descriptions of content. The vast majority of these responses were long, detailed "adventures" which included a wide variety of characters, events, and emotions. Indeed, the length and detail were very impressive and greatly exceeded that of ordinary spontaneous morning recall. Only 11 of the responses from 160 NREM awakenings (7 percent) met our criteria. In addition, five of these positive NREM responses were elicited from the 17 awakenings that were done within eight minutes of the spontaneous termination of an REMP (recall rate—29 percent). In the remaining 132 NREM awakenings that followed the termination of REMPs by more than eight minutes or did not follow REMPs at all (occurring in the initial NREM sleep preceding the first REMP or in NREM sleep following an interrupted REMP), there were only six positive reports (4 percent).

The interpretation of these results was that dreaming (still undefined) occurred only during REM sleep, and that occasional instances of NREM recall occurred when the memory of the dream persisted long enough to be recalled at some increment of time (usually less than eight minutes) after it had actually ended. In addition, it was felt that a zero recall rate should never be obtained since the general confusion of being abruptly aroused from sleep would predispose to an occasional confabulatory report. Thus, even when a rare positive NREM response was not preceded by an uninterrupted REMP, it would not undermine the basic interpretation.

The practical value of the hypothesis that dreaming occurred only during REMPs was that the total amount of dreaming in a single night could be easily evaluated objectively by recording eye movements and brain waves.

In order to feel complete confidence that the results typified by the Dement and Kleitman experiments justify such an interpretation, it is necessary to know exactly what is meant by dreaming both from the subjects' and the experimenters' points of view. Our subjects were uniformly asked, upon awakening, "Were you dreaming just then?" A large number of NREM awakenings elicited the reply, "No, I was not." Does this mean that no subjective experience had occurred, or that certain kinds of experience *had* occurred which were not labeled "dream," and thus were not mentioned? If the latter possibility were true, it would at least suggest that a certain uniformity existed in the labeling of dream experiences. The range of dream recall during REM periods for the 5 intensively studied subjects in the Dement and Kleitman report was 65 to 90 percent and the NREM range was 3 to 12.5 percent. The dream narratives themselves backed up the implication of the percentages. They were all descriptions of an experience that included a temporal dimension (that is, something took place in time) and usually several modes of imagery. The imagery was generally highly complex and predominantly visual. If we assume that experiences had to include these characteristics before subjects would label them as dreams, what might have been left out?

*"Thinking" reports.* This is best illustrated by referring to another study recently published by Foulkes (1962). In this study, subjects were awakened at various times and asked if they were dreaming; but, if they said they were not, they were then asked if anything was "going through your mind." This would presumably elicit recall of additional material that was *not* labeled as a dream. And in fact, Foulkes found that 20 percent of NREM awakenings elicited reports of subjective experience labeled not as dreaming but as "thinking."

Rechtschaffen, Verdone, and Wheaton also conducted a study (1963) in which an interest in more than just the mental activity labeled as dreaming was communicated to the subjects. They, too, obtained reports of "thinking" from NREM awakenings, but at a lower rate (about seven percent) than Foulkes.

*Criteria of dream recall.* Even though these results raise the problem of what kinds of mental activity ought to be included in an explicit definition of dreaming, the fact remains that the subjects ordinarily differentiated between "dreaming" and "thinking," and reports of the latter did not account for the high NREM dream recall rates obtained by some investigators as opposed to others. What does appear to explain the wide variation in NREM dream recall is brought out in the unpublished study of Orlinsky cited by Kamiya (1961). Orlinsky rated subject responses on an eight-point scale as follows: (0) subject cannot remember dreaming; no dream is reported on awakening. (I) Subject remembers having dreamed, or thinks he may have been dreaming, but cannot remember any specific content. (II) Subject remembers a specific topic, but in isolation: for example, a fragmentary action, scene, object, word, or idea unrelated to anything else. (III)

Subject remembers several such disconnected thoughts, scenes, or actions. (IV) Subject remembers a short but coherent dream, the parts of which seem related to each other: for example, a conversation rather than a word, a problem worked through rather than an idea, a purposeful rather than a fragmentary action, and so forth. (V) Subject remembers a detailed dream sequence, in which something happens, followed by some consequence, or in which one scene, mood, or main interacting character is replaced by another (different from III either in coherence of change or on the development of the several parts of the sequence). (VI) Subject remembers a long, detailed dream sequence involving three or four discernible stages of development. (VII) Subject remembers an extremely long and detailed dream sequence of 5 or more stages; or more than 1 dream (at least 1 of which is rated V) for a single awakening.

Of 400 NREM responses, Orlinsky found that 57 percent fell in the categories I through VII. Combining only categories II through VII, the percent of "dreaming" was 46. The categories II through VII would more or less correspond to a definition of dreaming as any mental activity occurring during sleep, or any report containing specific content regardless of how labeled. The percentages declined progressively as fewer categories were combined. For example, combining categories IV through VII gave 27 percent recall of dreaming, and combining only VI and VII yielded only seven percent. What emerges very clearly from this study is that the percentage of NREM dreaming is very sensitive to the criteria used in defining dream recall.

This principle goes a long way in explaining the differing NREM results in other reports. Dement and Kleitman's criteria, although vague, were obviously fairly exclusive. Only "coherent, fairly detailed" descriptions were rated as dream recall, and "vague" or "fragmentary" impressions were not. These experimenters obtained a low NREM rate.

Wolpert and Trosman (1958) distinguished a category of

recall called "fragment only." Excluding this category from the definition of dream recall, they obtained no dream reports from 36 NREM awakenings. If "fragment only" had been counted as a dream, the NREM recall rate would have been 28 percent.

Foulkes (1962), whose definition of a dream was "any occurrence with visual, auditory, or kinesthetic imagery," or "any phenomenon lacking such imagery but in which the subject either assumed another identity than his own or felt that he was thinking in a physical setting other than that in which he actually was," not surprisingly obtained a high NREM dream recall rate of 54 percent.

Rechtschaffen, Verdone, and Wheaton (1963) found that subjects reported some "specific content of mental experience" in 23 percent of NREM awakenings of which 63 percent were labeled as dreaming. Thus 14 1/2 percent of all NREM awakenings elicited "dreams."

*Reality of NREM experiences.* Although the results of these various studies might be viewed as controversial by some, it is my opinion that taken together they present a clear and consistent picture of the subjective aspects of sleep. In order to see the over-all picture, however, we must ignore the "dream recall" figures, which for the reasons already mentioned do not represent a standardized body of data, and try to look at the reports themselves.

If we do this, it becomes apparent that *all* phases of sleep are associated with some kind of subjective experience or mental activity whether it be called "dreaming," "thinking," "static imagery," or whatever. This is tantamount to saying that conscious mental activity does not cease at any time during sleep. We ought not to be disturbed by this because certainly nothing is known about the neurophysiology of any phase of sleep which dictates that the mind must be completely inactive, that is, that we are unconscious during sleep. Sleep, literary metaphor to the contrary notwithstanding, is not death. All we can say about sleep is that many physiological activities seem to reach a rather low and regularized level at certain times, but we certainly do not know whether this level or any level above death itself represents an *absolute* cut-off point for the activities of the mind. In addition, as we have previously pointed out, it is possible to achieve a rather low level of physiological activity in the waking state by relaxation and recumbency, and we surely would not deny the presence of thought, sensation, and/or imagery at this time. Finally, although it does not pertain to subjective activity *per se*, some recent work has shown that rather high level discriminatory and operant responses can be elicited during NREM sleep (Granda and Hammack, 1961; Oswald *et al.*, 1960).

Thus, there is no compelling physiological reason for refusing to accept NREM responses, whether they be labeled "dreaming" or "thinking," as valid accounts of subjective experience during sleep.[3] A more serious objection is: how do we know that these reports represent activity that actually occurred during sleep and not, for example, in the moment of awakening? The answer is that we do not know. There are no temporal landmarks available for NREM mentation which may serve to localize it *within* the sleep period as there are for REM experiences (that is, the correspondence between specific REM patterns and dream events). In the absence of absolute proof, there are, however, several reasons for accepting NREM reports as valid descriptions of experiences occurring *during* sleep:[4]

(a) Since it has been shown that some reports of subjective experience can be unquestionably localized to the sleep period (REM reports), we may regard other sincere reports with at least a little less skepticism.

[3] Those who consider "abstract thought" the highest and noblest function of the human mind may be unwilling to accept the possibility of its occurrence during sleep. However, they must remember that directed thinking to solve a problem is one thing and the idle, drifting nature of undirected thinking quite another.

[4] In making these points, the author has drawn rather freely from the arguments of Rechtschaffen, Verdone, and Wheaton (1963).

(b) Some of the NREM reports, including those characterized as imageless thought, are sufficiently complex so that it is difficult to assume that they were conjured up in the act of awakening, often a fraction of a second at best. Even in the full waking state we do not ordinarily consider ourselves capable of "lightning" thought. An example of an NREM response taken from Rechtschaffen *et al.* (1963) will serve to illustrate what is meant by sufficient complexity.

"This time I recall no dreaming at all. 'Thought' I guess you would call it. These thoughts, there was no obvious correlation between them. They were just various things that I would like to do, going from wanting a sailboat, say, which is one of them, to doing something with various interests, chemistry particularly, and metallurgy, which I happen to be interested in. Then it would drift back to the sailing. Then I would think about school—going back to school. They were all things that are either very important to me or were very relevant to the near future."

(c) Preliminary experiments in our laboratory indicate that very early changes in falling asleep (which can be pinpointed in the recordings either as the first slow, rolling eye movements, or the first attenuation of alpha rhythm, or both simultaneously) are associated with an equally sharp change in mental activity. Although it is a moot question as to when we would say that frank NREM sleep is present, the point is that the entrance into NREM sleep is correlated *not* with a cessation of subjective experience, but with a change in quality, usually from abstract thought to so-called hypnagogic imagery. A second point is that, if we do accept the early onset of sleep as part of the NREM phase, we shall have unquestionably localized a subjective experience within it. Furthermore, since the physiology of the early sleep onset period is virtually indistinguishable from later NREM sleep, particularly if preceded by a period of quiet wakefulness, there is no reason to doubt that the hypnagogic imagery continues right into the NREM phase. Figure 2.11 illustrates these experiments.

A subject with EEG and EOG attachments is lying relaxed in bed. A buzzer is sounded at periodic intervals and he responds by reporting what was "going on in his mind" just prior to the signal. While he remains awake, as indicated by the persistent alpha rhythm and *absence* of slow eye movements in the lower tracings, he monotonously reports "abstract thought" after each signal. When a signal occurs a few seconds after the first sign of sleep (the slow eye movement in the upper tracings of Figure 2.11), he reports a change from abstract thought to hypnagogic image. The report associated with the slow eye movement in Figure 2.11 was as follows: "I had to urinate and I was idly wondering if I should call you (the experimenter) and suddenly I saw an old man standing in front of a toilet who was going to urinate."

Of course it is no surprise that hypnagogic imagery is associated with falling asleep. The reason for emphasizing these experiments, however, is that a similar objection can be applied to hypnagogic imagery as is applied to other NREM content—that it may have actually occurred earlier or in the instant of arousal. We feel that these results serve to localize hypnagogic imagery within the sleep onset period.

(d) Sleep talking seems to occur most frequently during NREM sleep in conjunction with gross body movements (Kamiya, 1961; Rechtschaffen *et al.*, 1962). It often sounds like a description of some immediately preceding mental activity, although subjects aroused after an episode of sleep talking rarely recall anything.

(e) In a few trials, Rechtschaffen, Verdone, and Wheaton (1963) have found that a subawakening stimulus given a few seconds before an arousal was incorporated *within* an NREM experience, thus tagging it as having occurred during sleep.

If we accept these points as sufficient reason to grant that NREM reports probably are valid descriptions of mentation during sleep, then, since REM mentation is certainly well established, we must conclude that to all intents and purposes, the mind is continuously active *all* during sleep. Should we

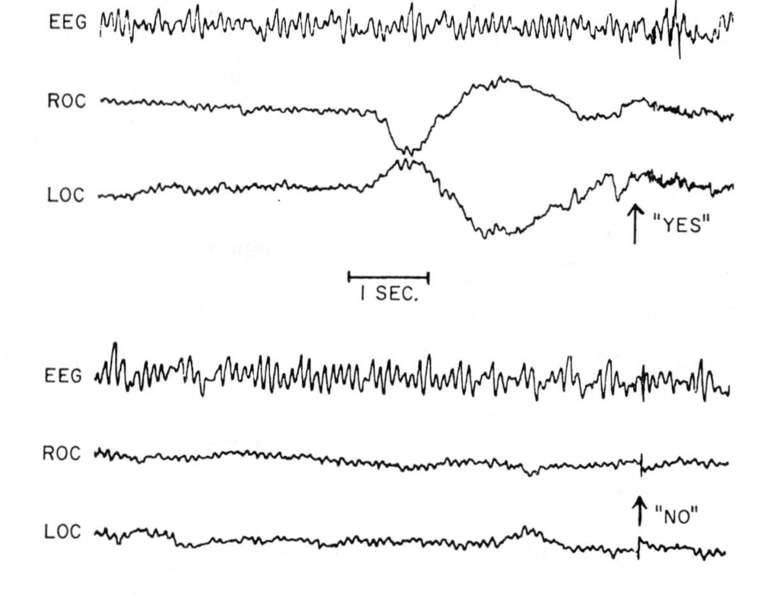


*Figure 2.11.* Relation of slow eye movements to hypnagogic imagery. Electrode placements: EEG, monopolar parieto-occipital electrode; ROC, right outer canthus monopolar electrode; LOC, left outer canthus monopolar electrode. With these derivations, a conjugate eye movement will give a potential change that is out-of-phase on the two eye pens. In the upper eye tracings there is a rightward, leftward, rightward sequence of slow swings after which the buzzer is sounded (arrow). Note that each directional component lasts about one second as compared to .05 to .1 second for rapid movements. In the lower tracings, the buzzer (arrow) is sounded when there are no eye movements. Although there is no change in the continuous waking alpha rhythm in the EEG, the subjects reported hypnagogic imagery in instances illustrated in the upper tracings, and abstract thought in instances illustrated in the lower tracings. If the buzzer had not been sounded, the slow eye movements would have continued and in a few seconds the EEG would have undoubtedly changed to Stage 1 sleep onset patterns.

then say that we are *dreaming* at all times during sleep? How would we reconcile such a possibility with the markedly different physiological properties of the REM and the NREM phases? Actually, there *are* consistent differences between the psychological activities of the two phases. REM reports are often long, complicated, and vivid, and consist of a coherent series of events. NREM reports are often fragmentary, thought-like, brief, and so on. Rechtschaffen, Verdone, and Wheaton (1963) made a detailed study of the content of reports from REM and NREM sleep. They found many significant differences and summarized their results as follows: "As compared with REM mentation, subjects report NREM mentation as more poorly recalled, more like thinking and less like dreaming, less vivid, less visual, more conceptual, under greater volitional control, more plausible, more concerned with their contemporary lives, occurring in lighter sleep, less emotional, and more pleasant. Our impression is that NREM mentation resembles that large portion of our waking thought which wanders in a seemingly disorganized, drifting, nondirected fashion whenever we are not attending to external stimuli or actively working out a problem or a daydream."

Even so, these differences are all quantitative and, if we confine ourselves to the content of the reports, we shall find no element that could tell us in every instance with which phase of sleep we are dealing.

## RECAPITULATION

A number of studies have shown that REM sleep is associated with a high probability of dream recall if subjects are awakened during its presence. The demonstration of an association between the spatio-temporal patterns of the electrically recorded eye movements and the specific activities that are recalled, supports the conclusion that the subjective experience has a temporal dimension and actually takes place during REM sleep. The relative independence of the degree of recall from the exact method of inquiry further attests to the veridicality of the verbal report.

Awakenings from NREM sleep, on the other hand, may or may not result in a substantial percentage of dream recall depending upon the technique of interrogation and certain other factors. The NREM responses in optimal situations include reports of "abstract thought," reports of vague, fragmented imagery, and a small proportion of lengthy, complex adventures. The physiological nature of NREM sleep is such that no temporal landmarks (such as the individual eye movements in REM sleep) exist which can aid in establishing that the material reported has actually occurred during sleep. A number of arguments can be made, however, which suggest that the most plausible assumption is that NREM reports are valid accounts of mental activity that occurred during the immediately prior period of sleep. There are quantitative distinctions between REM and NREM reports such that the more dreamlike experiences seem to take place during REM sleep, but no matter how we define dreaming, the best we can say is that most dreaming, or the most intense dreaming, occurs during the REMPs.

## THE ESSENTIAL NATURE OF DREAMING

The situation as we have described it up to this point is not very satisfactory. Although the elucidation of a physiological sleep cycle with two markedly contrasting phases seemed to hold out great promise as a way to approach the study of dreaming, the demonstrated psychological relationships were not sufficiently distinct.

At first it looked as if the REM phase were the only time that subjective experience occurred, and further, that this experience would conform to what is commonly described as dreaming. If this had been true, we would not have needed to worry about what nuances of experience to include in a definition of dreaming. We would have merely defined dreaming in terms of the REM phase and any subjective experience occurring therein would have been included.

Unfortunately for such a definition, subjective experience occurs *outside* of the REM phase of sleep. If we define dreams fairly inclusively, we must conclude that dreaming occurs all during sleep. In this case, the usefulness of our physiological techniques is lost. The possibility of a meaningful relationship between brain activity and mental activity is minimized, since a striking, qualitative change in nervous function is associated with only a quantitative change in dreaming; and the differences that *do* exist in the psychological properties of the two phases of sleep are not accounted for. Even if we arbitrarily exclude imageless thought from our definition of dreaming, we would still not be able to say that the REM phase was the only time that dreams occurred.

The only way to accomplish this would be to insist that only very long, complex experiences be called dreams. Then we would find that virtually 100 percent of all "dreams" occurred during REM periods. We would also find, however, that not only would shorter, less complex "non-dream" experiences regularly occur in the NREM phase, they would also crop up during the REM period. In short, it is virtually impossible to construct a reasonable content-based definition of dreaming that adequately differentiates the REM phase from the NREM phase.

Is there some way in which this large body of data can be assimilated without losing the usefulness of our objective techniques and blurring the psychological significance of the remarkable physiological differences between REM and NREM sleep? If the physiological and psychological properties are viewed together as part of a single over-all process in each phase, the author believes that there is an interpretation that will satisfactorily account for most of the experimental data thus far reported and, at the same time, will allow us to construct a meaningful definition or model of dreaming which confines it exclusively to the REM period.

First, let us consider the waking state. All conscious mental activity during wakefulness can be divided into two categories: (*Class I*) mental activity that is directly dependent upon, and the result of, on-going sensory input from the environment. In other words, Class I is the sphere of mental life that may be described as sensation and perception, and includes seeing, hearing, smelling, feeling (touch), tasting, and so forth. It is our continuous but continually shifting awareness of the outer world as it is communicated to us by the constant flux of messages from our various sense organs. *Class II* includes all mental activity not of Class I, specifically, that which is independent of, or only conditionally elicited by, ongoing sensory input. This would include all of what is loosely characterized as abstract thought, apperception, decision making, imagery, problem solving, and so forth.[5]

An important point is that on the basis of content alone, it would often be difficult to distinguish between these two categories or classes. Abstract or imageless thought is easily assigned to Class II, but with phenomena falling more under the heading of imagery, ranging all the way from vague imagery with the eyes closed, to hallucinations, the differentiation from Class I is not so simple. For example, as far as the *content* of the mental experience is concerned, there is no difference between an hallucination and a sensory perception. They can only be distinguished on the basis of whether or not they are associated with an appropriate sensory input (that is, whether or not the object perceived is really present in the environment). Even with Class II imagery of less than hallucinatory

[5] The terms "Class I" and "Class II" are used only to facilitate the argument and should be dropped thereafter. We do not presume to add to the official nomenclature in this difficult area. Furthermore, the distinction is not quite so easy and sharp as would be implied by a formal terminology.

intensity, content could not provide a basis for differentiation. How would we tell the difference between, "I saw my mother," and "I had an image of my mother," on the basis of the content? In the absence of absolute certainty as to which was associated with sensory input, we might separate them on the basis of intensity or "realness," the sensory perception being the more vivid. However, if we were completely isolated from the environment, as in sleep, our identification of Class II images on the basis of their relative intensity would eventually break down because of the absence of a continuous flux of optimally vivid sensory perceptions with which to compare them.

The only way to distinguish adequately between Class I activity and Class II activity of a similar order would be to monitor the sensory input. All activity appropriately associated with sensory input would be assigned to Class I, all other activity, regardless of how similar in content, would be assigned to Class II. Such a procedure theoretically would approach 100 percent accuracy.

To repeat, all mental activity or awareness, or conscious experience in the waking state, can be divided into two categories: Class I, that which is the direct result of ongoing sensory input; and Class II, that which is not. On the basis of intensity or content alone, it would sometimes be difficult to distinguish certain types of Class II experience from those of Class I. However, with knowledge of the sensory input we could theoretically achieve perfect accuracy in assigning any mental activity to the proper class.

Now let us consider the sleep state. As we have seen, the usual preparations for sleep have the aim of drastically reducing environmental stimuli. In other words, we tend to create a state in which Class I activity is minimized or eliminated from our mental sphere. As we lie in the dark awaiting the arrival of sleep, our physiological activities are slowing down and our minds drift aimlessly from random thought to image to thought, and so on. In other words, as we approach NREM sleep, our minds are almost entirely dominated by Class II mentation, although it is of a low order.

We cannot as yet identify the essential change in passing from this relaxed, resting-awake state to a state of frank sleep. Perhaps it is merely the final shutting down of our outside awareness. But we *do* know that whatever the essential nature of the change, Class II mentation does *not* cease. It merely shifts its emphasis from a predominance of abstract thought to a predominance of hypnagogic imagery. Should hypnagogic imagery be considered dreaming? It is certainly "mental activity during sleep," and furthermore, it fulfills the more stringent condition (Hall's definition) of being a "succession of images, predominantly visual in quality, which are experienced during sleep." We will not answer the question at this juncture, but will merely point out that hypnagogic images are almost always regarded by subjects as "not real" (Dement and Kleitman, 1957b; Maury, 1861).

At any rate, as we progress further into NREM sleep, Class I activity continues to be absent and Class II activity persists —a fluctuating, often aimless series of thoughts and images of varying complexity. If we are awakened at this point (NREM sleep), we are very likely to report a subjective experience, and the report may sound like a dream.

Now, let us suppose that at certain times, in an entirely physiological sense, a high level of sensory input is suddenly added to the Class II activity. If it originates from the environment (an alarm clock, for example), we awaken and resume our Class I experiencing. On the other hand, let us suppose that at certain times "sensory input" is somehow generated by the nervous system itself, independent of the environment—that at some level in the sensory pathways, neural elements begin to discharge in a pattern similar to that induced by external sensory stimulation. That such an occurrence is at least a possibility is supported by recent demonstrations of the central regulation of sensory input in the waking state (Livingston, 1959). During sleep these central regulatory mechanisms, rather than modifying discharge patterns, might actually induce them. At any rate, whenever such an internal "sensory input" occurred, we would, in effect, be experiencing Class I activity during sleep, and this is what we propose to define as dreaming.

*The basic assumption of our model of dreaming is that during the REM periods of sleep, the brain is somehow generating the neurophysiological background for Class I experiencing.* Therefore, REM periods are dream periods and dreams are experiences that include Class I (perceptual) activity in both a physiological and psychological sense. Before considering its implications, let us see how this hypothesis jibes with the known facts.

*Psychological aspects.* We may assume that the more or less continuous Class I activity of the waking state is almost always associated with concurrent Class II activity. In other words, sensations and perceptions normally evoke thoughts, images, and memories. When the waking behavior is of a purposeful or "problem-solving" type, the Class II activity tends to be more organized, concentrated, and "bound" to Class I, and also more easily recalled. On the other hand, when the waking behavior is more automatic or routine, Class II activity is more like what might be called "background thoughts." It wanders in a seemingly aimless fashion, continually interrupted and started anew by the shifting flux of perceptions and sensations. At such times, Class II activity is often difficult to recall or report, but is probably always present. We can remember driving down the street on our way to work and some of the things we saw, but can we remember what we were thinking? In general, it is more this kind of Class II activity that we assume occurs during NREM sleep in isolation, and during dreaming in association with Class I activity. Occasionally, these background thoughts and images are fairly vivid and more easily remembered. However, this is infrequent, and one will usually find the REM experiences are described solely in terms of sensory percepts except for an occasional, ". . . and I thought, 'How strange it looks.' "

On the basis of a comparison with Class I and Class II activities in the waking state as formulated above, we would expect that REM experiences would be more easily recalled. Every study of recall in various phases of sleep indicates that this is true. On the other hand, we would not expect perfect recall for the Class I experiences of dreaming anymore than we would for the Class I experience of the waking state, which is also shown by the experimental data. In addition, we might expect to get a small fraction of recall from REM sleep which is Class II in nature, just as on rare occasions we remember only what we thought, but not what we saw or heard in the waking state. The studies of Foulkes (1962) and Goodenough *et al.* (1959) indicate that REM awakenings do elicit some reports of "thinking," but not nearly so often as do NREM awakenings. And, of course, since Class II activity continues all during sleep, we find that zero recall never results from a large series of NREM awakenings.

We would expect Class I memories from REM awakenings to be more "vivid" or "real" than NREM images, which is what subjects generally report. More important, we would expect that on the basis of content, some NREM recall would be indistinguishable from REM recall. This, of course, is what occurs, and it is the main source of controversy in assigning dreaming solely to the REM phase. The probable reason for this lack of distinction is that NREM sleep becomes the only phase in the entire range of human existence when, for all practical purposes, Class I activity is not present. Therefore, it becomes difficult to distinguish NREM images from perceptions even on the basis of relative intensity, and thus, descriptions of the former may sound like descriptions of the latter.

Because of their intrinsic nature and the greater persistence of their memory traces, we would expect accounts of REM experience to be longer and more complex than accounts of NREM experience. This is readily confirmed if one examines the actual verbal responses rather than the abstract data of statistical tabulations. However, we would like to go a step farther, and suggest that the Class I activity of dreaming is not only more complex, but presents an essentially complete perceptual field. In other words, just as in the waking state, all sensory modalities are ordinarily present in the dream and with many details in each mode. This is not usually apparent from the dream narratives, because subjects tend to omit all details that are not immediately relevant and to emphasize single modalities depending upon the focus of attention. Visual imagery is, of course, the most prominent, with other modalities mentioned as the need arises.

Various compilers of dreams, cited by Ramsey (1953), have tabulated the occurrence of different perceptual modes and have found visual imagery to be the most frequent, followed by auditory, tactile, gustatory, and olfactory in order of decreasing incidence. Unfortunately, this has led some people to talk about dreams as if they were limited to a single modality ("visual" dreams versus "auditory" dreams, and so on). While this may be true for NREM imagery, we do not believe that it typifies REM experiences. For example, the dream from Roffwarg's study quoted earlier under the heading "Dreaming during REM Sleep" would undoubtedly be classified as an "auditory" dream, although visual perception was present and the specific REM pattern was appropriate to it. The dreamer was "staring" at the wall. Further questioning would probably have revealed the additional presence of proprioceptive and tactile sensation as an awareness of his recumbent position in bed and of the "feel" of the sheets. It is my impression from years of collecting dream (REM) reports that most, if not all, experiences recalled with reasonable clarity involve all modes of perception with an order of emphasis similar to that in the waking state. In other words, dreams are no more limited to a single mode than are real experiences, although in describing either, one mode of perception may be emphasized. "I *saw* the movie." "I *heard* him say——." "I *felt* the cold wind." Again, it is my opinion that when the subject positively denies the occurrence of more than one mode ("I heard a voice, but there was absolutely nothing else in the dream."), the explanation is faulty recall.

This whole concept is exemplified in the results obtained by Kahn *et al.* (1962) in a recent study of color in dreams. It has long been thought that a very low percentage of dreams contain color. Twenty-nine percent was the figure reported by Hall (1951), 21 percent by Monroe (1897), and 14 percent by Knapp (1956). Nevertheless, Kahn found that, while color was *spontaneously* mentioned in only 25.3 percent of REM experiences, its presence could be demonstrated in 82.7 percent if attention were discretely directed toward color by asking a series of questions about the dream objects (size, shape, location, and so forth) in which a color question was often "hidden." For example, one of his subjects mentioned that she saw "a bar of soap in the bathtub with the baby." After completion of the dream narrative, in which no reference was made to color, Kahn asked, "What did the soap look like?" The subject replied, "Like any bar of soap looks. It was round, it was *pink*, and the baby was playing with it in the bathtub." Thus, in terms of the color dimension, dreams involve "complete" perceptions. Kahn has obtained some preliminary data which suggests that the memory for color fades more rapidly than the memory for form, which means that the occasional "black and white" dream is probably an artifact of recall.

As has been suggested, if subjects were extensively questioned about each dream, a tremendous amount of detail would undoubtedly be added to their original narratives. One reason for the lack of extensive detail in the absence of thorough questioning is that a highly detailed description takes time, while the subjects' foremost desire is usually to go back to sleep as soon as possible. However, such questioning would immediately give rise to the objection that the subjects were being unduly influenced or "led" by the experimenter. Occasionally, a subject has both an excellent memory and sufficient motivation to provide us with extensive detail spontaneously. One such subject in our series was awakened 25 times during REM sleep. Beyond arousing him at the appropriate times by sounding a buzzer, the experimenter had no contact with the subject. Twenty-one dream sequences were recalled (84 percent) and dictated into a tape recorder.

Of these sequences, 100 percent contained visual perceptions, 90.3 percent contained auditory perceptions, color was described in 52.4 percent, specific thoughts evoked by the perceptions were mentioned in 62 percent, and specific emotions or feeling tones were mentioned in 52.4 percent. Only one narrative included the mention of a specific tactile sensation and there was only one reference to taste. These sensations seemed to be taken for granted, however. For example, there were several instances of eating, such as "I ate several pieces of chocolate, and so forth," but should the subject have been expected to describe the taste unless specifically asked? In this instance he would only have said that they tasted like chocolate, which was already implied by the description. In order to be sure, we would have to ask if he actually remembered tasting the chocolate. The only time guestatory sensation was specifically mentioned was in describing a glass of beer that "tasted unusually bitter."

*Physiological aspects.* The main reason for assuming that Class I activity occurs during REM sleep is derived from the truly remarkable physiological properties of this state. We might pause and ask the reader to recall the various attributes of REM sleep that were outlined in a previous section. The physiological data describe a central nervous system that is, in fact, behaving as if it were receiving a high level of sensory input from the environment; or, to put it another way, its neurophysiological properties resemble those of the active waking state. Thus, Evarts (1962a; 1962b) and Huttenlocher (1961) have shown that the discharge rates of individual neurons are very high during REM sleep, and that these rates only occur in the waking state when the animal is actively "inspecting" something. Also, the cortical blood flow is greatly increased (Kanzow *et al.*,

1962) and these levels are matched in the waking state only when the animal is actively attending or responding to external stimuli (Kanzow, 1961).

This notion is supported by several less specific measurements. For example, in subhuman animals, the low-voltage, fast cortical EEG rhythms during REM sleep are indistinguishable from the patterns that are present during active wakefulness, while slower components appear when the animals relax but are still awake. Characteristic sinusoidal waves, called "theta" activity, are continuously recorded from the hippocampal areas of the brain during REM sleep (Grastyan, 1959; Shimazono *et al.*, 1960). These waves are identical to the "theta" waves that are elicited by "meaningful" stimuli in the waking state.

Some of the most important data are on the output side. An analysis of the individual REMs has revealed that the human dreamer is behaving as if he were actually looking at something. It is difficult to imagine that the oculomotor apparatus could elaborate such highly integrated behavior if it were not receiving impulses similar to those that would be generated by "real" visual stimuli. Also, it is not true that any image will elicit active "viewing" or scanning. Certainly, what we have called the Class II imagery of NREM sleep is not actively scanned by the subject. The best illustration of this point is seen at the sleep onset where vivid, often fairly complex, hypnagogic imagery is always concomitant with slow, repetitive, side-to-side movement of the eyeballs. About the only thing that could account for this slow movement as active "viewing" would be an image of a swinging pendulum which rarely, if ever, occurs.

The high level of pyramidal tract discharge seen during REM sleep (Arduini *et al.*, 1963) suggests that the central nervous system is also elaborating an integrated motor output for the skeletal muscles, most of which, fortunately for the continuation of sleep, is apparently blocked at a lower level, probably via direct inhibition of the alpha motor neurons in the spinal cord (Pompeiano, 1963). Thus, if we had the technical resources to examine the higher levels of the sensory and motor apparatus in infinite detail, according to our hypothesis we would find that the patterns of neuronal activity during REM sleep were analogous to those associated with waking behavior. Of course, in order to make such a comparison, we would have to know a great deal more about the active waking state. At any rate, the essential differences between REM sleep and the active waking state ought to occur in the periphery where the former should be associated with very little activity in the peripheral receptors and a markedly reduced number of impulses in the peripheral motor nerves. We do not know exactly how or where this hypothesized internal sensory input could be elaborated, but such knowledge is theoretically within the range of our present-day experimental methods and techniques.

A final point is that we *do* know that Class I subjective experience can be elicited "internally," and is not ineluctably dependent upon some unique quality contained only in environmental stimuli. Direct stimulation of peripheral nerve trunks will evoke sensations that are referred to the appropriate areas of the body, and the work of Penfield and his collaborators (1952; 1954) has shown that sensation in specific modalities can also be elicited by stimulating the appropriate projection areas of the cerebral cortex. If we had sufficiently delicate techniques and knew the critical parameters of stimulation, we could probably evoke true perceptions. Perceptual experiences have been elicited by stimulating the temporal lobes (Penfield and Jasper, 1954), although it is a moot question as to whether the brain function in this case is strictly analogous to that when it is actually perceiving. Finally, in animals, a number of investigators (Morrell, 1961) have shown that direct stimulation of the brain can substitute for either the conditional or the unconditional stimulus in the classical learning paradigm and can be used to reinforce behavior in the operant situation (Olds, 1956).

## SUMMING UP

In essence, the psychophysiological model of dreaming that we have proposed states that insofar as we limit ourselves to what is going on *inside* the brain, dreaming is the same as being awake. The differences lie in the periphery where some endogenous activity is being substituted for sensory input and the motor outflow is being blocked. The mechanism of the latter has received some elucidation from the work of Jouvet, and we have at least been able to suggest a possible mechanism for the former. However, we do not wish to push the concept of a dreaming-waking identity too far. It is a useful hypothesis and future research will reveal the full extent of its application. We can only say that at the present state of our knowledge, the similarities between REM sleep and wakefulness seem far more striking than the differences. In other words, whatever degree of uniqueness it may eventually be found to possess, *at the present moment the salient feature of the dream state is its neurophysiological similarity to active wakefulness.*

The main value of the psychophysiological model is that it attempts to describe the essential nature of the dream experience, and it accounts for the apparent contradictions that have arisen from the content-based definitions of dreaming in previous studies of recall from various phases of sleep. It also renders the precisely measureable REM period synonymous with "dream period." Of course, in terms of applying a label, this is strictly a matter of taste. We could still apply the label, "dream," to *any* subjective experience arising in sleep, and say that there are two kinds of dreams, those with perceptual elements and those without. However, this would probably tend to perpetuate the confusion that already exists. The fact is that REM experience does conform rather closely to what is generally called dreaming, and furthermore, it is quite likely that REM experience has contributed most of the material that has been labeled "dreaming" in the past, and will constitute the major share of the "dreams" that will be collected by daytime interview and questionnaire techniques in the future. Thus, the REM definition is preferable because it provides a concept of dreaming that is verifiable by physiological experimentation and at the same time is consonant with generally accepted meanings. We need only keep in mind that "dreaming" is not the only subjective experience during sleep. It is also possible that "dreams" and NREM mentation may have differing unconscious meanings and motivations.

# FURTHER ASPECTS OF DREAMING AS EQUATED WITH REM SLEEP

## TOTAL DREAM TIME

In an early report, Dement and Kleitman (1957a) suggested that "an objective measurement of dreaming may be accomplished by recording REMs during sleep." They added that it might be possible "to study objectively the effect on dreaming of environmental changes, psychological stress, drug administration, and a variety of other factors and influences." The subsequent demonstration of the apparent occurrence of dreaming during NREM sleep, however, raised grave doubts about such a possibility. Nevertheless, although a wide variety of "factors and influences" have not as yet been investigated, several studies of the duration and incidence of REM sleep were accomplished; and if we are now ready to accept an REM definition of dreaming, we may proceed to describe the quantitative aspects of the dream experience in terms of these data.

A total of 71 undisturbed all-night recordings were made on 33 subjects ranging in age from 16 to 60 by Dement and Kleitman (1957b). Regular periods of REM sleep were seen on every night, *without exception.* Figure 2.12, a composite diagram of a single night of sleep, constructed from these data, shows the typical EEG curve and the average durations and times of occurrence of successive dream (REM) periods. In the first 6 hours of sleep, the total dream time averaged 64 minutes, or 17.7 percent, and the mean cycle length was very close to 90 minutes.

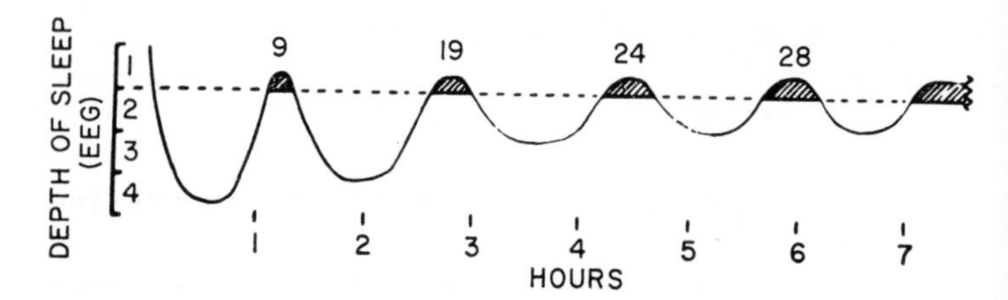


*Figure 2.12.* The typical night of sleep. The depth of sleep *in terms* of brain waves fluctuates regularly. Whenever it reaches the Stage 1 level, dreaming (shaded area) starts, accompanied by rapid eye movements, and continues until the downswing of the cycle. The numbers over the shaded areas indicate the average length of successive eye movement (dream) periods. (Reprinted, by permission, from Dement, W. and E. Wolpert, The relation of eye movements, body motility, and external stimuli to dream content, *J. exp. Psychol.*, 1958, *55*, 543-553.)

Recently completed experiments by Fisher and Dement included 221 uninterrupted all-night recordings from 32 subjects. The composite data for all these nights were almost identical with the earlier study, attesting to the remarkable stability of the sleep cycle. The total dream time at the end of the fifth cycle was 109 minutes, or 21.2 percent of the mean sleep time of 7 hours 48 minutes. There was, however, considerable individual variation. For example, single dream periods ranged from one minute to more than 80. The percentage of dreaming sleep on single nights ranged from about 10 to 30. One of the most interesting parts of the data was the variation in total dream time in terms of individual subjects. Some subjects characteristically dreamed more than others. The mean subject percentages ranged from 14 to 27.4, which to some extent reflected the wide variation in age of the group. Among the 22 "young adults," aged 21 to 34, the range in the mean percentages of dreaming was 17.2 to 25.4, but most of this group tended to cluster around 21.2 and the standard deviation was plus or minus 2. Finally, it should be emphasized again that, in the entire 292 nights of these 2 studies, there was not a single exception to the cyclic appearance of dreaming.

According to the study of Roffwarg, Dement, and Fisher (1964), infants and young children have a much higher *percentage* of dreaming than adults while the percentage in older children and adolescents is slightly less. Because they sleep much longer than adults, the latter group actually experiences more dreaming in terms of number of minutes. Elderly people have the lowest percentage and, because they generally do not sleep as long, experience by far the least amount of dreaming. The small amount of information that is available on other factors that may influence dreaming will be mentioned in appropriate sections.

## DREAM RECALL

The apparent universality of dreams as indicated by the foregoing data serves to emphasize one of their most perplexing properties: the extreme difficulty we ordinarily have in remembering them. In spite of the fact that each of us dreams 1 to 2 hours every night of our lives, it is the rare person who is able to recapture even a small fraction of his nocturnal experience. As we have seen, a large part of the difficulty is obviated when the attempt to recall a dream is made in close proximity to its actual time of occurrence; that is, immediately after being awakened from REM sleep. When this is done, the number of dream episodes recalled and their length and detail is often spectacular. Unfortunately, space limitations have discouraged investigators from publishing complete transcripts of some of the longer narratives elicited from REM awakenings, and the full impact of the detail and richness of the REM experience cannot be conveyed by statistical tabulations. In order to fill this gap and in keeping with the more comprehensive scope of this essay, the full transcript of one typical REM response is included here. It is by no means the longest or most detailed dream that we have ever obtained, but it is a fairly representative example of a report that does not appear to have been decimated by forgetting. This report was elicited from an awakening that followed, or rather interrupted, 23 minutes of REM sleep. The events seem to encompass much more time than 23 minutes, but close attention to the narrative will make it apparent that this is due to the effect of "telescoping," sudden changes of scene that could only be accounted for in real life by assuming the passage of time. Parenthetically, it should be remembered that the length of a description is not always exactly proportional to the duration of that which is described. A few minutes at the height of a battle may require an entire chapter in a book, while the events of an ordinary day may be summed up in a sentence.

This dream began in the opera house. I was sitting in the orchestra. I noticed that one of my close friends was sitting in one of the boxes with his fiancée who is very, very pretty. I waved and tried to talk to them but we were too far apart to hear each other. Then I was looking at my program and I believe it said something about this being the opening of a ballet that hadn't been performed for a very long time and that it was very unusual with a lot of strange choreography. And then on the stage there was a Japanese scene of a—I don't know, they were holding things and moving them up and down, tall papier-mâché figures. And then all of a sudden, the biggest curtain opened and there were a bunch of people dressed in Chinese costumes on swings. And the swings flew way out over the heads of the audience and the girls were moving their legs to make the swings propel themselves and it was very exciting. There was no singing, or very little singing so there was a kind of chattering. It was very colorful, and immediately after that everyone started to leave, but the performance wasn't over yet, and Robert Merrill (noted opera star) came out onto the stage and burst into an aria and I shouted to an old man in front of me who was ready to leave and said, "You must sit down, it's Robert Merrill singing." And he said, "Of course, dear." So he sat down, and everyone else sat down again. And then it was over and I was getting my gloves from my pocket and gathering my things together when this young man came up to us and he said, "Isn't Merrill's fiancée beautiful?" I said, "Yes, she's a very pretty girl, but of course, Merrill has his own taste, you know." And he just looked at me very oddly and then he said, "I'm a very good friend of Merrill's and I know that." I said, "Well, if you're such a very good friend of his, you must know about me." And he said, "Yes, I do." And he went on to say that Merrill had very good taste and that he hadn't used it or had kept it in reserve until the moment when he met this girl. And I said, "Of course, it isn't true because you know he used to date me and he was in love with me." And Merrill's friend said, "Oh yes, but you didn't really count," which made me feel a little annoyed. Well anyway, apparently we had gotten out of the opera house and as we were going into a bus, John didn't have change and I gave him some from my purse—John was my escort. He didn't say anything the whole time, he was just with me. I had one dime, a quarter, a couple of nickels, and about 15 pennies. Although I wanted to take the nickels, in the rush I was going to take the pennies. But John didn't want to take the pennies and I got very upset. Then it finally dawned on me that on this bus we could only ride for two stops and then we had to take a crosstown bus, and for the crosstown bus obviously we needed to save six pennies for the transfers. After we were on the bus, the bus driver abruptly got out of his seat to everybody's dismay and he turned around and said, "Hey, ladies and gentlemen, taking care of the coin box is more important than driving. It's a psychological process." Well, then he gets up and leaves the steering wheel. I'm sitting in those three seats right behind the driver that face the other side of the bus and I look out of the window and see that we're moving down the street in a very strange way, horizontally. The pedestrians aren't aware that the driverless bus is a threat to them and they smile and wave. Then the bus noses into a construction and sort of tips up a little. The bus driver smiles as though he expected this to happen and that it was sort of a little trick he played on the passengers. Then he takes the coin box and gets back into his seat and that seemed to be the end of the scene. Then we seemed to be in the hospital where I'm supposed to sleep. John disappears and I'm with another girl. I'm not quite sure who it is. No, I do know who it is, it's an elderly woman, someone that I met at the opera. She's coming too. She's sort of heavy set. I have to bring her along with me because it isn't Dr. Smith that's putting on the electrodes—setting up the experiment, but it's this young man (this is a representation of the experimental situation). This young man—actually he was in the dream earlier. While we were on the bus, apparently this young man got on the bus and sat down. John said that he was ready to kill him and I said that I didn't like him either. Anyway now we're at the hospital and I see him again. He's setting up the experiment instead of Dr. Smith. And this time he's all dressed in white and he doesn't speak English too well. He makes a lot of grammatical errors. And then he brings in three girls, three very pretty girls. They look like Americans in spite of the fact that they're tawny. He sits them down and gives the instructions to tell about dreams or something like that, and is starting to put the electrodes on. And he calls them "broads" (subject laughs). I immediately stiffened and the girls stiffen. They look at him and say, "This isn't what we came for. What kind of ideas do you have? Is this America, the land of the free and the home of the brave, where people can do as they please and are free? Is this what we came for, so you can be free and do just what you please and we're under your subjugation?" They were very upset and they thought certainly he was going to try to rape them during the night. I laughed to this elderly woman I was with and I said, "My goodness, I just don't think he knows what the term, 'broad,' means. He must have heard it in some movie and just thinks it is a term for girls." These three girls were getting very, very upset and he was proceeding to undress them and put one of those white robes on them, and one of them walked up behind and took out a razor blade—it was very shiny. Then the girls started to threaten him. They weren't going to leave, but if he had any intention of having intercourse with them, he would have a fight on his hands. At first the situation was very amusing. Then I became very alarmed because I realized that this poor young man was very innocent. So I went to the medicine chest and got out this big knife and my friend got out something else. But I didn't do anything. I was just watching them, and somehow the girls' attitude softened. They saw the young man's complete bewilderment. Then the three of them went back and sat down together on this low couch or bed and the young man went over to the sink. I went with him and there was a big scar on the back of his hand. It wasn't really a scar, it was just sort of a coating of blood that looked like a scar and sort of brownish. He wiped it off. Then he went to this old lady—the one I'd brought from the opera—and he had her get into the bed. He told her that if she had a dream, she was supposed to make a humming sound. She was very uneasy because she was certain that she would never make a sound, but the doctor assured her that she would. And I reassured her that she would be able to do it. Then the three girls came over to me and suggested that we should go get something to eat. Just as we were starting to leave, the buzzer woke me up.

Although a great deal of "unconscious" material is expressed rather openly, the dream is not unique in this respect. It was chosen only to illustrate the length and detail that frequently characterize REM responses. It is appropriate to point out that the dreamer's concern about being a "good" subject is clearly expressed toward the end. The desire to be a "good" subject and to please the experimenter is undoubtedly a very important factor in determining how well a dream is recalled and described.

It has already been suggested that REM events are better recalled then NREM events, because the former are, in effect, true perceptions while the latter resemble "background" thought. When awakenings interrupt ongoing REMPs, many subjects are able to remember a dream nearly every time. However, REM events certainly do not have the persistence of waking perceptions, because when the dream period ends *spontaneously*, they are forgotten almost at once.

In a group of ten subjects studied by Wolpert and Trosman (1958) detailed dreams were recalled in 85.2 percent of 54 awakenings that interrupted REMPs. *No* dreams were recalled in 11 instances when the awakenings were done within 5 minutes of the spontaneous termination of REMPs.

Approximately 87 percent of the time, the end of an REM sleep period is marked by the occurrence of a gross body movement. Even when Wolpert and Trosman awakened their subjects *during* these terminating body movements, which presumably meant that only a few seconds had elapsed since the end of the dream, the recall rate dropped to 69.1 percent (of 123 such instances). In addition to demonstrating that the memory of a dream decays rapidly in time after the cessation of the dream experience, these results also suggest that remembering a dream tends to be an all-or-nothing process. Thus, if we are awakened during REMPs, we often remember entire dream sequences which may extend back in time for 10 or more minutes. Only 2 or 3 minutes after the cessation of REMPs, we often remember nothing at all. Do the dream experiences simply fail to form permanent memory traces, or is there a repressive force at work? The rather abrupt massive forgetting might favor the latter possibility. However, part of it may be the sudden jolt of the body movement. In the waking state, if we are concentrating on something and are suddenly interrupted and distracted, we occasionally forget the entire episode. At any rate, forgetting seems to occur maximally at the points where gross body movements interrupt REMPs.

Dement and Wolpert (1958a) found this to be true not only of body movements terminating REMPs, but also of those occurring *within* the period. They examined all narratives elicited from awakenings that interrupted 10 or more minutes of REMs and found 45 that were unusually short. Of these 45 narratives, 37 were associated with records that showed the presence of a large body movement 2 to 5 minutes prior to the arousal. This suggested that a previous dream episode had been terminated and forgotten at the point of the body movement, and that another had started up prior to the awakening. Thus, it seemed that the over-all period of dreaming might be divided into a series of more or less independent dream episodes by the gross body movements occurring within the period.

In order to test this possibility, dream transcriptions were carefully screened for (a) long narratives of smoothly related, continuously progressing events, and (b) accounts consisting of 2 or more distinct, seemingly unrelated dream episodes. Of 46 dreams that fulfilled the first requirement, 32 were associated with REMPs that contained *no* gross body movements. Of 31 narratives that contained 2 or more unrelated episodes, 21 were associated with REMPs containing 1 or more gross body movements.

There has been some confusion in the literature about this very important point. As we have seen, the typical night of sleep includes 4 to 6 REMPs. These REMPs are usually referred to as "dreams," therefore implying that we have 4 to 6 dreams a night. Actually, depending upon the number of times that each individual REMP is fragmented by body movements, we may have as many as 10 to 20 distinct dream episodes a night. (A distinct, self-contained episode is probably what most people would call a single dream.) Accordingly, in the usually accepted connotation, it would be fairer to say that we ordinarily have 10 to 20 dreams in a night rather than 4 to 6.

Up till now, we have been considering the recall characteristics of the subject who typically reports prior to participating in the sleep experiments that, like most people, he remembers a dream every so often—perhaps once a week, or more often under certain circumstances. With the optimal conditions of REM awakenings, such a subject will ordinarily produce dream material about 80 percent of the time.

Occasionally, subjects are encountered who say they remember dreams only rarely, or that they "never" dream and wouldn't know a dream if they saw one. Not too much information is available on the exact proportion of such individuals among the general population. Antrobus *et al.* (1964) had an unselected group of 185 females between the ages of 20 and 29 keep a daily "dream diary" and found that 28 (15.1 percent) recalled dreams from only once every 3 months to never.

The first question to answer about these apparent "non-dreamers" was whether or not they had REMs during sleep. Goodenough *et al.* (1959) made recordings on a group of 8 male subjects who said they recalled dreams less than once a month. A typical sleep cycle with "emergent" Stage 1 and REMs was found in each subject, which led the authors to suggest that such individuals be called "non-recallers" rather than "non-dreamers." The subjects *did* recall dreams when awakened during REMPs, but at a relatively low rate (46 percent). Since the REMPs were interrupted to elicit dream recall, figures for total nightly dream time could not be calculated.

Antrobus *et al.* (1964) compared all-night measurements of undisturbed sleep in a group of 11 subjects who remembered dreams *less than once every three months* (including several who "never" dreamed) with 11 subjects at the opposite end of the spectrum who recalled at least 1 dream every second or third night. The two groups were carefully matched for age, intelligence, sex (all were females), and total sleep time on experimental nights. The mean dream time percent for the "recaller" group was 23.8 and for the "non-recaller" group, 18.9. Although statistically significant, the difference obviously could not account for the enormous variation in spontaneous dream recall. Other aspects of the sleep cycle showed little difference except for the somewhat surprising result that the "non-recallers" exhibited a greater number of individual ocular deviations per unit time in REM sleep. The best interpretation of these results would seem to be that dream memories are being actively suppressed in "non-recallers" and that this psychological factor is strong enough to effect a small curtailment of REM sleep itself.

Since they seem to possess all the physiological attributes of dreaming sleep, we have assumed that even the most extreme "non-recallers" experience substantial amounts of dreaming. Thus, when a person goes through his life dreaming an hour or more every night without recalling a single iota of the experience, a rather profound degree of repression is suggested, which ought to be reflected in other aspects of his personality. Schonbar (1961) found that "people who recall few dreams also recall them as being fairly bland or less unpleasant than do people who recall more frequently." She reasoned that "people who repress more of their available experience, as in forgetting dreams, reveal this repression rather generally by also toning down the affect." In another study, Schonbar (1959) found that frequent recall of dreaming was associated with higher intelligence and more overt anxiety. However, Lachmann, Lapkin, and Handelman (1962) showed that "non-recallers" might not necessarily be "repressers" as measured by another index.

If a subject who has dictated dream narratives after several REM awakenings during the night is asked to repeat them the next morning, two tendencies are apparent. Whole episodes previously recalled are entirely forgotten. On the other hand, those that *are* remembered are generally described in more detail and in a clearer and more precise fashion. The latter tendency is undoubtedly due to the fact that the descriptive powers of the subject are greater in the morning than in the middle of the night. The former tendency suggests that certain dream events may be more subject to repression than others. No one has as yet exploited the differences in REM recall and morning recall to study the shades of significance and meaning in dream experience.

Finally, we should be reminded that although we are interested in the marked evanescence of dream memories, it may actually be a great boon to mankind that dreams are not remembered as efficiently as waking experiences. If they were, we would have to be continually asking ourselves, "Did that really happen to me, or was it a dream?" This would be especially true if our dreams were a little less bizzare and improbable. There is one condition in which this kind of confusion does occur. It has recently been found that patients with narcolepsy, in contradistinction to all other subjects that have been studied, enter the REM phase immediately at the sleep onset (Rechtschaffen *et al.*, 1963). We have also found that the brief sleep attacks (10 to 20 minutes) these patients suffer during the day usually consist only of REM sleep. It frequently happens that the immediate environmental setting is maintained as the background in the dreams that are experienced during these attacks. Under these circumstances, when the patients awaken, they are never quite sure whether or not the dream really took place. For example, one patient fell asleep during the day in the laboratory and apparently dreamed that he was in the exact same situation but that the experimenter entered the recording room and had him take a pill. When he awakened a few minutes later he asked, "What was in that pill you had me take?" When the experimenter assured him that no such event had taken place, he said with surprise, "Oh, I must have been asleep."

## SOME ASPECTS OF THE CONTENT OF DREAMS

Perhaps the most fascinating and puzzling aspect of normal dreams is the wildly unpredictable nature of their content. This is even more striking and variable when one has the opportunity to sample the content from each REMP. I recall one subject who ran the gamut from being with "two hippopotamuses in a millpond" through "a taffy pull in the Soviet Embassy" to "hearing Handel's 'Messiah' sung by a thousand-voice chorus in this beautiful cathedral," and back to "writing at my desk," all in a single night. Even if we accept the existence of latent dream thoughts and their regressive transformation into dream images, we are still confronted with the problem of why a certain *one* of many possibilities is selected to represent the underlying thought. The explanation that a particular symbol or image is overdetermined is only partly satisfactory. It is possible that at its point of origin, the hypothesized internal sensory input is relatively nonspecific. Accordingly, the content of the perception is "created" by the cerebral cortex as it attempts to analyze this nonspecific input. In this sense, "perceptual set" would be all important and this might be why the dream images have such important associative links. We must admit, though, that a complete explanation of the truly incredible series of "adventures" and "sights" that are conjured up in a single night still eludes us.

One of the most time-honored explanations for the specific content of dream images, espoused by Aristotle and subsequently by many others, is that they are distorted and exaggerated perceptions of random stimuli from the environment. Thus, the glow of a candle becomes a raging conflagration, a knock on the door the thunder of horses' hooves, and so forth. If we allow that the exaggeration and distortion may be so great that we can no longer recognize the source, and that the most trivial stimuli such as our own breathing may be effective, then this theory can never be completely refuted. However, the regular cyclic appearance of dreaming in the face of the omnipresence of such stimuli makes it unlikely. Furthermore, the evidence to date does not even suggest an important role for more significant external stimuli. Dement and Wolpert (1958a) stimulated sleeping subjects by means of either a tone, a flashing light, or a spray of cold water. When these stimuli were given during NREM sleep, they uniformly failed to initiate dreaming (REMPs). They were also given *during* REMPs; if an immediate awakening did not occur, the subjects were aroused after one or two minutes of additional REM sleep by a loud buzzer and their dreams were examined for evidence of incorporation of the stimuli. Only 9 percent of the flashing light stimuli seemed to have modified the content of the dream, while the tone was effective in 23 percent of the trials, and the water spray in 42 percent. The relative effectiveness of the cold water suggests that the degree to which a stimulus is "unusual" or "noxious" may be an important factor in determining its ability to modify an ongoing dream. The authors concluded from these results that "although external stimuli can at times interject a new element, the basis for the images and particular story of a dream must exist mainly within the dreamer." Kamiya has found that verbal stimuli (spoken sentences) given during REMPs had no effect whatsoever (personal communication).

Dement and Wolpert also attempted to evaluate the effectiveness of an internal stimulus (1958a). Three subjects on 5 occasions completely restricted their intake of fluids for periods of 24 hours or more prior to sleeping in the laboratory. On all occasions, they reported that they were very thirsty when they went to bed, and twice their thirst had reached distressing proportions with dry lips and tongue, inability to salivate, and so forth. Fifteen dream narratives were elicited under these somewhat extreme conditions. *In no case* did the dream content involve an awareness of thirst or descriptions of actually drinking something. Ten dreams seemed completely unrelated to this external stimulus, while 5 contained elements that *might* have been related, as follows:

a. "I was in bed and was being experimented on. I was supposed to have malabsorption syndrome."
b. "I started to heat a great big can of—a great big skillet of milk. I put almost a quart of milk in it."
c. "Just as the bell went off, somebody raised a glass and said something about a toast. I don't think I had a glass."
d. "While watching TV I saw a commercial. Two kids were asked what they wanted to drink and one kid started yelling, 'Coca-cola, orange, Pepsi,' and everything."
e. "I was watching a TV program and there was a cartoon on with the animals that are like those in the Hamm's beer advertisement."

The dehydrated state undoubtedly exerted some influence on the content of the dreams, but it is puzzling, in view of the wish-fulfillment theory of dreaming and the subjects' suffering and overwhelming preoccupation with their thirst, that none were able to slake their thirst directly as did Freud who, after eating anchovies, frequently dreamt of "swallowing down water in great gulps, and it has the delicious taste that nothing can equal but a cool drink when one is parched with thirst" (Freud, 1955, p.123).

Another puzzle about the dream experience is the conspicuous lack of critical judgment on the part of the dreamer. The most incongruous, illogical, and impossible happenings are accepted as "real" and, with rare exceptions,[6] tax our credulity

[6] Every once in a while, the sheer impossibility of an occurrence seems to get through to us and we think, "This must be a dream." Many of these instances occur when nightmarish events have aroused extreme anxiety. We think, "This is only a dream," and usually wake up. The recognition of dreaming may actually be part of the awakening process. On the other hand, Arnold-Forster (1921) makes the claim that she overcame the plague of frequent nightmares by learning to say, "This is only a dream," and instead of awakening, she continued to dream, but the experience was somehow divested of its terror.

not at all. Kleitman (1957) voiced the opinion that dreaming represents a state of "low-grade cerebral activity" in which critical judgment is suspended—a state analogous to the wakefulness of a very small child or an alcoholic. This may be true, although as yet there is little evidence to support the notion that the higher levels of the nervous system are not functioning maximally during the dream. The fact that dream experiences are accepted as real may indicate that the perceptual impulses of dreaming reach the higher levels of the nervous system over the same pathways as "real" information in the waking state and thus cannot be distinguished. In other words, we cannot "doubt the evidence of our senses." However, this does not explain the lack of incredulity. If we were confronted in the real world by some of the things we see in dreams, we would surely be literally paralyzed with astonishment. This seems to imply that, although the conscious quality of the dream experience is an intense sense of reality, at some other level of awareness we know that we are dreaming. Freud arrived at the same opinion over a somewhat different route, saying, "I am driven to conclude that throughout our whole sleeping state, we know just as certainly that we are dreaming as we know that we are sleeping" (Freud, 1955, p. 571). This stands in marked contrast to the views of Malcolm (1959) mentioned earlier.

One aspect of the content of dreams that is particularly accessible to investigation by means of REM awakenings is the interrelatedness of dreams occurring on a single night. Dement and Wolpert (1958b) examined sequences of 4 to 6 individual dreams each, from 38 nights of sleep distributed among 8 adult subjects. They found that no single dream was ever exactly duplicated by another dream, nor were the dreams of a sequence ever perfectly continuous, one taking up just where the preceding had left off. For the most part, each dream seemed to be a self-contained drama independent of those that preceded or followed it. There were, however, many seemingly trivial relationships among contiguous dreams and occasional similarities in plot with some duplication of the action and environmental setting. An important finding was that on seven of the 38 nights, all the dreams seemed to be clearly united by a common theme or maintained a rough but recognizable continuity from one to another. The most dramatic example of the seven was as follows:

*First REM awakening.* I was dreaming something about a woman. The last scene was something about some kind of involvement where she's trying to do something about an inheritance and I'm trying to thwart her. I must have thwarted her pretty well, but she still has something she can do, and I'm saying—we're in some kind of a dining room—"Let me see your trump card. Let me just look at you." I went over and looked at her in the face and I said, "How can I possibly be afraid of you?" She wouldn't let me look her in the eye. She just kind of turned away a little. And just as the bell went off I was chasing her out and I shouted, "You god damn bitch." The woman was a woman I'd never seen before.

*Second REM awakening.* I was watching a guy standing in the street. Suddenly he raised his gun and shot a woman in the back. I'm sure it was a woman. And I ran. There was a little frame house sitting on the street. Just a few rooms, five or six. I ran in the front door and started running out the back. I was afraid this guy would come out the back door. Somehow I knew he was on my side, yet I was afraid he would come after me. I felt frightened and anxious when I woke up.

*Third REM awakening.* This dream started out at a—no, it didn't. Oh, Lord, it started out with Sara Smith (pseudonym for well-known entertainer). She seduced me. That's how it started. I don't remember how we got undressed or anything, but we got undressed and she was kind of neurotic and I had a queer feeling I was being manipulated. She scorned any way of conventional intercourse. I'd try to do it conventionally and she'd just sneer at me. She had me doing all these different things. First I was on my back and then that didn't satisfy her. There were three of us actually. Some other girl was helping her, and it was funny because they were just casually explaining what they wanted me to do and I didn't feel embarrassed or anything. But this other girl would take my penis and say, "Well, you've got to do it this way," and Sara Smith was very impatient. "Let's get on with it," she said. Finally I got mad and left. I got mad and went into my room and leaned on a chair. I leaned resting my right hand on it and was tuning a TV set with my left. So then I came back and sat down to dinner. And all of a sudden I looked at my hand. It seemed like we were in a family circle and I was part of an entirely different family than I should have been. And then I looked at my hand and it had started bleeding. First my little finger was bleeding and then it looked like my whole hand was bleeding. And then there were a series of cuts clear up my arm. I was kind of stunned and somebody said there was a razor blade on that chair. I remember remarking that I'd like to clobber the guy who left a razor blade there, and the memory came to me in the dream that I had left a razor blade there myself previously and had forgotten about it. And then I was amazed that I didn't feel myself cutting myself when I had my hand on the chair. I got up and started to leave when the bell rang."

*Fourth REM awakening.* It had something to do with bridge. We were sitting at the bridge table. Just three of us, these two women and I. There was something about how a hand had been played wrong. I was very puzzled about the way it had been played. Then I looked at my cards and they were the wrong kind of cards. I didn't know what to do, and then I woke up.

In the first dream, the dreamer wins a consummate victory over his female competitor in the struggle for an inheritance as he scorns her "trump card," calls her a "god damn bitch," and chases her from the room. He is no longer as certain of himself in the second dream, and when a woman is shot in the back (compare this cowardly act to the bravado of the first dream when the dreamer wanted to look the woman straight in the eye) by a male associate who may represent the dreamer himself, he runs, fearing that he may be betrayed by his shadowy male friend. In the third dream, he is subjected to the humiliation of accepting a passive sexual role with Sara Smith and another woman. Immediately afterwards he cuts himself on a razor blade he had left on a chair. If the "shadowy friend" mentioned above actually represented the dreamer himself, in both dreams he would be the instrument of his own injury. Demonstrating how far the reversal of position has gone in the reported dream series, the final dream finds the dreamer playing cards with two women and discovering that his cards are "wrong." A far cry from the first dream in which he felt no fear of even his female competitor's trump cards!

This dream sequence resembles a classical tragedy to a surprising degree. The hero is first presented in a triumphant role, but as the sequence progresses, he is vanquished by the very forces that were originally within his control. It is as if the ancient law of *hubris* had been invoked and, once the dreamer exalted in his triumph over a woman, he was doomed to be destroyed by another woman.

The authors pointed out that conclusions drawn from such a study of nightly dream sequences would always be weakened by the fact that each dream must be interrupted before its spontaneous termination is reached to insure recall. The normal uninterrupted sequence could never be known, and the awakenings themselves together with the telling of the dream may to some extent have influenced the content of the next one.

Trosman *et al.* (1960) studied two subjects intensively, gathering 106 dreams in 32 nights of recording. They found only one night in which all the dreams were directly related on the manifest level, each subsequent dream representing a further development of the previous dream. Otherwise, their findings were similar to those of Dement and Wolpert. They also examined the latent contents of the dreams by obtaining associations at the time of the awakenings and in later clinical interviews. In terms of latent material, they noted a cyclic relationship for sequential dreams. "It seems that as need pressure accumulates in the early dreams of a sequence, it is discharged in a pitch of excitement either directly or by highly dramatic visual representation, and is followed by a period of regression or quiescence." An example of this, with the authors' comments, is as follows:

"*Dream 1. I am making my own bed.* This reversed the actual experimental situation in which the experimenter made the subject's bed, and reflected the subject's generally more competitive attitude toward the experimenter at this time. The dream thus may represent a competitive, aggressive act by the subject.

*Dream 2. I am being chased by witches who have been released from boxes where they were imprisoned. At the same time I am chasing a girl. All this is very exciting.* The subjects association indicated that he had erotized the competitive, aggressive striving of the first dream and had converted it into an overtly heterosexual situation.

*Dream 3. I return to the dormitory where I lived as an undergraduate. A friendly woman gives me a message.* The excitement of the second dream is not allowed free reign but is modulated by the threat of punishment or reprisal. In reaction to the conflict of the second dream, the third dream of the sequence indicates regressive longings which are more acceptable and less threatening."

In view of these studies and other experiences with REM recall, the author is inclined to think that reports of repetitive dreams are greatly exaggerated, except possibly in the case of the traumatic neuroses (Kardiner, 1941). When most of these claims are carefully scrutinized, it usually turns out that by "repetitive" was meant "some element of similarity." To the author's knowledge, there is no documented instance of the frequent repetition of a dream in which each occurrence was exactly identical in every respect.

Offenkrantz and Rechtschaffen (1963) obtained dream sequences on 15 different nights from a patient in psychotherapy. They made the interesting observation that similar elements in the manifest dreams recurred in the same position in the sequence on different nights. For example, on 5 nights the dream associated with the third REMP was about the patient's relationship to his employer; in 9 dreams occurring after 4:30 A.M. on 8 different nights, the manifest content was located in a geographical setting of childhood or adolescence whereas childhood scenes never occurred early in the night.

Whitman *et al.* (1962) have pointed out that the single, most important factor in determining the content of dreams elicited in the laboratory is probably the experimental situation itself. They found that 32.4 percent of 111 dreams contained manifest elements dealing directly with the experiment, and an additional 36 percent were obviously related to the experiment although in a disguised fashion. The number of such dreams did not diminish on successive nights in the laboratory. The authors felt that these dreams were expressing the subjects' considerable anxiety about participating in the experiment. The data seemed to indicate that additional exposure to the situation did not allay the anxiety.

If valid, these results would raise the reservation in using REM techniques that the contents of dreams elicited in the laboratory were highly artifactitious. This consideration moved me to analyze all the dream narratives in our files available from previous work for the presence of references to the experimental situation. The analysis is not yet completed, but it is very clear from about 500 dreams so far examined, that while the number of dreams dealing with the experiment is high on the first night (around 30 percent), it drops to a fairly low level on the second night in the laboratory and remains low thereafter (about 10 to 15 percent). The main reason for the difference is probably that Whitman's subjects slept in a hospital environment with all the anxiety it entails, while our subjects generally slept in nonclinical settings.

## SLEEP TALKING

Audible vocalizations during sleep do not seem to be particularly related to dreaming. Kamiya (1961) noted 98 instances of spontaneous vocalization in his laboratory subjects, of which only 12 (12.3 percent) occurred during REMPs. The vast majority were associated with gross body movements. Rechtschaffen, Goodenough, and Shapiro (1962) observed 84 incidents of actual speech during their various sleep experiments. Only 8 percent occurred during REMPs, but when the data were corrected for unequal subject distribution, the figures rose to 14 percent, which is not far from what might be expected in terms of the REM fraction of the total sleep time if talking occurs at random throughout the entire sleep period. All the NREM sleep-talking incidents were associated either with gross body movements or EMG tension artifacts in the EEG and EOG leads. Often the speech sounded as if the subject thought he had been aroused for dream interrogation, although no dreams were reported. Generally, the NREM material was very brief, only a few words, and very flat in emotional tone. In contrast, 5 of the 7 REM incidents were associated with no movement or EMG artifact whatsoever, and contained a great deal of affect.

The relative sparsity of talking during dreaming is not surprising from what we know about the inhibition of motor function during the period. Occasionally, speech activity in the dream must break through this inhibition and achieve motor expression. Rechtschaffen, Goodenough, and Shapiro found that the REM incidents did reflect the speech in the dream, and further, that the dream events at the time were quite "disturbing" to the subject. Most NREM incidents seem to be either inarticulate vocalizations occurring as part of an over-all gross movement or stretching, or articulate verbalizations that occur when the subject wakes himself up by moving but, assuming the experimenter has aroused him, groggily says something appropriate. Of course, there may be a small number of sleep-talking episodes that actually reflect NREM mentation. Unfortunately, subjects do not seem to remember them. An interesting observation was made by Major Harold Williams of the Walter Reed Army Institute of Research. He was studying a subject who several times awakened abruptly out of Stage 4 NREM sleep with a bloodcurdling scream. Each time, Williams rushed into the sleeping room to find the subject sitting up in bed in a state of fright, but with no explanation for the scream, and no memory of a dream or any other occurrence.

In view of these results, it is likely that most vocalizations heard in a home setting, for example, the groaning or occasional calling out of sleeping children, also have nothing to do with dreams.

## PARADOXICAL NATURE OF THE DEPTH OF SLEEP

In his monograph on sleep, Kleitman (1939) stated, "The depth of sleep, like its quality, is an elusive characteristic." After reviewing the pertinent studies, he concluded, "The depth of sleep for a particular night cannot be expressed by a single curve with one peak or even two peaks, but is an undulating line with multiple maxima and minima varying slightly in height and duration at different hours of the night and depending, among other influences, upon the variable measured."

The origins of the concept of depth of sleep undoubtedly lie in the personal, subjective evaluation of sleep as "deep" or "good" when one feels rested and restored in the morning; and "bad" or "restless" or "light," if one does not. Naturally such subjective evaluations do not necessarily reflect a consistent trend in the objective measurements of depth of sleep. We have seen subjects arise after nights of extreme experimental disturbance feeling that they had enjoyed a wonderful, deep sleep. We have also found that subjects are generally unable to distinguish on the basis of the subjective quality of their sleep, whether they received sedatives, stimulants, or placebos on the night before.

On the other hand, there is the time-honored charactrization of sleep as a slowing down of bodily functions and reactions, and accordingly, the depth of sleep would be an expression of the degree of the slowing, or to put it another way, of the distance from the waking state. Depth of sleep, in this sense, is measured by recording one or more physiological variables which are assumed to represent at some level of abstraction, the over-all activity and reactivity of the organism. Unfortunately for the concept, the peaks and troughs of the curves executed by individual variables fail to occur simultaneously during the course of the night. For example, high voltage slow waves in the EEG are most prominent in the first two or three hours of the night (Dement and Kleitman, 1957b), the lowest heart rate occurs in the sixth and seventh hours, and the lowest body temperature is seen in the middle of the night. Probably the most meaningful and widely used criterion of the depth of sleep, aside from the EEG, is the arousal threshold which is usually measured in terms of the intensity of some stimulus required to awaken a sleeper. Using this measure, Kleitman (1939) found many fluctuations in depth of sleep throughout the night with some tendency for greater depth in the early hours, but with wide individual variation.

With regard to the EEG, there can be no doubt that some of the reasoning behind its almost routine service as a measure of depth of sleep borders on the intuitive. In the early days of electroencephalography, it was undoubtedly felt that the low voltage patterns represented lighter sleep simply because they looked more like waking patterns than did the high voltage slow waves. In terms of the hypothesis that cortical waves represented synchronous activity of neural elements, it followed that the slow waves would indicate deeper sleep since, in this stage, neural elements would be beating slowly and with a high degree of synchrony. Another point was the well-ordered sequence of brain wave changes after the sleep onset starting with the gradual disappearance of alpha rhythms and progressing through spindle stages to high voltage slow activity. Since it was obvious that depth of sleep could not be greatest at the instant of falling asleep, but must gradually deepen, it also followed that the gradually increasing depth of sleep should coincide with the progression of EEG events from Stage 1 (light sleep) to Stage 4 (deep sleep).

Most people have assumed that dreams must occur in light or "disturbed" sleep, particularly members of the "stomach-ache" school,[7] although Arnold-Foster (1921) and a few others have talked about the great depth of dreaming sleep. The verdict of the majority seemed to be rather solidly confirmed by the findings of Dement and Kleitman that REMs and dreaming were, in fact, associated with periods of Stage 1 ("light sleep") EEG. The acceleration of heart and respiratory rates during REMPs also suggested light sleep.

The real controversy began with the study of REM sleep in the cat. Jouvet (1962) found that the arousal threshold tested by direct mesencephalic stimulation was 300 to 500 percent higher than NREM (slow wave) sleep. The later arousal threshold studies of Benoit and Bloch (1960) gave exactly the same results. Similar findings were obtained with external auditory stimulation, although they were somewhat more variable. The complete loss of muscle tone also suggested to Jouvet that REM sleep was very deep. The contrast between these indicators and the concomitant "activated" EEG which looks as if the cat were awake, led Jouvet to coin the very apt term, "paradoxical sleep," for the REM phase. He also found that, contrary to the human, the heart rate was usually decreased during REM sleep although the respiratory rate was uniformly increased. The findings of a marked lowering in blood pressure by Candia *et al.* (1962) seemed to confirm the great

[7] Also called the "cheese and pickle" school, whose adherents subscribed to the notion that dreams arose from the discomfort following gastronomic indiscretion.

depth of REM sleep; in fact this group has used the term "deep sleep" as its more or less formal nomenclature of the REM phases. Of course, the neuronal discharge data of Evarts and Huttenlocher suggest a very active, or lightly sleeping animal. In another study, Huttenlocher (1960) found that the mesencephalic electrical responses to auditory stimuli were greatly reduced during REM sleep. He suggested as a possible explanation that the intrinsic spontaneous activity was so great that the incoming impulses were occluded. Thus, the paradoxical nature of REM sleep in the cat was fully apparent. Some measurements suggested that it was a very light phase of sleep and others indicated that it was a very deep phase of sleep. It was a great blow to those who felt that the EEG was the final arbiter of depth of sleep to find high voltage slow waves associated with a relatively low arousal threshold and the low voltage, fast patterns ordinarily indicative of the alert waking state not only occuring during behavioral sleep, but associated with a very high arousal threshold.

The next question was, would the difference in arousal threshold between REM and NREM sleep found in the cat also be found in the human? Several studies (Blake and Gerard, 1937; Coleman *et al.*, 1959; Zung and Wilson, 1961) of arousal threshold in relation only to the EEG (done before the REMs had been discovered, or in ignorance of their existence) indicated that the human and the cat would not be the same. In these studies, when all the trials for each EEG stage were averaged, it was found that the EEG (Stage 1 to Stage 4) was correlated with depth of sleep as indicated by the arousal threshold. However, there was wide variability among individual trials and one group (Coleman *et al.*, 1959) stated, ". . . often a response was difficult to evoke when the EEG was characteristic of 'light' sleep." The apparent explanation for these results was the failure to differentiate the sleep onset Stage 1 from the "emergent" Stage 1 associated with REMs—an important omission, particularly since repeated awakenings due to the stimuli greatly increased the amount of the former.

Dement and Klietman (1957b) compared the two types of Stage 1 and found that the arousal threshold was barely above the waking threshold at the sleep onset and as much as 1800 percent higher during REMPs. Williams *et al.* (1963) were the first to make the distinction in all-night studies. In a very elegant study in which the stimuli were pulses of white noise at various exact-decibel levels above waking threshold delivered to the subjects by means of a small earphone, they found that the threshold for eliciting a behavioral response was lowest during sleep onset Stage 1, next lowest in Stage 2, and Stage 3, then REM Stage 1, and finally, Stage 4. Since Stage 2 and 3 comprise the bulk of NREM sleep, it may certainly be concluded that, in terms of arousal threshold, REM sleep is generally deeper then NREM.

The paradoxical nature of REM sleep in both the cat and the human may be explained as follows: When the organism falls asleep, the level of physiological activity and the level of behavioral responsiveness are both decreased by a variable amount. At the onset of REM sleep, the brain abruptly becomes much more active, and in this sense, sleep is drastically lightened. However, a portion of this accelerated activity is directed toward the active inhibition of muscle tone, body movement, and perhaps the lowering of blood pressure. Insofar as these indices are used to measure the level of sleep, it is much deeper. Other functions, notably eye movements and respiration, cannot be inhibited, and their behavior thus reflects the basically active state of the central nervous system. On the other hand, the high degree of spontaneous activity greatly interferes with the capacity to react to outside stimuli. This may be due to occlusion of incoming impulses, active inhibition of behavioral responses to the stimuli, or both. In the human, there may be the additional factors that strong external stimuli are incorporated into the ongoing dream and accordingly stripped of their arousing potential, or are not able to distract the subjects attention from the dream. The relative infrequency with which this occurs may be because the majority of the stimuli never obtain access, due to the occlusive mechanism mentioned above. In view of all this, we can see that depth of sleep does not have any general application in relation to a cluster of individual functions, and without this general validity it has no conceptual usefulness.

A final task is to account for the uniquely high arousal threshold during Stage 4 in the human. There is apparently no portion of NREM sleep in the cat characterized by an arousal threshold that is higher than REM sleep. Roffwarg *et al.* (1964) suggest that the high arousal threshold during Stage 4 in the human may follow the development of the diurnal cycle. Whereas human infants show no particular differentiation of successive NREM periods, young children show very long periods of Stage 4 during NREM sleep early in the night and almost none later. It was suggested that the development of the diurnal cycle with its attendant periods of sustained wakefulness (up to 16 or more hours in the adult) leads to a great accummulation of fatigue, particularly in children who are more active physically during the entire day as compared to sedentary adults, so that when they finally go to sleep, it is more like falling into a coma. Indeed, the basic distinction between sleep and coma is the lack of arousability in the latter, and some children literally cannot be aroused during the first two or three hours of the night. Thus, the Stage 4 early in the night represents a new stage of sleep with a very high arousal threshold peculiar to the human, which results from the development of the diurnal cycle. If such a diurnal cycle were well developed in cats, it is likely that they, too, would have an early period of NREM sleep in which the arousal threshold would be higher than in REM sleep.

## DRUG STUDIES

Not too much information is available about the effects of pharmaceutical agents on the sleep cycle. One of the reasons is that such knowledge does not seem to have an immediate practical application of sufficient importance to inspire the tremendous effort of taking many all-night recordings with both drug and control series in order to get statistically significant results. Oswald *et al.* (1963) found that 400 mg. of heptabarbitone greatly decreased the duration of REMPs and also the frequency of REMs within those periods. Fisher and Dement have some preliminary data which show that small doses of sodium seconal have little effect on the sleep cycle, while higher doses (around 300 mg.) will completely block the appearance of eye movements, although the other attributes of REM sleep including its duration seem unaffected. Thus, individual barbiturate compounds may have different effects. Rechtschaffen and Maron (1964) studied the effects of the CNS stimulant, dexedrine sulphate, and surprisingly found that it seems specifically to suppress the REM phase of sleep while leaving the NREM phase essentially unaltered. We have confirmed this result in our laboratory. In the cat, Jouvet has found that atropine tends to suppress REMPs, while eserine augments them (1962). The effect of psychotropic drugs on dream content has been examined by Whitman *et al.* (1960; 1961). They found interesting changes in such content dimensions as hostility, dependency, heterosexuality, homosexuality, motility, and anxiety.

## THE BASIC FUNCTION OF DREAMING

### DREAM DEPRIVATION

In view of the universality of substantial amounts of REM sleep, Fisher and Dement were led to ask whether or not this nightly amount of dreaming was in some way a necessary and vital part of our existence. Would it be possible for human beings to continue functioning normally if their dream life were completely or partially suppressed? Should dreaming, if necessary, be considered so in a psychological or a physiological sense, or both?

The obvious attack on these problems was to study subjects who had somehow been deprived of the opportunity to dream. The method employed was fairly simple, although it involved a tremendous experimental effort (Dement, 1960; Dement and Fisher, 1963). Each time subjects began to dream, as indicated by the appearance of REMs and Stage 1 EEG patterns, they were awakened, kept awake for a few minutes, and then allowed to go back to sleep. This procedure was continued throughout the entire night. On the first night, the total dream time could be reduced about 90 percent by perhaps ten such awakenings, which still allowed a nearly normal amount of sleep. In general, the over-all procedure was as follows: Subjects slept in the laboratory without disturbance for several nights to evaluate their average nightly sleep time and average nightly dream time. They were then "dream deprived" by the above technique for two to five *consecutive* nights, and immediately following this, were again allowed to sleep without disturbance for an additional number of "recovery" nights. They also had daily psychiatric interviews as a check on their daytime behavior. At the present time, 21 subjects have taken part in these experiments. For purposes of description and interpretation, the results may be divided into physiological and psychological categories. The most striking and clear-cut results occurred in the physiological sphere, and were as follows:

(a) In all 21 subjects, it took a progressively greater number of awakenings on each successive night to suppress dreaming. In other words, the REMPs began to appear progressively more often.

(b) On "recovery" nights immediately following the awakening nights in 20 of the 21 subjects, there was a marked increase in the amount of dreaming, often to more than 50 percent above the range of baseline nights. It was as if the dreaming that had been lost was being made up—that an increased tendency to dream had built up during the period of suppression.

If REMPs were considered to be light sleep, this would be a truly remarkable result. The subjects were being disturbed and they were losing sleep. Instead of their usual 7 to 7½ hours, they were sleeping 5 to 6. Therefore, their tendency should have been to sleep more deeply and to dream less.

It might be objected that the awakenings were so disturbing and emotionally upsetting to the subject, just by virtue of repeated arousals, that they induced a sort of "excited state" which was reflected in the changes in total dream time and the number of dream onsets. Each subject, however, underwent an additional series of awakenings which exactly duplicated the dream deprivation series, except that the awakenings fell outside of rapid eye movement periods. Each time an eye movement period started, it was allowed to continue without interruption. In this situation, the subjects were equally disturbed and lost an equal amount of sleep, but on recovery nights, there was no significant rise in dream time.

If it is accepted that dreams express or effectively discharge a certain amount of infantile or repressed impulses, it might be assumed that the continued nightly interference with such discharge and consequent accumulation of tensions would lead to difficulties in the waking state. In our series, 11 subjects, of which 3 were females, had dream deprivation for 5 consecutive nights. On the psychological side, all showed, in one way or another, deteriorating tendencies during the period of dream deprivation that were not apparent during the period of control awakenings. They suffered greater or less degrees of anxiety, irritability, inability to concentrate, tiredness, etc. Two male subjects became markedly agitated. One female, who denied any loss of well-being, showed a marked change in Rohrschach responses scored for primary process manifestations by the method of Holt (1956). The other 2 females showed evidence of hallucination during photic stimulation at the height of the dream deprivation but not during the baseline or control periods. The males did not receive photic stimulation. Six of the male subjects developed ravenous appetites and showed significant weight gain during dream deprivation.

In interpreting these results, Fisher and Dement have adopted the tentative hypothesis that dreaming is necessary, or has special significance for the well-being of the human organism apart from its contribution to the total amount of sleep. It is possible that if dream-deprived long enough, perhaps 20 or 30 nights, subjects might become disorganized, hallucinatory, or even frankly psychotic in the waking state. Kubie (1962) has criticized these results on the basis of his contention that it is impossible to estimate *amounts* of dreaming by the frequency and/or duration of dreams, and that dreams might occur *without* REMs. As is readily apparent, these reservations depend solely on the definition of dreaming, and Kubie's does not coincide with ours.

In view of the "dream deprivation" findings in the human, certain experiments of Jouvet (1962) acquire an added interest. As was previously mentioned, the destruction of a circumscribed area in the pons (brain-stem nucleus pontis caudalis) led to a complete elimination of the REM phase of sleep in an otherwise normal animal. However, after the operation, a series of remarkable changes in behavior took place. On about the fourth post-operative day, occurring periodically 2 or 3 times an hour, the cats would suddenly stare fixedly in front of them with their heads raised and their pupils dilated. Then they would begin to hit at an imaginary object with their paws. By the sixth to eighth post-operative day, the animals had become perpetually agitated and restless with their heads always held up. They moved their feet continuously as if standing on a hot surface. There was a progressive increase in heart rate from 100 beats per minute on the first post-operative day to 160 beats per minute on the fifth day and 210 on the 12th day. Finally, some of the animals showed a great increase in eating and drinking behavior.

In some cats, there was a reappearance of the REM phase of sleep after a varying number of days, probably because the lesion was incomplete. If this occurred, all the aforementioned changes in behavior rapidly disappeared. However, Jouvet reports that the cats in which REM recovery did not take place died in a state that seemed to resemble acute manic delirium.

Thus, in cats, the nucleus pontis caudalis and/or REM sleep seems to be necessary for life. Deprived of these factors, cats underwent what resembled a psychotic breakdown with intermittent hallucination progressing to manic delirium, exhaustion, and death. The dramatic remission of these signs in the cats that recovered even a very tiny amount of REM sleep suggests that such dramatic results were not obtained by suppressing REM sleep in the human because, actually, small amounts of dreaming were allowed to precede each "dream deprivation" awakening.

The fact that these signs occur in the cat minimizes the importance of psychological factors in explaining the necessity of REM sleep, but we cannot push the analogy between cat and man too far. Humans are unique in having to exert a high degree of control over their aggressive and sexual impulses, and they may accordingly have a greater need to discharge these impulses in a safe way. Along this line, if we assume that dreams are, in effect, real experiences from the standpoint of what is going on in the brain, it would give some solid body to the wish-fulfillment hypothesis. An experience in a dream ought to be gratifying in a way that fantasies and day dreams never can. In the fullest sense, we are able to "blow off steam" in our dreams. The view that dreams might be the "safety valve" of the mind was held long ago by Robert (1886).

The occurrence of REM sleep in decorticate humans and cats has also been demonstrated by Jouvet (1962; Jouvet *et al.*, 1960). Originally he suggested that, because REMs took place in these preparations, they were probably not related to the visual imagery of dreaming in humans. The same might be concluded from the fact that REMs are present in neonatal infants (1964). It should be obvious that this does not necessarily follow. In the decorticate cats and humans and newborn infants, they are merely a random motor expression of the heightened activity of the REM phase. Faulkner and Hyde (1958) have shown that conjugate eye movements can be elicited in the totally decerebrate cat by stimulating the brain stem. The findings of Jouvet merely show that eye movements during sleep can occur in the absence of dreaming, assuming that a cerebral cortex is necessary for the experience of the latter. In the intact human, as the mind develops to the level where dreaming can take place, the oculomotor and psychological events are integrated. It would be very interesting to see if the "dream deprivation" findings could be elicited in the decorticate preparation (increase in REM sleep after its suppression). This would certainly emphasize the physiological side of the coin, but such a study has not been systematically undertaken as yet.

## RELATION OF DREAMS TO MENTAL ILLNESS

If dreaming is the "safety valve" of the mind, as Robert has suggested, what might be its role in mental illness? Does it cease to function? Or, is dreaming itself the mental illness, in the sense that the same mechanism which produces it in sleep may become abnormally active and produce dreaming in the waking state? Many people have commented on the similarity of dreams and psychosis.

Relatively little has been done in this area. In a very early study (Dement, 1955) a group of chronic schizophrenics was observed. They apparently had a fairly normal sleep cycle although the measurements at that time were not overly precise.

The most fascinating observations have been initiated by Fisher on borderline patients. To date, 5 borderline cases have been studied, 1 of whom became overtly psychotic (Fisher and Dement, 1963). The first patient in the series was studied intensively. Over a 5-month period he slept in the laboratory 13 nights. On individual nights, his total dream time ranged from 27 to 36 percent and averaged about 30, a value considerably above that of normal subjects. At the end of this 5-month period he rather precipitously developed an acute paranoid psychosis. He first became delusional and then began to hallucinate in both the visual and auditory spheres. He was in severe panic, would run through the streets and over roof tops fleeing from imaginary pursuers. Within several days after the onset of hallucinations, he was placed on massive doses of Stelazine and 18 consecutive nights of sleep were recorded. The first of these nights was obtained while he was still hallucinating and the recording began only about 8 hours after the first dose of Stelazine. On this first night, his dream time was about 50 percent, as measured by REM techniques, which is by far the highest that we have ever encountered. On the second night, the percent was around 29, but when the daily dose of Stelazine was decreased, it rose on the third night to about 40 percent. By the fourth night the hallucinations had disappeared and the dream time was again 30 percent. It hovered around this value for the remainder of the recordings while the delusional activity gradually diminished and he became more amenable to psychotherapy. After the drug was discontinued, a number of additional recordings were obtained and all showed the pre-psychotic level.

It was suggested by Fisher that this patient showed an unusually high percentage of dreaming in his pre-psychotic period because of intensified drive pressure in the presence of weak ego organization. As drive pressure mounted and defenses became weaker, his dream time percent rose to an even higher level and, at the point where he became acutely psychotic, delusional, and hallucinating, it had attained a level of 50 percent. As the psychotic symptomatology rapidly abated, presumably under the influence of Stelazine, the total dream time rather quickly returned to its pre-psychotic level.

Similar *baseline* findings were made in four additional potentially schizophrenic patients. The mean percentage for all 5 borderline patients was 26.5 as compared to about 21 for a comparable age group of normals. Dream-time percentages of 30 or more on individual nights were common. It was proposed from these data that the total dream-time level in any given patient on any given night is the outcome of the balance between the pressure of instinctual drives toward discharge and the adequacy of the defensive and controlling functions of the ego. The question, of course, arises as to whether or not the elevated dream time is a passive reflection of the particular balance in borderline patients, or whether it is actively fulfilling a therapeutic or compensatory function.

If there is a similarity between dreams and psychosis, just what is its basis? Is it possible that one aspect of psychosis is an abnormal activation in the waking state of the pontine-limbic dream system described by Jouvet? Or, is it more likely that for some reason, the dream function fails and drive pressure piles up to break out as hallucinations and delusions. In the latter case, it may fail by virtue of being eliminated (as in dream-deprived subjects or Jouvet's cats), or by not reaching high enough levels to be effective (as is possible in Fisher's patient). The fact that Jouvet's cats seemed to become psychotic in the absence of the key neuroanatomical structure in the dreaming mechanism, suggests that this structure may actually control the psychotic process and keep it in check by permitting controlled discharge during sleep. When the nervous system is deprived of this control, it runs wild.

These are all only speculations, but it is tempting to assume that dreaming and psychosis must be linked in some way, and that the coming together of physiology and psychology in the study of the former may eventually lead to an additional understanding of the latter.

Although it is somewhat dramatic, we might close this section by citing a statement of John Rosen (1962) who has had much experience working with psychotics. "Psychosis is often like a continuous nightmare from which the sleeper, that is, the psychotic, is not able to awaken himself; further, the psychosis on occasion is like a simple dream, devoid of terrifying anxieties, but likewise a "dream" from which there is no awakening."

## EPILOGUE

In this essay, the author has tried to combine fact and speculation in reasonable proportions. The main purpose was to formulate a useful, meaningful description of what might be called the essential nature of dreaming. In order for an experience to be a dream, it must have occurred during sleep and it must contain perceptions. If the perceptual activity cannot be determined from the narrative report (as opposed to vague imagery or abstract thought), it must be differentiated on the basis of neurophysiological measurements that will detect the neural basis of the perception. At this time, the latter step has not been taken. Rather, the presence of the neural substrate is inferred from the properties of the REMs and the more general characteristics of the activity of neuron populations. This allows us to substitute temporarily for this last step, differentiating on the basis of recording the EEG and REMs which will detect the period of true dreaming.

Many people may not be accustomed to such glib assumptions that neural activity and perceptions are really related even in the waking state. Of course, this can never be established in an ultimate sense, but we have certainly reached a point in the development of our knowledge about the human organism where we know that "mental activity" is consistently related to many parameters of neural function. We may accordingly infer the same thing about mental activity and neural function in dreaming. The main difference is that the study of the nocturnal side has lagged far behind the daytime side.

Why there should be two kinds of sleep remains an evolutionary riddle. The location low in the brain stem of the REM-triggering mechanism suggests that it is archaic. It may be that primitive organisms had only one kind of "sleep"—the actively enforced immobility of what is now called the REM phase. However, it would seem that this would have been evolutionarily fatal since REM sleep appears to render the organism less sensitive to the environment and its dangers. There may be other, as yet unsuspected positive traits connected with REM sleep, biochemical or metabolic, which may have outweighed this disadvantage.

In reviewing the physiological and psychological studies that followed Aserinsky and Kleitman's breakthrough in the study of dreaming, the author has restricted himself to reports that included some use or implication derived from REM techniques. Some studies have been emphasized more than others but this does not necessarily reflect on the quality of the work. Although we have made great strides in our understanding of the nature of dreaming, there is still much to be learned. It is not yet conclusively established whether the dream should be considered as a sort of psychic vermiform appendix or whether it plays a crucial role in relation to the over-all psychic economy. The hints that favor the latter possibility do not indicate whether its importance lies in the experiential aspects or in the unique physiology of REM sleep.

A final point that has not been touched on in this essay is the possible role of the cultural background in augmenting the potential usefulness of dreams. Except for psychoanalytic influences, the significance of the dream has certainly been deemphasized in present-day Western civilization. In cultures where this is not the case, dream memories may be more vivid and persistent and the dream experiences may be brought to some extent under the voluntary control of the individual through a lifetime of interest and concern. Kilton Stewart (1962) has given the example of the Senoi culture of Central Malaya where dreaming is of paramount importance and is encouraged and cultivated from early childhood. In this atmosphere, the members of the culture have attained a high level of spontaneous recall of dreams together with a certain amount of control, and, according to Stewart, they are able to achieve a high order of creative thinking in the dream. It may be hoped that the recent physiological contributions to the understanding of dreams will lend new impetus to their study from a sociological point of view.

## REFERENCES

Andress, J. An investigation of the sleep of normal school children. *J. educ. Psychol.*, 1911, *2*, 153-156.

Antrobus, J., W. Dement, and C. Fisher. Patterns of dreaming and dream recall: an EEG study. *J. abn. soc. Psychol.*, 1964, *69:* 341-344.

Arduini, A., G. Berlucchi, and P. Strata. Pyramidal activity during sleep and wakefulness. *Arch. ital. Biol.*, 1963, *101*, 530-544.

Arnold-Foster, H. *Studies in dreams.* New York: Macmillan, 1921.

Aserinsky, E., and N. Kleitman. Regularly occurring periods of eye motility, and concomitant phenomena during sleep. *Science*, 1953, *118*, 273-274.

Asher, E., and R. Ort. Eye movement as a complex indicator. *J. gen. Psychol.*, 1951, *45*, 209-217.

Benoit, O., and V. Bloch. Seuil d'excitabilité reticulaire et sommeil profond chez le chat. *J. Physiol. (Paris)*, 1960, *52;* 17-18.

Berger, R. Tonus of extrinsic laryngeal muscles during sleep and dreaming. *Science*, 1961, *134*, 840.

Berger, R., P. Olley, and I. Oswald. The EEG, eye-movements, and dreams of the blind. *Quart. J. exp. Psychol.*, 1962, *14*, 183-186.

Berger, R., and I. Oswald. Eye movements during active and passive dreams. *Science*, 1962, *137*, 601.

Blake, H., and R. Gerard. Brain potentials during sleep. *Am. J. Physiol.*, 1937, *119*, 692-703.

Blank, H. Dreams of the blind. *Psa. Quart.*, 1958, *27*, 158-174.

Bremer, F. Cerveau "isolé" et physiologie du sommeil. *C.R. Soc. Biol.*, 1935, *118*, 1235-1241.

Bulow, K. Respiration and wakefulness in man. *Acta Physiol. Scand.*, 1963, *59*, suppl. 209, pp 1-110.

Candia, O., E. Favale, A. Giussani, and G. Rossi. Blood pressure during natural sleep and during sleep induced by electrical stimulation of the brain stem reticular formation. *Arch. ital. Biol.*, 1962, *100*, 216-233.

Chow, K. Changes of brain electropotentials during visual discrimination learning in monkey. *J. Neurophysiol.*, 1961, *24*, 377-390.

Coleman, P., F. Gray, and K. Watanabe. EEG amplitude and reaction time during sleep. *J. appl. Physiol.*, 1959, *14*, 397-400.

Dement, W. Dream recall and eye movements during sleep in schizophrenics and normals. *J. nerv. ment. Dis.*, 1955, *122*, 263-269.

Dement, W. The occurrence of low voltage, fast, electroencephalogram patterns during behavioral sleep in the cat. *EEG clin. Neurophysiol.*, 1958, *10*, 291-296.

Dement, W. The effect of dream deprivation. *Science*, 1960, *131*, 1705-1707.

Dement, W. Eye movements during sleep. In M. Bender,

(Ed.), *The Oculomotor System.* New York: Hoeber, 1964.

Dement, W., and C. Fisher. Experimental interference with the sleep cycle. *Canad. Psychiat. Assoc. J.*, 1963, *8*, 400-405.

Dement, W., and N. Kleitman. Incidence of eye motility during sleep in relation to varying EEG patterns. *Fed. Proc.*, 1955, *14*, 216.

Dement, W., and N. Kleitman. The relation of eye movements during sleep to dream activity: an objective method for the study of dreaming. *J. exp. Psychol.*, 1957a, *53*, 339-346.

Dement, W., and N. Kleitman. Cyclic variations of EEG during sleep and their relation to eye movements, body motility, and dreaming. *EEG clin. Neurophysiol.*, 1957b, *9*, 673-690.

Dement, W., and E. Wolpert. The relation of eye movements, body motility, and external stimuli to dream content. *J. exp. Psychol.*, 1958a, *55*, 543-553.

Dement, W., and E. Wolpert. Relationships in the manifest content of dreams occurring on the same night. *J. nerv. ment. Dis.*, 1958b, *126*, 568-578.

Ellis, H. *The world of dreams.* Boston: Houghton Mifflin, 1922.

Evarts, E. Effects of sleep and waking on activity of single units in the unrestrained cat. In G. Wolstenholme, and M. O'Connor (Eds.), *The nature of sleep.* Boston: Little, Brown, 1960.

Evarts, E. Patterns of neuronal discharge on visual cortex during visual inspection, waking, and sleep. *Proc. Int. U. Physiol. Sci.: XXIIth Int. Cong.*, 1962a, *1*, 448-450.

Evarts, E. Activity of neurons in visual cortex of the cat during sleep with low voltage fast EEG activity. *J. Neurophysiol.*, 1962b, *25*, 812-816.

Faulkner, R., and J. Hyde. Coordinated eye and body movements evoked by brain stem stimulation in decerebrated cats. *J. Neurophysiol.*, 1958, *21*, 171-182.

Fischgold, H., and B. Schwartz. A clinical, electroencephalographic and polygraphic study of sleep in the human adult. In G. Wolstenholme, and M. O'Connor (Eds.), *The nature of sleep*. Boston: Little Brown, 1960.

Fisher, C., and W. Dement. Studies on the psychopathology of sleep and dreams. *Am. J. Psychiat.*, 1963, *119*, 1160-1168.

Foulkes, W. Dream reports from different stages of sleep. *J. abn. soc. Psychol.*, 1962, *65*, 14-25.

Freud, S. *The interpretation of dreams*. New York: Basic Books, 1955.

Goodenough, D., A. Shapiro, M. Holden, and L. Steinschriber. A comparison of "dreamers" and "nondreamers": eye movements, electroencephalograms, and the recall of dreams. *J. abn. soc. Psychol.*, 1959, *59*, 295-302.

Granda, A., and J. Hammack. Operant behavior during sleep. *Science*, 1961, *133*, 1485-1486.

Grastyan, E. The hippocampus and higher nervous activity. In M. Brazier (Ed.), *The central nervous system and behavior*, Trans. Sec. Conf., New York: Macy Foundation, 1959, pp. 119-205.

Hall, C. What people dream about. *Sci. Amer.*, 1951, *184*, 60-63.

Hall, C. *The meaning of dreams*. New York: Harper & Row, 1953.

Hawkins, D., H. Puryear, C. Wallace, W. Deal, and E. Thomas. Basal skin resistance during sleep and "dreaming." *Science*, 1962, *136*, 321-322.

Holt, R. Gauging primary and secondary processes in Rohrschach responses. *J. proj. Tech.*, 1956, *20*, 14-25.

Hubel, D. Single unit activity in striate cortex of unrestrained cats. *J. Physiol.*, 1959, 147, 226-238.

Huttenlocher, P. Effects of state of arousal on click responses in the mesencephalic reticular formation. *EEG clin. Neurophysiol.*, 1960, *12*, 819-827.

Huttenlocher, P. Evoked and spontaneous activity in single units of medial brain stem during natural sleep and waking. *J. Neurophysiol.*, 1961, *24*, 451-468.

Jouvet, D., J. Valatx, and M. Jouvet. Etude polygraphique du sommeil du chaton. *C. R. Soc. Biol.*, 1961, *155*, 1660-1664.

Jouvet, M. Recherches sur les structures nerveuses et les mécanismes responsables de differentes phases du sommeil physiologique. *Arch. ital. Biol.*, 1962, *100*, 125-206.

Jouvet, M., F. Michel, and J. Courjon. Sur un stade d'activité electrique cérébrale rapide au cours du sommeil physiologique. *C. R. Soc. Biol.*, 1959, *153*, 1024-1028.

Jouvet, M., F. Michel, and D. Mounier. Analyse electroencephalographique comparée du sommeil physiologique chez le chat et chez l'homme. *Rev. Neurologique*, 1960, *108*, 189-205.

Kahn, E., W. Dement, C. Fisher, and J. Barmack. Incidence of color in immediately recalled dreams. *Science*, 1962, *137*, 1054-1055.

Kamiya, J. Behavioral, subjective, and physiological aspects of drowsiness and sleep. In D. Fiske, and S. Maddi (Eds.), *Functions of varied experience*. Homewood, Illinois: Dorsey Press, 1961.

Kanzow, E. Electrical activity and blood flow of the cerebral cortex of unanesthetized, unrestrained cats correlated to behavior. *Excerpta Medica. Int. Cong. Series*, 1961, *37*, 97-98.

Kanzow, E., D. Krause, and H. Kuhnel, Die Vasomotorik der Hirnrinde in den Phasen desynchronisierter EEG-Aktivitat im naturlichen Schlaf der Katze. *Pflugers Archiv.*, 1962, *274*, 593-607.

Kardiner, A. *The traumatic neuroses of war*. New York: Hoeber, 1941.

Kleitman, N. Sleep. *Physiol. Rev.*, 1929, *9*, 624-665.

Kleitman, N. *Sleep and wakefulness*. Chicago: University of Chicago Press, 1939.

Kleitman, N. Sleep, wakefulness, and consciousness, *Psychol. Bull.*, 1957, *54*, 354-359.

Kleitman, N. Patterns of dreaming. *Sci. Amer.*, 1960, *203*, 82-88.

Kleitman, N., F. Mullin, N. Cooperman, and S. Titelbaum.

*Sleep characteristics.* Chicago: University of Chicago Press, 1937.

Knapp, P. Sensory impressions in dreams. *Psa. Quart.*, 1956, *25*, 325-347.

Krauss, R. *A hole is to dig. A first book of first definitions.* New York: Harper & Row, 1952.

Kris, C. Vision: electro-oculography. In O. Glasser (Ed.), *Medical Physics, Vol. III.* Chicago: Year Book Publishers, 1960, pp. 692-700.

Kubie, L. The concept of dream deprivation: a critical analysis. *Psychosomatic Med.*, 1962, *24*, 62-65.

Lachmann, F., B. Lapkin, and N. Handelman. The recall of dreams: its relation to repression and cognitive control. *J. abn. soc. Psychol.*, 1962, *64*, 160-162.

Ladd, G. Contribution to the psychology of visual dreams. *Mind*, 1892, *1*, 299-304.

Levin, M. Reconstruction dreams. *Amer. J. Psychiat.*, 1939, *96*, 705-710.

Lewin, B. Sleep, the mouth and the dream screen. *Psa. Quart.*, 1946, *15*, 419-434.

Livingston, R. Central control of receptors and sensory transmission systems. In *Handbook of Physiology*, 1959, *1*, 741-760, Amer. Physiol. Soc., Washington, D.C.

Loomis, A., E. Harvey, and G. Hobart. Cerebral states during sleep as studied by human brain potentials. *J. exp. Psychol.*, 1937, *21*, 127-144.

Luckhardt, A. Contributions to the physiology of the empty stomach. XXXII—The effect of dreaming on the gastric hunger contractions. *Amer. J. Physiol.*, 1915-1916, *39*, 330-333.

Magoun, H. *The waking brain.* Springfield, Illinois: Charles C. Thomas, 1958.

Malcolm, N. *Dreaming.* New York: Humanities Press, 1959.

Masserman, J. Language, behavior and dynamic psychiatry. *Int. J. Psa.*, 1944, *25*, 1-8.

Maury, A. *Le sommeil et les rêves.* Paris: Didier, 1861.

Monroe, W. Note on dreams. *Amer. J. Psychol.*, 1897, *9*, 413-414.

Morrell, F. Electrophysiological contributions to the neural basis of learning. *Physiol. Rev.*, 1961, *41*, 443-494.

Moruzzi, G., and H. Magoun. Brain stem reticular formation and activation of the EEG. *EEG clin. Neurophysiol.*, 1949, *1*, 455-473.

Nauta, W. Hippocampal projections and related neural pathways to the mid-brain in the cat. *Brain*, 1958, *81*, 319-340.

Offenkrantz, W., and A. Rechtschaffen. Clinical studies of sequential dreams. *Arch. gen. Psychiat.*, 1963, *8*, 497-508.

Offenkrantz, W. and E. Wolpert. The detection of dreaming in a congenitally blind subject. *J. nerv. ment. Dis.*, 1963, *136*, 88-90.

Olds, J. A preliminary mapping of electrical reinforcing effects in the rat brain. *J. comp. physiol. Psychol.*, 1956, *49*, 281-285.

Oswald, I. Falling alseep open-eyed during intense rhythmic stimulation. *Brit. med. J.*, 1960, *1*, 1450-1455.

Oswald, I., R. Berger, R. Jaramillo, K. Keddie, P. Olley, and G. Plunkett. Melancholia and barbiturates: a controlled EEG, body and eye movement study of sleep. *Brit. J. Psychiat.*, 1963, *109*, 66-78.

Oswald, I., A. Taylor, and M. Triesman. Discriminative responses to stimulation during human sleep. *Brain*, 1960, *83*, 440-443.

Penfield, W., and H. Jasper. *Epilepsy and the functional anatomy of the human brain.* Boston: Little, Brown, 1954.

Penfield, W., and T. Rasmussen. *The cerebral cortex of man.* New York: Macmillan, 1952.

Pompeiano, O. Supraspinal control of reflexes during sleep and wakefulness. C.N.R.S. Symposium on aspects anatomo-fonctionnels de la physiologie du sommeil. Lyon, France, September, 1963.

Ramsey, G. Studies of dreaming. *Psychol. Bull.*, 1953, *50*, 432-455.

Rechtschaffen, A., E. Wolpert, W. Dement, S. Mitchell, and C. Fisher. Nocturnal sleep of narcoleptics. *EEG Clin. Neurophysiol.*, 1963, *15*, 599-609.

Rechtschaffen, A., D. Goodenough, and A. Shapiro. Patterns of sleep talking. *Arch. gen. Psychiat.*, 1962, 7, 418-426.

Rechtschaffen, A., and L. Maron. The effect of amphetamine on the sleep cycle. *EEG Clin. Neurophysiol.*, 1964, *16*, 438-445.

Rechtschaffen, W., P. Verdone, and J. Wheaton. Reports of mental activity during sleep. *Canad. Psychiat. Assoc. J.*, 1963, *8*, 409-414.

Robert, W. *Der Traum als Naturnotwendigkeit Erklart*. Hamburg, 1886.

Roffwarg, H., W. Dement, and C. Fisher. Observations on the sleep-dream pattern in neonates, infants, children and adults. In E. Harms (Ed.), *Problem of sleep and dream in children*. London: Pergamon Press, 1964.

Roffwarg, H., W. Dement, J. Muzio, and C. Fisher. Dream imagery: Relationship to rapid eye movements of sleep. *Arch. gen. Psychiat.*, 1962, 7, 235-258.

Rosen, J. *Direct psychoanalytic psychiatry*. New York: Grune and Stratton, 1962.

Schonbar, R. Some manifest characteristics of recallers and non-recallers of dreams. *J. consult. Psychol.*, 1959, *23*, 414-418.

Schonbar, R. Temporal and emotional factors in the selective recall of dreams. *J. consult. Psychol.*, 1961, *25*, 67-73.

Shapiro, A. Observations on some periodic and non-periodic phenomena in normal human sleep. *Ann. N. Y. Acad. Sci.*, 1962, *98*, 1139-1143.

Shimazono, Y., T. Horie, Y. Yanagisawa, N. Hori, S. Chikazawa, and K. Shozuka. The correlation of the rhythmic waves of the hippocampus with the behaviors of dogs. *Neurol. medico-chir.*, 1960, 2, 82-88.

Snyder, F. Dream recall, respiratory variability and depth of sleep. *Am. Psychiatric Assoc.*, April, 1960.

Snyder, F., J. Hobson, and F. Goldfrank. Blood pressure changes during sleep. *Science*, 1963, *142*, 1313-1314.

Stewart, K. The dream comes of age. *Mental hygiene*, 1962, *46*, 230-237.

Stoyva, J. The effect of suggested dreams on the length of rapid eye movement periods. Unpublished Ph.D. dissertation, University of Chicago, 1961.

Strumwasser, F. Long-term recording from single neurons in brain of unrestrained mammals. *Science*, 1958, *127*, 469-470.

Swisher, J. Manifestations of "activated" sleep in the rat. *Science*. 1962, *138*, 1110.

Trosman, H., A. Rechtschaffen, W. Offenkrantz, and E. Wolpert. Studies in psychophysiology of dreams. IV. Relations among dreams in sequence. *Arch. gen. Psychiat.*, 1960, *3*, 602-607.

Vaihinger, H. *The philosophy of as-if*. London: Paul, 1924; New York: Harcourt, 1924.

Weitzmann, E. A note on the EEG and eye movements during behavioral sleep in monkeys. *EEG clin. Neurophysiol.*, 1961, *13*, 790-794.

Whitman, R., C. Pierce, and J. Maas. Drugs and dreams. In L. Uhr, and J. Miller (Eds.), *Drugs and behavior*. New York: Wiley, 1960, pp. 591-595.

Whitman, R., C. Pierce, J. Maas, and B. Baldridge. Drugs and dreams II. Imipramine and prochlorperazine. *Comp. Psychiat.*, 1961, 2, 219-226.

Whitman, R., C. Pierce, J. Maas, and B. Baldridge. The dreams of the experimental subject. *J. nerv. ment. Dis.*, 1962, *134*, 431-439.

Williams, H., J. Hammack, R. Daly, and W. Dement. Auditory arousal and the EEG stages of sleep. *EEG clin. Neurophysiol.*, 1964, *16*, 269-279.

Wolpert, E. Studies in psychophysiology of dreams. II. An electromyographic study of dreaming. *Arch. gen. Psychiat.*, 1960, *2*, 231-241.

Wolpert, E., and H. Trosman. Studies in psychophysiology of

dreams. I. the evocation of sequential dream episodes. *Arch. Neurol. Psychiat.*, 1958, *79*, 603-606.

Zung, W., and W. Wilson. Response to auditory stimulation during sleep. *Arch. gen. Psychiat.*, 1961, *4*, 548-552.

# 3 EMERGING TECHNOLOGIES FOR MAKING DECISIONS

WARD EDWARDS, HAROLD LINDMAN,
AND LAWRENCE D. PHILLIPS

UNIVERSITY OF MICHIGAN

Unaided machines make decisions all the time. Your automobile decides, with no intervention by you, when its engine is warm enough so that water should be permitted to circulate through the radiator. Your house decides whether it is too hot or too cold, and then takes appropriate corrective action. The more intelligent houses consider whether it is day or night in choosing what action to take, and may even initiate the action ahead of time, so that the house does not actually get too cold or too warm.

Nevertheless, an executive who orders a million dollars' worth of computer-controlled milling machines in the morning may proclaim that same afternoon that computers will never replace men as decision-makers, that decision making is *the* inescapably human function which cannot be automated. So sweeping a claim is nonsense, and yet there may seem to be some plausibility to it. Though the examples indicate clearly that machines make decisions, and it would be easy to find more complicated examples of unaided machines making much more complex, much more important decisions, we still feel that those thermostats cannot decide alone. They need men to tell them what to do, to program them. Why? Not because such programming is necessary to the daily functioning of decision-making machines; it is entirely possible to manufacture thermostats preset for particular temperatures, as in the automobile cooling system. The point is that man knows best what effect he wants a decision-making machine to produce. He designs a decision-making system so that he can conveniently communicate his preferences to them, perhaps once and for all or perhaps day by day or decision by decision. One indispensable human function in decision making, then, is evaluation of the anticipated consequences of decisions.

Into what separable functions can the process of making a decision be analyzed? For which of those functions are men indispensable? We ask the latter question not primarily because of its technological importance, but rather because of its usefulness in identifying the limitations of knowledge. If we can build a machine to perform a function, we understand the nature of that function. If not, we may or may not understand its nature; often we do not. If we knew in detail how heredity and environment have managed to shape a man's value system, we could design a machine to set his house thermostat for him, though we probably would not. And certain other functions included in the process of making a decision are still more mysterious.

A functional analysis of decision making should be very useful for reasons more important than reassurance of executives who fear their own technological unemployment. Research and experience suggest the ego-deflating conclusion that men often make poor decisions. Automation of certain automatable functions that are parts of the process of making a decision will often substantially improve the resulting decision, we believe. Practical techniques for such partial automation of decision making are one topic of this chapter.

The fundamental step in understanding decision making, then, is formal analysis of the process into separable functions, and detailed further analysis of each such function. Most of this paper is devoted to such a formal analysis. By "formal" we mean explicit and precise—and it turns out, in decision making as everywhere else, that explicit and precise analyses of difficult problems require the use of mathematical tools. Decision making has interested its students for a long time, and mathematicians have developed many tools important in analyzing it. Among them are probability theory, utility theory, the theory of games, classical and Bayesian statistics, and operations research. We will touch on each of these topics, but we have kept mathematics to a minimum.

After presenting a formal analysis of decision making, we shall discuss several emerging technologies that permit full or partial automation of some of those functions. Our conclusion will be that these technologies offer immense promise for improving the quality and speed of decision making, but that human beings will continue to be indispensable for certain functions for the foreseeable future.

## SOME DISTINCTIONS AMONG MODELS

Decision theorists often distinguish two classes of models, or theories: normative and descriptive. A normative model or theory is a set of rules specifying what people should do; a normative model for decision-making, then, specifies what decision you should make. A descriptive model attempts to predict what people do do; a descriptive model of decision making predicts what decision you in fact will make. Almost all of the familiar psychological models or theories are descriptive, not normative.

This distinction between normative and descriptive models is a lot less clear-cut than it sounds. For example, a normative model of decision making will predict correctly the behavior of anyone who is willing and able to apply that model in making his own decisions. The larger and more important the decision, the more likely is the decision-maker to calculate carefully the potential consequences of his act and so try to make the normatively correct decision. Moreover, descriptive considerations have changed the content of normative models of decision making over the years. The earliest normative model of decision making in effect attempted to prescribe not only how one should go about implementing one's value system, but also to some extent what that value system should be. Such prescriptions turned out to be so different from the actual behavior of reasonable men that the content of the normative model was re-examined, and much of the prescription of values was removed. Contemporary normative models for decision making are no more than sets of rules designed to ensure that acts will be coherent or internally consistent with one another in the pursuit of whatever goals the decision maker may happen to have. Nevertheless, this requirement of coherence or internal consistency is a very strong one, so strong that no one seems able to satisfy it fully.

Every descriptive model in psychology actually contains two parts. One is a description of the environment and task facing the organism; the other is a description of the basic response tendencies that the organism brings to that environment and task. The interplay of these two kinds of descriptions produces the detailed predictions about the behavior of the organism in the situation. Often, perhaps usually, the description of the environment and of the task is very much more sophisticated than is the description of the response tendencies that the organism brings to that environment and task and the predictive success of many descriptive models in psychology depends, not on the effectiveness of their description of the organism, but on the effectiveness of their description of the environment. Since normative models of decision making are descriptions of an environment and of a task with few assumptions about the response tendencies that the organism brings with it, they are incomplete as descriptive models. Yet they provide most of the intellectual substance that descriptive models need. It is relatively simple to add to these normative models rather trivial assumptions about the way that men behave in response to decision-making tasks, and come up with very sophisticated predictions about what men will actually do. This is especially so because men very often attempt to do the best they can in a decision-making task; that is, men attempt to behave as a normative model would prescribe. From this point of view, a normative model is simply an incomplete descriptive model.

This chapter is continually concerned with the interweaving of normative and descriptive models of decision processes. But its primary emphasis is on the normative rather than the descriptive models, since the normative models are more profound, more explicit, and form the basis from which the descriptive models depart. We will try to make clear whether each theoretical concept is primarily normative, primarily descriptive, or both.

We need to specify one more taxonomic distinction among models for decision making. This distinction has been given various names: static versus dynamic decision theory, single-stage versus multistage decision processes, and others. We shall call it the distinction between the static and dynamic theories. Static theories are especially appropriate to some classes of decision tasks and dynamic theories are especially appropriate to others; hence we shall apply the static-dynamic distinction to tasks as well as to theories. A static theory applies to the following setting: the decision maker has a problem and a supply of information relevant to that problem. He considers that information and uses it to make a decision, receives some payoff or prize—and then the situation ends. The decision maker never has an opportunity to make a second decision in which he might make use of whatever he learned as a consequence of the first. A general explanation of how people make one-shot bets in horse-racing is a descriptive static theory. A dynamic theory, on the other hand, conceives that a decision maker faces a sequence of decisions that may or may not be related to one another, and that may or may not all seek the same goal. Almost any learning experiment requires a dynamic theory for its interpretation. Only the dynamic approach can hope to do justice to the complexity of the real world. But of course the dynamic approach is intellectually and mathematically far more complicated than the static approach. The simpler static approach is far more tractable and it is easier to understand, and many, though by no means all, decision tasks are so designed that the static approach makes considerable sense for them in spite of its air of unreality. In addition, static theories can serve as a basis for the more realistic but more complicated dynamic theories.

This paper introduces all of the basic ideas of decision theory in the context of the static approach, and thereafter turns its attention to the dynamic approach.

## AN EXAMPLE

Suppose that, some Sunday morning, you decide to spend the afternoon either playing golf or sailing. You can't decide which activity to choose because the weather is uncertain; the sky is overcast and a mild wind is blowing. If the sky clears and the wind stays the same or increases, the afternoon will be ideal for sailing. Golf will be less desirable because the wind will interfere with your modest golfing skill. But if the wind dies, golf will be preferable to sailing.

There is also some possibility of rain in the afternoon. If it rains and the wind holds, sailing in your open cockpit boat will be unpleasant, but so will golf. If it rains and the wind dies, sailing will be impossible and uncomfortable. If you are golfing when the rain starts, you can at least make a quick dash for the clubhouse.

The problem as stated above is obviously oversimplified. In a real problem of this kind, there are many more factors to consider, for instance the possibility of lightning striking your boat's mast if the rain turns out to be a thunderstorm. You may also want to consider other kinds of weather, or various wind velocities. However, our simplified version makes an adequate example.

The factors that you must consider fall into two reasonably distinct categories: certain and uncertain. You can predict with near certainty that playing golf on a windy day will result in a poor score. You are positive that if the wind dies while you are sailing you will miss supper. If the wind does not pick up until the evening, you will have to sail the boat back at night, and your boat has no lights. But you are very uncertain about the afternoon's weather. Thus, you must make the best possible choice without knowing the answer to the crucial question. Moreover, in this example, you cannot hope to find out the answer, or even to reduce substantially your uncertainty about it, before making your decision. (You could consult the weatherman, but he predicted the whole day would be clear and sunny.)

Decision situations in which uncertainty is important can usefully be characterized by a matrix such as Figure 3.1. In it, the rows, labeled $A_1$ and $A_2$ (for Act 1 and Act 2) represent the two possible courses of action, "go sailing" and "go golfing," respectively. The columns represent the possible states that nature might be in, or will be in. A state of nature, in this context, means the state of any relevant variable that the decision maker cannot control. If this definition seems vague now, it will be clarified in examples later.

In this case, the states consist of the possible types of weather that will occur in the afternoon. For our example, there are, of course, a theoretically infinite number of states possible. For convenience, however, we have classified them into 4 categories. The first, $S_1$, is wind and no rain. The second, $S_2$, is no wind and no rain. The third, $S_3$, is wind and rain, while the fourth, $S_4$, is rain and no wind.

For each act by you and each state there will be a final result, or outcome. These outcomes are the cells of the matrix in Figure 3.1 (a). Outcome $O_{11}$, for example, is the result of your choosing to go sailing and the weather's being windy with no rain. Presumably, this is a very desirable outcome—a fine afternoon of sailing.

Before you can make a decision, you should consider the value, or attractiveness, or desirability, or utility of each possible outcome. A matrix like that in Figure 3.1(b), in which each cell contains the value of that outcome expressed in some convenient unit, is called a payoff matrix. In filling out a payoff matrix, you should consider all relevant aspects of the outcome. For example, the value of $O_{11}$ depends not only on the desirability of sailing itself, but also on the consequences to your physical well-being, for you might get a sunburn or become very tired. The outcome $O_{24}$, rain forcing you to stop your golf, has a value that depends not only on the unattractiveness of having to stop golfing, but also on the value of

| ACTS | STATES: Windy, no rain $S_1$ | No wind, no rain $S_2$ | Windy, rainy $S_3$ | No wind, rainy $S_4$ |
|---|---|---|---|---|
| Go sailing, $A_1$ | Good sailing $O_{11}$ | Becalmed $O_{12}$ | Uncomfortable sailing $O_{13}$ | Uncomfortable and becalmed $O_{14}$ |
| Go golfing, $A_2$ | Poor golfing $O_{21}$ | Good golfing $O_{22}$ | Stop golfing, take shelter $O_{23}$ | Stop golfing, take shelter $O_{24}$ |

(a)

| | $S_1$ | $S_2$ | $S_3$ | $S_4$ |
|---|---|---|---|---|
| $A_1$ | 100 | 20 | −20 | −50 |
| $A_2$ | 30 | 90 | −35 | −35 |

(b)

*Figure 3.1.* An example illustrating acts, states, outcomes, and payoffs assigned to outcomes. (a) Acts, states, and outcomes; (b) Payoff matrix.

spending the remainder of the afternoon at the bar of the clubhouse.

In real world contexts, filling out such a payoff matrix may be very difficult. For one thing, it often requires reduction of values on quite different dimensions to common units. How much sunburn is worth an hour of sailing? As another example, suppose you wish to decide which of two secretaries to hire. The fact that one requires $100 a month more salary than the other is easy to translate into dollars. But suppose that one takes shorthand at only 50 words per minute, while the other can take 150; suppose too, that one is a gorgeous unmarried redhead while the other is middle-aged and matronly. It will tax your introspective abilities to reduce these facts to a single value unit. The example also illustrates the second difficulty: many entries in payoff matrices are themselves contingent on still other uncertainties. How long is the redhead likely to remain an unmarried secretary rather than a married housewife?

Moreover, it is not enough to reduce the inconsistent value dimensions of the real world to a single dimension. As the dollar scale suggests, the judged or subjective value that controls a decision may not be at all identical with the objective value that may be entered in a payoff matrix. The 12-year-old will chase a wind-blown dollar bill for a block; the blasé millionaire who dropped it may not care enough to watch it as it whirls away. The technical name for subjective value is *utility;* it is the utilities, not the objective values, of outcomes that control and should control decisions. For that reason, payoff matrices should contain utilities rather than objective measures of value. But for modest amounts of money it is frequently reasonable to suppose utility nearly linear with dollars; for that reason, it is sometimes convenient to fill in payoff matrices in dollars. In this chapter we will consider utility in much more detail and will discuss the problem of reducing many value dimensions to one as a practical problem in the technology of decision making.

To return to the sailing–golfing example, you need another

set of numbers in addition to those entered in the payoff matrix. You often have quite a lot of information about the state nature is in. You may not be sure what the weather will be in the afternoon, but you may have good reason to believe that the state "wind and no rain" is more likely than the other states, and that "wind and rain" is the least likely. Such information can be stated more precisely as a set of numbers called probabilities, one for each state; each probability is a quantitative measure of your opinion about how likely that state is to be the true one, or more technically, to *obtain.* Such numbers should be assigned in such a way that they sum to one across a mutually exclusive and exhaustive set of states, that is a set of states of which one and only one must obtain. Such a set is called a *partition.* If in your opinion this coin must land heads or tails, and your probability that it will land heads is 0.5, then your probability that it will land tails, the other state in the partition, should also be 0.5.

The use of the word "probability" as a name for numbers that describe opinions is controversial. More traditionally the probability of heads would be defined as the ratio of heads to total flips as the number of total flips increases without limit. Such a definition of probability is called the *frequentistic* definition, since it appeals to the relative frequency of heads to total flips. Obviously relative frequencies should affect opinions. But many opinions may be described by numbers between zero and one that behave in all ways like probabilities except that they have nothing in particular to do with repeated or repeatable events. (Example: what is the probability that the next President of the United States will have at least one teen-age daughter? A count of the number of past Presidents with teen-age daughters would be a rather inappropriate approach to the answer.) Such opinion-describing probabilities are called *personal* probabilities; whenever the word probability is used in this chapter, personal probability is meant. A strong case can be made for the assertion that no other kind of probability is meaningful, and we happen to believe that—but the arguments between the personalists and the frequentists, although they make interesting reading, are irrelevant to this chapter. The bibliography contains some references.

The sailing–golfing example includes all the elements of the formal analysis of every decision situation under uncertainty. First, there is a set of available acts, or things that the decision maker may do. Such acts are defined so as to be mutually exclusive. Next, there is a set of possible states of the world that affect the consequences of the acts. Associated with each combination of an act and a state there is an outcome; associated with each outcome there is a payoff. And the decision maker has an opinion about how likely each state is. Such opinions are always to some degree vague in the complex decision situations found outside the gambling casinos and psychological laboratories. The remainder of this article examines these elements of the formal analysis of decision situations in more detail, and discusses procedures for obtaining appropriate numbers for use in real decisions. One idea not yet introduced will dominate the discussion: how the decision maker can choose the *best* course of action available to him. It will take some effort to decide what we mean by the best course of action, and even more effort to show why the best course of action should be taken even though it may often not lead to the best possible result.

The discussion of what we mean by best will inevitably be dry and abstract, but we cannot avoid it. When it is over, we can return to livelier topics.

## THE CONCEPT OF RATIONALITY

We all feel that decisions should be made rationally, but are unsure of what we mean by rational. A reading of the formal mathematical and philosophical literature about rationality unfortunately only increases the confusion. Perhaps 20 or 30 criteria by which a rational decision can be distinguished from an irrational one have been proposed and seriously studied. Each, considered separately, claims to be a rule that no one would willingly violate when the stakes are high. Unfortunately, some of them contradict others. Several consistent lists of 6 or 7 of these criteria (mathematicians call them axioms) have been proposed as definitions of rationality, but no proposer has been able to persuade his colleagues that all criteria on his list belong there and that no others do.

This chapter makes no attempt at an exhaustive list of criteria of rationality. We will, however, list 4 propositions that appear on most lists and that seem to contain the essence of the idea, one more that, while more controversial, we wish to defend as rational, and a rule or theorem that is the goal of most definitions of rationality.

The first uncontroversial principle of rationality is sometimes called *decidability*. Given any two outcomes, *A* and *B*, a decision maker should be able to tell whether he prefers *A* to *B*, or *B* to *A*, or whether he is indifferent about them. Do you prefer steak to lobster, lobster to steak, or have you no preference? A similar principle applies to acts, and to the probabilities of states. Though the formal consequences of this principle are profound, it seems empirically trivial; we cannot conceive of a real-world situation that would violate it.

The second uncontroversial principle of rationality is more important, both theoretically and empirically. It is called the principle of transitivity, and it too is primarily defined on outcomes but applies also to acts and probabilities. If you prefer Outcome A to Outcome B and Outcome B to Outcome C, it would be irrational of you to prefer Outcome C to Outcome A. If you prefer steak to lobster and lobster to pork chops, then you should prefer steak to pork chops. If you preferred pork chops to steak, you would exhibit intransitivity. We all have in fact behaved intransitively on occasion, so transitivity clearly fails as a description of human behavior. But we ordinarily would admit that such intransitive patterns of judgment or decision are mistakes, and that truly rational choices would be transitive. In fact, a man who was deliberately and systematically intransitive could be used as a money pump. You might say to him: "Here, I'll give you pork chops. Now, for a penny I'll take the pork chops back and substitute lobster for them." Since he prefers lobster to pork chops, he accepts. Next you offer to replace lobster with steak for another penny, and again he accepts. You complete the cycle by offering to replace steak with pork chops for still another penny, and since he prefers pork chops to steak, he again accepts, and thus is 3¢ poorer, back where he started, and ready for another 3¢ round.

Presumably he will continue to be a money pump till he is pumped broke—or till he learns the wisdom of not being determinedly intransitive. The fact that we have never met such a money pump suggests that no one is in fact deliberately and systematically intransitive.

The third relatively uncontroversial principle of rationality is concerned with rules for determining preferences, rather than with consistency relations among preferences. The principle of *dominance* (more technically, weak dominance) is simple, sweeping, and common to all conceptions of rationality. If for every possible state of the world Act A produces at least as desirable an outcome as Act B, and if for at least one state of the world the outcome of Act A is definitely better than that of Act B, you should never prefer Act B to Act A. For example: if you would prefer a convertible to a closed top car except when it is raining, and even then the two seem equally desirable on all dimensions including price, then you should certainly get a convertible. A general, two-act, three-state example is shown in Figure 3.2. Dominance does not occur in the example of Figure 3.1. One function of this principle is to eliminate certain acts, those dominated by other acts, from serious consideration. In some happy situations, dominance will eliminate all but one act; that will always be true in situations in which no uncertainty exists, for example. But ordinarily dominance directly applied is not enough; more sophisticated principles of rational choice are required.

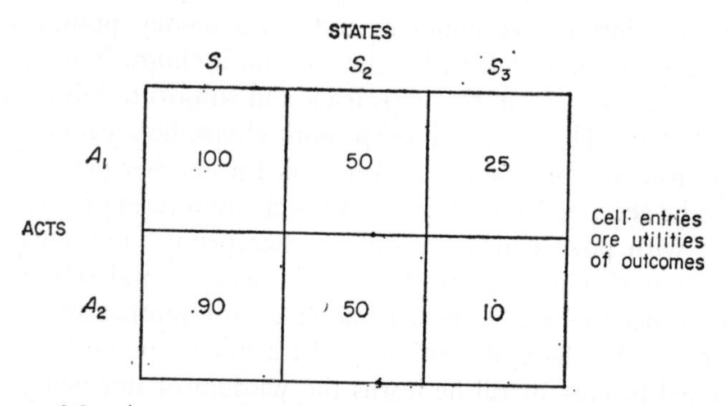


*Figure 3.2.* An example of dominance. If $S_1$ obtains, $A_1$ is preferred to $A_2$; if $S_2$ obtains, $A_1$ is just as good as $A_2$; if $S_3$ obtains, $A_1$ is preferred to $A_2$. Therefore, $A_1$ should be preferred to $A_2$.

The fourth relatively uncontroversial principle, called the sure-thing principle, states that when you are making a choice between two possible actions, outcomes that do not depend on your choice should not influence your choice. Suppose, for example, that you wish to invest $500 in stocks. You have your choice of two companies, Stable Industries and Speculation, Inc. Stable is a much safer stock; if the economy becomes worse, you probably will not lose more than a hundred dollars or so if you invest in it. If times become better, however, you cannot expect to make much money either. On the other hand, the Speculation stock can be expected nearly to double in value if times become much better, but you will lose most of your investment if times become worse. An example of an outcome that does not depend on your choice would be a market collapse as in 1929; in this case, you would lose your entire $500 no matter which stock you invested in. Figure 3.3 illustrates this situation. In this case, since the outcome is the same no matter which choice you make, this possibility should not influence your choice of which stock to buy. It may, of course, influence you in deciding whether or not to buy stock at all, but once you have decided to buy, it should have no more influence on your choice.

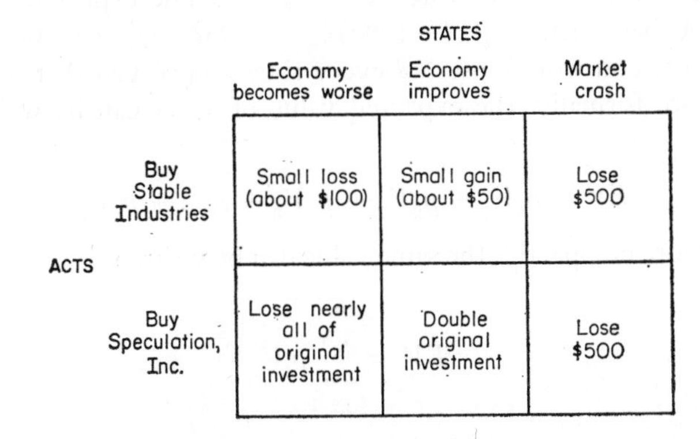

| ACTS \ STATES | Economy becomes worse | Economy improves | Market crash |
|---|---|---|---|
| Buy Stable Industries | Small loss (about $100) | Small gain (about $50) | Lose $500 |
| Buy Speculation, Inc. | Lose nearly all of original investment | Double original investment | Lose $500 |

*Figure 3.3.* An illustration of the "sure-thing" principle. Because the outcomes in the right column are identical, the possibility of a market crash should not influence the choice between the two stocks.

We must pause for two paragraphs to introduce one of the two mathematical ideas of this paper: the idea of an *expectation.* This idea, a fundamental concept of probability theory, is nothing other than a weighted average. Consider the following bet. You will throw a fair coin three times. If it comes up heads all three times, we shall pay you $1. If it fails to come up heads all three times, you will pay us 15¢. What is the average payment to you on each trial, over a large number of trials, of that bet? Clearly it is larger than − *15¢* and smaller than +100¢. Equally clearly you could not find it by adding those two numbers and dividing by 2, since the −15¢ will happen far more often than the +100¢. The payoffs should be weighted by the probability of obtaining each; such a weighted average is called an expectation. In this example the quantities being averaged are values, and so the average is called an expected value. To calculate the expected value of that bet, we need only use a little probability theory to find that the probability of three heads in three tosses of an unbiased coin is $\frac{1}{2} \times \frac{1}{2} \times \frac{1}{2} = \frac{1}{8}$; the probability of not getting three heads must therefore be $1 - \frac{1}{8} = \frac{7}{8}$. The expected value of the bet, then, is $\frac{1}{8}(+100¢) + \frac{7}{8}(-15¢) = -\frac{5}{8}¢$. On the average, you would lose $\frac{5}{8}¢$ every time you played that bet.

More formally, the expected value of a bet can be written as

$$EV = p_1V_1 + p_2V_2 + p_3V_3 + \ldots + p_nV_n$$

Or, more compactly, the same value can be written

$$EV = \sum_{i=1}^{n} p_iV_i$$

Of course $p_1$ is the probability that State 1, of the $n$ different states included in the partition, will turn out to be the one that obtains, and $V_1$ is the payoff (which may be negative) that will accrue to the decision-maker if that state obtains, and similarly for the other $p$'s and $V$'s. The symbol

$$\sum_{i=1}^{n}$$

is called an operator; translated into words, it reads "There are $n$ different quantities of the form specified by the symbols immediately following. Find their sum." When the place at which the running index $i$ begins (in this case, at 1) or ends (in this case, at $n$) is obvious from context, it is permissible to write

$$\sum_{i}$$

or even

Σ

Not all expectations are expected values. The expectation of any kind of quantity involved in a bet-like situation can be calculated. We shall be primarily concerned with expected utilities rather than expected values. An expected utility is calculated in exactly the same way as any other expectation, but the quantities being averaged are utilities rather than objective quantities such as numbers of dollars, bushels of wheat, kisses, or ice cream cones.

The four principles of rationality listed above, combined with some others that are of minor importance and are not worth listing here, turn out to imply a very strong and sweeping conclusion. The conclusion is that a rational decision-maker chooses that available act whose expected utility is greatest. In effect, the substance of the conclusion is that a consistent set of weights that will behave like probabilities of states and will be consistent with the rational decision-maker's choices can always be found.

We have played a mathematician's trick on you. We led you along, presenting premise after premise, each apparently innocent and acceptable. Then all of a sudden we showed (or rather asserted, since this chapter is no place to present formal proofs of theorems) that these individually innocent premises jointly imply a very strong and perhaps controversial conclusion. Now you face the alternatives of accepting the conclusion or rejecting at least one of the premises. (Or you could dig deeply enough into the mathematics of the matter to check up on our assertions; the basic reference is an excellent book by L. J. Savage named *The Foundations of Statistics*.)

Our conclusion, a controversial one that is coming to be accepted by most students of the theory of decision making, is that there is really only one candidate for the title of optimal or rational strategy for making decisions. That is the strategy of choosing the act with the largest expected utility; more formally, it is called the strategy of maximizing expected utility. We shall call it the EU strategy, or *EU model*, for short. To apply this model, you assign a numerical utility to each outcome and determine a numerical probability for each state. Then multiply the utility of the outcome of an act if a given state obtains by the probability of that state, and sum these products over the various states. Do this for each available act, and choose the act for which that sum is largest. If you are offered the bet that turned out to have an expected value of $-5/8$¢, and can accept or reject it, and if for you the utilities of the amounts of money involved are equal to the dollar values, you should reject the bet, since the expected utility of rejecting the bet is 0, which is larger than $-5/8$.

Although we shall often use bets as examples, the EU model applies to all kinds of choices. Utility is in some decisions closely related to nonfinancial variables: the probability of survival, fuel remaining, palatability of food—any dimension or combination of dimensions that has value for you.

In terms of the sailing–golfing example, suppose that we call the local weatherman and ask him for a revised forecast for the afternoon. Specifically, you ask him for the probabilities of the 4 types of weather of interest to you. He gives you these values:

| | |
|---|---|
| $S_1$, windy and no rain, | 0.3 |
| $S_2$, no wind, no rain, | 0.4 |
| $S_3$, windy and rainy, | 0.1 |
| $S_4$, no wind, rain, | 0.2 |

Then, the expected utility of $A_1$, sailing, is

$$0.3\,(100) + 0.4(20) + 0.1(-20) + 0.2(-50) = 26$$

The expected utility of $A_2$, golfing, is

$$0.3(30) + 0.4(90) + 0.1(-35) + 0.2(-35) = 34.5$$

And so, being an EU maximizer, you decide to play golf.

Before leaving this principle of rational choice, we must digress long enough to discuss its main competitor. A branch of mathematical analysis called the theory of games gave birth to a proposed optimal strategy called the *minimax* principle. A person applying the minimax principle acts as if, no matter what act he may choose, nature will subsequently turn out to be in that state which is least favorable for that act. The appropriate strategy under such conditions is to choose that act whose worst possible outcome is least unpleasant—in more concise language, to minimize the maximum loss (hence the name minimax). For decisions in which nature or chance is the "opponent," such a strategy is unduly pessimistic, and indeed it was not proposed primarily for "games against nature." In competitive situations in which the decision-maker faces a rational opponent, the strategy makes more sense. But in competitive games, also, the minimax strategy turns out to be too conservative; it gives up most possibilities of exploiting an opponent's mistakes. It is safe to say that a minimax businessman or poker player would soon go broke. The minimax principle is attractive to frequentists because it does not require its user to know the probabilities of the states, or, in competitive games, to know the probability that the opponent will use each strategy open to him. But the personalistic view of probabilities invites you to use whatever you may know about your opponent to judge the probabilities that he will use the various strategies open to him, rather than your adopting a strategy equivalent to assuming that he will always use the strategy that you consider least favorable to you.

We must add one more principle of rationality, more controversial, more technical, and less important than those so far discussed. The principle of *column linearity* applies to payoff matrices like Figures 3.1 and 3.2, and in effect it asserts that the addition of a constant to each entry in a column of a payoff matrix should not change a rational decision-maker's preferences among the acts. Such transformations on payoff matrices that should not affect a decision-maker's preferences are called *strategically irrelevant* transformations. Suppose we promise to pay you a dollar if the weather turns out to be windy and rainy regardless of which act you choose, golfing or sailing. That gift, according to the principle of column linearity, should not at all affect your decision. Since your choice makes absolutely no difference to whether or not you get the bonus dollar, the possibility that you might get it should not affect that choice.

The principle as stated requires two qualifications. It assumes that the gift does not change the set of possible acts (for example, by enabling you to pay the green fee which you couldn't pay before). It also assumes that the entries in the payoff matrix are utilities, or subjective values, not objective values. A gift of a million dollars might change your gambling behavior by changing your judgments about the value of a dollar.

A convenient consequence of column linearity (and the reason why it is presented here while other principles with at least as much claim for inclusion in a discussion of rationality are not) is that it simplifies immensely the preparation of payoff matrices. It says that it is always permissible to add (or subtract) a constant to a column of a payoff matrix; and the constant may change from one column to the next. In particular, it is always appropriate to make a cell in each column 0 by subtracting its value from all cells in its column, as has been done in Figure 3.4. So a decision-maker need not determine in some absolute sense how valuable the various possible outcomes of a decision may be; the judgment need only be a relative one of how much more or less valuable one possible outcome is than another, given that a particular state obtains. Even such relative judgments are hard enough; the absolute judgments would be next to impossible. Column linearity is closely related to, but goes beyond, the idea to be discussed later that the origins of utility functions are arbitrary.

The philosophically minded will have noticed that these principles of rationality have to do with means rather than ends. They are concerned with the implementation of value systems, not with what values are worth implementing. We are

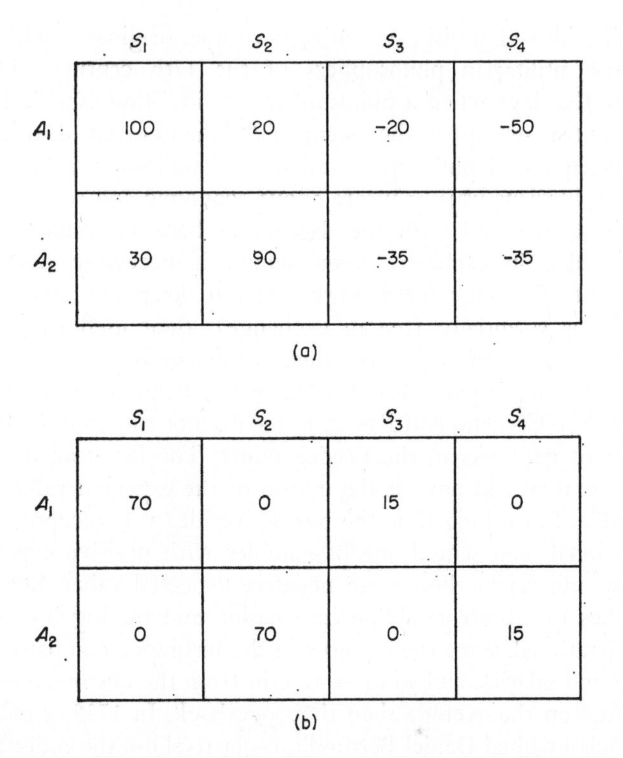

| | $S_1$ | $S_2$ | $S_3$ | $S_4$ |
|---|---|---|---|---|
| $A_1$ | 100 | 20 | -20 | -50 |
| $A_2$ | 30 | 90 | -35 | -35 |

(a)

| | $S_1$ | $S_2$ | $S_3$ | $S_4$ |
|---|---|---|---|---|
| $A_1$ | 70 | 0 | 15 | 0 |
| $A_2$ | 0 | 70 | 0 | 15 |

(b)

*Figure 3.4.* Transformation of the payoff matrix in Figure 3.1 by adding a (possibly negative) constant to each column. The transformed matrix is equivalent to the original matrix. (a) Original payoff matrix; (b) Transformed matrix.

inclined to feel that disputes about tastes are important, that some tastes are more desirable than others. But this kind of speculation is not our purpose here.

We must reiterate that this discussion of rationality has to do with what a decision-maker ought to do. What real decision-makers *do* do, and the degree to which it agrees with what they ought to do, is another story, and a much less abstract one. We turn to it next.

The idea of utility, or subjective value, originated with the British utilitarian philosophers of the 17th century. Those were the days when a philosopher was indistinguishable from a scientist—except to the extent of the then-current distinction between moral philosophy and natural philosophy. Actually, the utilitarians usually wrote about economic and social questions. Concerned with the distinction between value in use and value in exchange (you would if necessary pay any amount of money for enough water to keep you alive—but water is essentially free in exchange), they used the word "utility" to mean subjective value, or value in use.

Probability theory had begun, in the hands of mathematicians like Cardano and Pascal, as an attempt to guide the decisions of gamblers in the French court. The key tool in such advice, then and now, is the notion of the expected value of a gamble. For a long time the persuasive idea was accepted that a rational man would accept gambles with positive expected value and reject those with negative expected value. But this implies that both gambling in a casino and buying insurance are irrational, since the casino and the insurance company pay rent and salaries, and so must take in from the customers more money on the average than they pay back. In 1738, a mathematician named Daniel Bernoulli, eager to show the rationality of buying insurance, introduced the concept of utility and suggested that a decision-maker should maximize not expected value but expected utility. He further argued that a dollar is more valuable to a beggar than to a millionaire, and in general that the value of one more unit of anything is inversely proportional to the number of units you already have. This idea turns out to imply that utility is a logarithmic function of quantity. That is, if you arbitrarily call the utility of a dollar one utile (a name for the unit of utility, as pound is a name for a unit of weight) and the utility value of $10 two utiles, then the utility of $100 will be 3 utiles; $1000, 4 utiles; $10,000, 5 utiles; etc. In this interpretation, if you have a total fortune of $10,000, it takes a gift of $10 to make you as happy as a gift of

10¢ made you when your total fortune was only $100. A man with such a value system would be willing to pay a small amount (for example, an insurance premium) for certain in order to eliminate the danger of losing a much larger amount, even though the premium is larger than the expected value of the risk. He should not, however, be willing to buy a lottery ticket—not even a fair one. More sophisticated utility functions have been proposed that make the simultaneous purchase of insurance and lottery tickets "rational," but we shall not discuss them.

As an interesting sidelight on intellectual history, this 1738 paper by Daniel Bernoulli might appropriately be called the starting place of psychophysics. More than a hundred years later, Gustav Theodor Fechner, a German physiologist-philosopher much concerned about the relationship between mind and body, read Bernoulli's paper. It occurred to Fechner that the logarithmic relationship between a stimulus magnitude and perceived magnitude that Bernoulli had proposed for utility might well hold for other perceived magnitudes as well. Fechner knew of some physiological work on just noticeable differences by Ernst Heinrich Weber that seemed consistent with such an interpretation, so he devised a mathematical derivation that seemed to link Weber's findings with the concept of a logarithmic relationship between any stimulus magnitude and the resulting perceived magnitude, and thus was born what is nowadays called Fechner's Law. (We say "seemed to link" because, in fact, Fechner's mathematical derivation is based on two premises that are inconsistent with each other and so is mathematically incorrect. The formal relationship between Weber's Law and the logarithmic relationship called Fechner's Law does exist, but Fechner failed to demonstrate it.) Of course Fechner gave Bernoulli due credit, but most psychophysicists typically have not looked behind Fechner. Should that logarithmic relationship between stimulus magnitude and perceived magnitude perhaps be called Bernoulli's Law? (Perhaps it should, but it won't be.)

To go back to utility theory, little happened in its development between 1738 and 1944, when von Neumann and Morgenstern published their famous book on the theory of games. Since the entries in payoff matrices should be utilities rather than objective values, von Neumann and Morgenstern felt compelled to deal with the concept of utility. They did so in a first chapter (plus an appendix, in later editions of the book) that has probably had more influence than any other part of that epochal work, even though it was of only minor importance to the authors. Their basic contribution was to stand Bernoulli's idea on its head. They suggested that instead of specifying a utility function that would seem somehow appropriate and then prescribing behavior on the basis of it, one could instead observe actual behavior and infer from it the utility function that gave rise to it, assuming that the behaver was in fact behaving rationally.

The essence of their idea is the following. Suppose you must choose whether or not to play a bet in which you will either win or lose $100. If you refuse to play the bet, no money changes hands—that is, your "winnings" in this case would be 0 dollars. Presumably, your choice of whether or not to play the bet will depend primarily on the probability of winning. If you are almost certain to win, you will prefer to play the bet. If the probability of winning is gradually increased from 0 to 1, your aversion toward playing the bet should decrease gradually until, when the probability of winning becomes large enough, you will prefer to play the bet. There is, then, some probability of winning, such that if the actual probability of winning is smaller than this you will prefer not to play the bet, while, if the actual probability is larger, you will prefer to play it. At exactly that probability, you are presumably indifferent about playing and not playing; that is, playing and not playing are equally attractive to you. Von Neumann and Morgenstern proposed that equally attractive bets could be found by careful interrogation. They assumed, further, that if you were indifferent about playing and not playing, your expected utility of playing would be exactly equal to the expected utility of not playing. In terms of an equation this becomes:

$$p^* \cdot u(\$100) + (1 - p^*) \cdot u(-\$100) = u(\$0)$$

Where $p^*$ is the value of the probability of winning that makes you indifferent to playing and not playing, $u(\$X)$ represents the utility of $X$ dollars, and a minus $X$ represents a loss, rather than a gain, of $X$ dollars.

If we artibrarily define the utility of losing \$100 as 0 and the utility of not playing the bet as 1, the equation then becomes

$$p^* \cdot u(\$100) + (1 - p^*) \cdot (0) = 1$$

or

$$u(\$100) = 1/p^*$$

For the moment we will simply assume that the value of $p^*$ is known without worrying about exactly *how* it is obtained.

Note that in order to find the utility of 1 of the 3 amounts of money involved it was necessary to set arbitrarily the utilities of the other 2 amounts of money. If, for example, the utility of losing \$100 had been given a value of $-1$ instead of 0, the utility of winning \$100 would have been $(2 - p^*) / p^*$ instead of $1/p^*$. Once 2 utility values have been arbitrarily assigned, the utility of any other amount of money is then determined by that assignment and your preferences. Suppose, for example, that we wanted to find your utility of winning \$200. There are a number of ways we could proceed. One technique would be to ask you to choose between 2 alternatives. If you chose the first alternative you would play a bet in which you would win either \$200 or nothing. If you chose the second alternative you would receive \$100 as an outright gift. Again, preference between these two alternatives should depend on the probability of winning, and again there should be a probability, $p^{**}$, that makes you indifferent to the two alternatives. Since the utility of \$100 is already known to be $1/p^*$, the equation becomes.

$$p^{**} \cdot u(\$200) + (1 - p^{**}) \cdot (1) = 1/p^*$$

$$u(\$200) = (1/p^{**}) \cdot (p^{**} - 1 + 1/p^*)$$

Note that the utility of winning 0 dollars is the same as the utility of not playing the original bet above. The situation here is similar to that found in measuring temperature. The Fahrenheit scale arbitrarily assigns certain values to the freezing and boiling points of water. The centigrade scale arbitrarily assigns other values. Once these two values have been assigned, however, they determine all of the other values of the scale.

This idea of von Neumann and Morgenstern had two useful consequences. First, it firmly (perhaps too firmly) established the thought that a man's utility functions are up to him, and that an adviser on decisions should discover his client's relevant value systems, rather than prescribe them. Secondly, it made this thought practical by making explicit a technique of measuring utility by observing a man's choices among bets that had been implicit in Bernoulli's idea—and had been at least partially explicit in obscure papers published in 1928 by Ramsey and in 1937 by de Finetti.

A number of theoretical and experimental studies followed von Neumann and Morgenstern's book, using techniques analogous to those implied by our description of their idea. It soon became apparent that their idea had something basically wrong with it. When the techniques for inferring utility functions from gambles were applied to college student subjects choosing among real gambles, inconsistencies arose that could not be explained by even very sophisticated utility functions. If behaving in a way consistent with von Neumann and Morgenstern's idea was rational, these students were not. The trouble seemed to be that the weights used in calculating the weighted averages deviated in a systematic way from what they "ought" to be. In one series of experiments by Edwards, most subjects behaved as though an event that would happen about half of the time had a probability of about $\frac{9}{16}$, while an event that would happen about $\frac{3}{4}$ of the time had a probability of about $\frac{11}{16}$. If these probabilities were substituted for the "true" ones and the utility of money were assumed equal to its objective value, the EU model fitted the data pretty well—though by no means perfectly.

Is it irrational to behave as though the probability of getting heads when flipping a coin is $\frac{9}{16}$ instead of $\frac{1}{2}$? It certainly is if you behave as though the probability of getting tails is also $\frac{9}{16}$. But would it be irrational to behave as though the probability of heads were $\frac{9}{16}$ and the probability of tails $\frac{7}{16}$? That obviously depends on what you mean by "probability" and by "rational." We have explored rationality; now we must explore probability. Later, we will return to the topic of utility in a more modern guise.

## PROBABILITY

We have already said that a controversy exists about probability, and that our position is the unpopular one. We must explore the issues to some extent, though of course we cannot do justice to their mathematical or philosophical depth.

In a very important sense, everyone agrees about what a probability is. It is a number between zero and one, inclusive. These numbers obey several laws, all derivable from the simple rule that the sum of the probabilities assigned to a mutually exclusive set of events one of which must happen, is one. The arguments arise not over what these mathematical properties are, but over the rules we should use in relating these mathematical properties to observations that we could make of the real world. Three kinds of observations relate to such numbers.

## 1. RELATIVE FREQUENCIES

If a coin is flipped a large number of times, the difference between the number of heads and the number of tails increases with the number of flips. It is very unlikely that that difference would ever be 0 for a fair coin, after any substantial number of flips (that is, 10 or more). But the ratio of the number of heads to the total number of flips will, for a fair coin, be very likely indeed to be very close to 0.5. For excellent but very technical reasons, that ratio itself cannot be thought of as the probability that the coin will fall heads. But one viewpoint about how to relate probabilities to observations defines the probability of a coin's falling heads as the limit that the ratio of heads to total tosses approaches as the number of tosses increases without limit (that is, approaches infinity). From this viewpoint, the ratio of heads to total tosses for a finite number of tosses, while not the probability, is what is called an unbiased estimator (that is, a good though fallible guess) of that probability.

Using this conception of probability, most uncertainties that men experience cannot be described by means of probabilities. Uncertainty about matters of fact is one example: What is the probability that the eighth president of the U.S. had more than three children? We do not know whether he did or not, and yet we would certainly accept an even-money bet that he did not, provided that its offerer were as ignorant as we. Moreover, it may be quite difficult to determine whether a particular relative frequency is an appropriate estimator of a probability. The coin toss is the textbook example of relative frequencies. But how should the coin be tossed? The successive tosses should be under "substantially identical" conditions. But the conditions cannot be absolutely identical, or the coin would come up the same way every time. How much variation in tossing procedure from one toss to another is permissible? What kinds of variation are permissible and what kinds are not? If these decisions are arbitrary and subjective, the frequentistic conception of probability loses most of its "objective" character. But the frequentistic position offers no further specification of what "substantially identical" means. Finally, the frequentistic position would almost never lead you to conclude that the probability of getting heads in tossing a coin was ½. In any reasonably long finite sequence of tosses, the relative frequency of heads will almost certainly not be ½; moreover, it will vary from one occasion to another and from one coin to the next. But a frequentist's best estimate of a probability is the observed relative frequency, so he is stuck with estimates like 521/1000, or 5187/10,000—unless he is wise enough to ignore or (preferably) not collect relative frequencies when he has a better basis for probabilistic judgment, as he does for symmetric coins.

## 2. SYMMETRY AND NECESSARY VIEWS

Some mathematicians have attempted to treat probability as a branch of logic and have argued that at least some probabilities are logically necessary. Such views hinge on various versions of the notion that some partitions are sufficiently symmetric so that all elements of the partition should be considered equally likely. For example, even for biased coins, the probability of flipping first heads and then tails is equal to the probability of flipping first tails and then heads. There must be something of at least psychological importance in this idea, since one of our major industries is built around it. Every popular form of gambling except betting on contests of strength or skill depends on devices like shuffled cards, perfectly cubical dice, or symmetrically laid-out roulette wheels. All such devices use visible symmetry to support the idea that the symmetric elements are equally likely. This conception of probability seems to us more reasonable than the frequentistic conception, but it too is of very limited applicability, and, when applicable, is very difficult to distinguish from the personalistic view.

## 3. THE PERSONALISTIC VIEW

You might be willing to say "Heads on the next flip of this coin has probability ½" if and only if you would as soon guess heads as not, even if there were some important reward for being right. Your verbal statement of probability and your choices among gambles are devices whereby you can report your opinion about the coin. Such consistent opinions, we think, are the essence of probability. Your opinions about a coin can of course differ from your neighbor's. Hence the personal in the phrase "personal probability." Any probability should in principle be indexed with the name of the person, or people, whose opinion it describes; that indexing is usually unexpressed unless there is a special reason to expect that people will disagree.

The personalistic approach permits just as meaningful a discussion of the probability of a unique event as of the probability of a repeatable event—if an event can appropriately be called repeatable. Your probability that the next toss of this coin will be heads, your probability that the next President of the United States will be a Democrat, your probability that the next child to be born in your family will be a boy, your probability that the last child to be born to one of us was a boy, and your probability that the 200th decimal digit of $\pi$ is a 7 —all of these probabilities are the same kind of quantity, though they vary widely in the degree to which relevant relative frequencies can be defined. From this point of view then, all uncertainties can appropriately be dealt with as probabilities. However, not all opinions about uncertain events can be dealt with as probabilities; opinions, to be treatable as probabilities, must be consistent, which turns out to mean no more than that they must add up to one.

The personal approach to probability does not imply that "your guess is as good as mine" about what a probability is. Although your initial opinion about the future behavior of a coin, or about any other uncertain hypothesis, may differ radically from your neighbor's, your opinion and his will ordinarily be so transformed by the application of Bayes' theorem (which will be discussed later) to the results of a series of relevant observations as to become nearly indistinguishable. This approximate merging of initially divergent opinions is, as some people see it, one reason why inferences from relative frequencies and other such data are considered "objective." Personal probabilities are sometimes dismissed by the argument that scientific or other knowledge cannot be mere opinion. But obviously no sharp lines separate the conjecture that many human cancers may be caused by viruses, the opinion that many are caused by smoking, and the "knowledge" that many have been caused by radiation.

## BAYES' THEOREM AND THE REVISION OF OPINION IN THE LIGHT OF INFORMATION

The mathematical definition of conditional probability of an event $D$ given another event $H$ is

$$P(D \mid H) = \frac{P(D \cap H)}{P(H)} \tag{3.1}$$

unless $P(H) = 0$. The symbol $P(D \cap H)$ means the probability that both $D$ and $H$ will occur. The symbols $D$ and $H$ could stand for anything, but they have been chosen because they are the initial letters of datum and hypothesis.

A little algebra applied to Equation 3.1 now leads to one form of Bayes' theorem:

$$P(H \mid D) = \frac{P(D \mid H) \quad P(H)}{P(D)} \tag{3.2}$$

provided $P(D)$ and $P(H)$ are not 0.

In Equation 3.2, $P(H)$ is the prior probability of some hypothesis $H$. Though not written so, it is a conditional probability; all probabilities are really conditional. It is the probability of $H$ conditional on all information about $H$ available prior to learning $D$. Similarly, $P(H \mid D)$, the posterior probability of $H$, is the probability of $H$ conditional on that same background knowledge together with $D$. Here $P(D \mid H)$ is formally the probability that the datum $D$ would be observed if the hypothesis $H$ were true. For a set of mutually exclusive and exhaustive hypotheses $H_i$, the $P(D \mid H_i)$ represent the impact of the datum $D$ on each of the hypotheses. Obtaining the values of $P(D \mid H)$ for each $D$ and $H$ is the key step in applying Bayes' theorem to any kind of revision of opinion in the light of information. In statistical applications, $P(D \mid H)$ is typically obtained by computation from a so-called statistical model (like the assumption that a set of observations is normally distributed).

The probability $P(D)$ is usually of little direct interest. It is typically calculated, or eliminated, as follows. The hypothesis $H$ is one of a list, or partition, of mutually exclusive and exhaustive hypotheses $H_i$. Since the definition of probability requires that

$$\sum_i P(H_i \mid D) = \sum_i P(H_i) = 1 \tag{3.3}$$

Equation 3.2 implies that

$$P(D) = \sum_i P(D \mid H_i)P(H_i) \tag{3.4}$$

The choice of the partition $H_i$ is of practical importance but largely arbitrary. For example, tomorrow will be "fair" or "foul," but these two hypotheses can themselves be subdivided and resubdivided. Equation 3.2 is of course true for all partitions, but is more useful for some than for others. In principle, a partition should always leave room for "some other" possibility. Since it would be difficult to obtain $P(D \mid H)$ for the hypothesis that "some other possibility" is the true one, this "catch-all" hypothesis is usually handled in part by studying the situation conditionally on denial of the catch-all and in part by informal appraisal of whether any of the explicit hypotheses fit the facts well enough to maintain this denial.

A particularly convenient version of Bayes' theorem for some of the applications to be discussed in this paper is the odds-likelihood ratio form. For two hypotheses, $H_A$ and $H_B$, and one datum $D$, Bayes' theorem may be written twice thus:

$$P(H_A \mid D) = \frac{P(D \mid H_A)\, P(H_A)}{P(D)} \tag{3.5}$$

$$P(H_B \mid D) = \frac{P(D \mid H_B)\, P(H_B)}{P(D)} \tag{3.6}$$

Dividing Equation 3.5 by 3.6, we obtain

$$\Omega_1 = L\, \Omega_0 \tag{3.7}$$

In Equation 3.7, $\Omega_0$, the prior odds, is simply the ratio of the prior probability of $H_A$ to that of $H_B$. The same ratio after observation of D is $\Omega_1$; it is called the posterior odds. The ratio $L = P(D \mid H_A) \,/\, P(D \mid H_B)$ is called the likelihood ratio. The word "odds" here means exactly what it does at the race track, and the notion of likelihood ratio is just what it is in classical statistics. Equation 3.6 is as valid and appropriate a way of writing Bayes' theorem as is Equation 3.2—and in some applications is considerably more convenient.

There are many other ways of writing Bayes' theorem. The ways presented here have all been for discrete partitions, but it is equally possible to write Bayes' theorem for continuously variable hypotheses and continuously variable data, such as temperatures, weights, psychophysical judgments, or even probabilities. (Yes, the probability of a probability is a perfectly meaningful idea, and such probabilities of probabilities can be modified on the basis of evidence in exactly the same way that any other variety of opinion can be modified on the basis of evidence.)

Bayes' theorem is an elementary consequence of the fact

that probabilities add up to one. It is neither deep nor controversial. Nevertheless, a school of statistical thought called the Bayesian approach is currently responsible for one of the most vigorous scientific controversies in years. A part of the reason for the controversy is simply that the Bayesian approach leads to some practical conclusions that are heretical from the point of view of orthodox or classical statistics—such as the conclusion that it is appropriate procedure and indeed good science to collect data until you have enough to prove your point, and then to stop. But a more fundamental reason for controversy is that Bayes' theorem, like other normative models for human behavior, prescribes how men should think. More precisely, it specifies certain internal consistency relationships among opinions. All of these internal consistency relationships reduce, in one way or another, to the requirement that probabilities should add up to one. Nevertheless, they are not all behaviorally similar, even though their mathematical roots are the same, and they can appropriately be studied in quite different ways.

The static and the dynamic approaches to the problem of whether or not opinions are consistent are considerably more precisely differentiated here than they are in many other parts of decision theory. Static approaches seem well confined to examination of the question of whether opinions or judged probabilities do in fact add up to one; such studies make no use of Bayes' theorem. They may also inquire whether different methods of observing these opinions do or do not agree (in general, they do not). The dynamic studies, on the other hand, examine how opinions are changed by evidence. Here, of course, Bayes' theorem is the natural normative model with which to compare human performance, and the direct question of additivity assumes only secondary importance. A third question, somewhat unrelated to these first two, is whether probability opinions are numerically identical with, or close to, relevant relative frequencies.

## PSYCHOPHYSICAL ESTIMATES OF RELATIVE FREQUENCY

A number of experiments have examined the question of whether human beings can effectively estimate relative frequencies, simultaneously or sequentially presented, when the elements in the relative frequency for one reason or another cannot easily be counted. Philip (1947), in a rather primitive experiment of this kind, found extremely close agreement between displayed relative frequency and estimates. So, in more sophisticated experiments, did Stevens and Galanter (1957) and Shuford (1961). Perhaps the most elaborate experiment of this kind was performed by Robinson. Whereas Philip, Stevens and Galanter, and Shuford presented events simultaneously, Robinson (1962) used sequential presentation. Robinson sat his subjects in front of two lights, one or the other of which flashed once in each second (or other unit of time). The subject controlled a tracking handle with a meter slaved to it, and was asked to estimate continuously the probability that the right light would flash. The changes in probability were all actually step changes, but the subjects expected various kinds of changes and thought that they in fact had observed slow and steady ones as well as sharp and discontinuous ones. Performance in this task was remarkable. Subjects zeroed in on each new relative frequency quickly and with no substantial bias; the estimates with which they ended up were seldom off by as much as 2 percent. The conclusion from these relatively simple studies is that human beings are very competent estimators of observed relative frequencies—at least when there are only two classes of events to consider as was the case in all of these experiments. However, a series of studies by Erlick (1959, 1960, 1961) has shown that several factors other than displayed proportion will affect subjects' estimates of relative frequency. Some of these factors for studies involving two events are the difference in proportion between the two events, sample size, run structure or clustering of similar events in the sample, rate of presentation, and subjects' expectancy about the sample size. Whether human beings would be good at estimating 5 or 10 or 20 simultaneously displayed relative frequencies is another, and at present an experimentally unresolved question.

## SUBJECTIVE PROBABILITIES INFERRED FROM DECISIONS USING STATIC DISPLAYS: THE SEU MODEL

Although von Neumann and Morgenstern's procedure for measuring utilities implicitly assumed that the probabilities were known ahead of time, there is nothing about the expected utility maximization model that requires the probabilities to be of the form of relative frequencies or some similarly objectively observable or estimable quantity. When expected utility (EU) is calculated using subjective or personal instead of objective probabilities, however, it has become customary to call that quantity a subjectively expected utility (SEU) and so to call the model the SEU maximization model, or SEU model. Of course, in the SEU model considered as a normative model the probabilities will add up to one and so will obey Bayes' theorem, and consequently there will be no mathematical difference between it and the EU model except at the level of definitions. However, descriptive versions of the SEU model also exist in which the probabilities are not required to add up to any specified constant.

Such quantities that do not add up to anything should perhaps not be called probabilities at all. Nevertheless, real people might have such disorderly opinions, and assuming that they do not would prevent us from being able to find out whether or not they do. Consequently, both additive and nonadditive versions of the SEU model need to be considered when we are talking about descriptive rather than normative models of static decision making.

A number of the early studies of choices among bets, like those by Mosteller and Nogee (1951) and Preston and Baratta

(1949), recognized the possibility that such choices could be accounted for by means of either subjective probability functions or utility functions; Mosteller and Nogee calculated both kinds of functions from their data. But it has become clear since then that such studies must measure utility and subjective probability simultaneously. Only two satisfactory ways of doing this have been developed, so far as we know. One is a multistage procedure devised by Davidson, Suppes, and Siegel (1957). The other is a technique developed by Lindman (unpublished) which involves the simultaneous estimation of utilities and probabilities.

The first step in the technique devised by Davidson, Suppes, and Siegel is to find an event with a probability of exactly ½. The subject chooses between the two courses of action shown

| | State 1 | State 2 |
|---|---|---|
| Option 1 | Win 15¢ | Lose 8¢ |
| Option 2 | Lose 8¢ | Win 15¢ |

*Figure 3.5.* A payoff matrix for which the subject will be indifferent between Option 1 and Option 2 only if the probabilities of States 1 and 2 are equal.

in Figure 3.5, where the two states of the world controlling which payoff accrues to him are determined by some random device. Various random devices are tried until one is found such that the subject is essentially indifferent about the two actions. It is easy to see that he will be indifferent about them if and only if the expected utilities of the two actions are equal, which implies (for additive probabilities) that the probabilities of the two events are equal. Davidson, Suppes, and Siegel tried a number of different random events. They found their subjects biased as between heads and tails, and were unable to come up with satisfactory combinations when rolling a die. However, they obtained some special dice that had the nonsense syllable ZOJ on three faces and the syllable ZEJ on the other three, and found that the two nonsense syllables were considered equiprobable by all of their subjects.

Once any pair of events with known probability is available, whether that known probability is ½ or not, it is of course perfectly straightforward to use the method of determining utility proposed by von Neumann and Morgenstern and discussed above. Davidson, Suppes, and Siegel in fact determined utility functions for money in this way, and found them fairly linear with amounts of money, though not so precisely linear as would have been desirable. This incidentally is a typical finding; so much so that some investigators in more recent studies have been willing to assume the utility of money linear with amounts of money for small amounts and have therefore not considered it necessary to determine that utility before determining, for example, subjective probabilities. After determining utility functions for the subjects, Davidson, Suppes, and Siegel attempted to determine the subjective probability of an event with an "objective" probability (based on symmetry considerations) of 0.25, using essentially the same procedure as they used to determine utilities but treating the probabilities rather than the utilities as the unknowns in the equations. They did not reach any empirically important conclusions from this attempt.

The other utility measurement experiment that we want to summarize is an unpublished one by Lindman. Lindman's technique leads to simultaneous determination of utility and subjective probability functions. Experimentally, he first presents the subject with a bet and arranges for the subject to state a price at which he would be just willing to sell that bet. Thus, he can say that the SEU of the bet is equal to the utility of the selling price. Since the SEU of the bet has three or four unknown parameters, two utilities and one or two subjective probabilities, and the utility of the selling price constitutes another parameter, this equation has either four or five unknowns in it depending on whether or not the subjective probability of an event and that of its complement are assumed to add up to one.

It is, of course, not possible to solve one equation with five unknowns. But the number of equations can be increased by collecting from the subject more judgments about different bets. There will be four or five unknowns in each of these equations, but many of them will be the same from one equation to another. Thus, for example, many different bets may embody the same probabilities, and many different bets may involve many of the same amounts of money. An appropriately chosen matrix of bets can have almost as many equations as unknowns in it. The number of equations cannot be as large as the number of unknowns, however, so further simplifications are needed. The most appropriate further simplification is simply to assume that utility functions are reasonably regular or orderly. The assumption, for example, that the utility of a dollar is a little more than the utility of 95¢ and a little less than the utility of $1.05 implies so much about the utility of a dollar that for all practical purposes it becomes still another equation. Such smoothing techniques can be used in various ways. One particularly attractive way is to assume that the utility function belongs to some convenient, versatile family of mathematical functions with fairly few parameters. This technique is widely used in mathematics; one widely used family of functions for the purpose is called the power series. Actually, Lindman is using a different smoothing technique; he chooses to fit his data with straight-line segments instead; but the principle is the same.

While it is too early to present Lindman's data in detail, they do seem to indicate that at least for a very simple situation, subjective probabilities in fact add up to one. This finding is surprising, since the opposite conclusion had seemed to be justified by earlier and less methodologically sophisticated research. Lindman obtained utility functions that look surprisingly like the logarithmic function proposed by Daniel Bernoulli for amounts of money greater than zero. For amounts of money less than zero, they look rather similar; that is, a modest loss seems to be disproportionately painful compared with a much greater loss. Incidentally, the conception of utility used in this kind of experiment is somewhat different from the conception that Bernoulli originally had in mind. Ever since Mosteller and Nogee's experiment, it has been customary to treat a $6 gain obtained from a bet as being located at $6 away from 0 on the utility function, rather than $6 away from your current total fortune, whatever that may be. The point, of course, is that in the course of a gambling experiment, your current total fortune changes. It would be complicated to keep track of changes in current total fortune, and to plot utility functions in a manner that respected these changes. Moreover, the results would probably be unintelligible. Data and intuition combine to suggest that an increment of $6 in your current total fortune affects you about the same way whether that current total fortune is $5000 or $5200. If so, then any attempt to keep track of fluctuations in your current total fortune and to take them into account in determining utility functions could only mislead. Of course, the situation is different if the fluctuations in your current total fortune are large; in that case, they must be taken into account in some way or another in determining the form of your utility function.

## ACTUAL VERSUS OPTIMAL REVISION OF OPINION IN THE LIGHT OF INFORMATION

We have already pointed out that Bayes' theorem is an optimal model for the revision of opinion in the light of information. The last category of research that we will report concerns comparisons between the performance of that model and the performance of actual subjects. Most of these experiments have used bookbag-and-poker-chips (binomial) tasks. Imagine two bookbags filled with poker chips. One of them contains a proportion $p$ of red poker chips and $q = 1 - p$ of blue poker chips; the other contains the proportion $q$ of red and $p$ of blue poker chips. One of these two bookbags is chosen by flipping a fair coin, or perhaps by flipping a coin with a known bias. The question of interest is which bookbag was chosen. Different varieties of experiments could be designed around this basic situation; the ones of primary interest here all ask the subject to sample poker chips from the bookbag randomly one at a time with replacement, and to estimate after each sample how likely he considers it to be that the chosen bookbag contains more red poker chips than blue ones.

Try the experiment on yourself. One of the two bookbags, let us say, contains 70 percent red poker chips and 30 percent blue chips; the other contains 70 percent blue and 30 percent red. The choice between them was made by flipping an unbiased coin; consequently the initial or prior probability that the predominantly red bookbag was chosen is 0.5. Now in 12 samples from the bookbag, the following sequence of poker chips was obtained:

$$R, R, B, R, R, R, B, B, R, R, R, B. \text{ (8 reds, 4 blues)}$$

On the basis of these data, how likely do you consider it to be that this is the predominantly red bookbag? Make an intuitive estimate; write down a number between 0 and 1 on a sheet of paper.

In order to find out how good your estimate was, and in order to give an example of how to use Bayes' theorem, it is appropriate at this point to do a little arithmetic. The prior probability, in this example, is 0.5; in order to obtain the posterior probability all that is required is $P(D \mid H)$. How does one calculate $P(D \mid H)$ for this kind of example? To start with, a single red chip drawn from the bookbag that has 70 percent red chips in it has probability .7 by symmetry considerations. Two red chips in a row would have a probability $.7^2 =$ .49. Three red chips in a row would have probability. $7^3 =$ .343. And in general, $n$ red chips in a row would have probability $.7^n$. The same principle, of course, applies to blue chips. Now what about sequences of observations that include both red and blue chips? The same sort of technique that applied to homogeneous sequences of observations should also apply to heterogeneous sequences of observations; that is, if the probability of two reds from the 70 percent red bookbag is .7 x .7, then the probability of a red followed by a blue should be .7 x .3 and the probability of a blue followed by a red should be .3 x .7. In short, the probability of any particular sequence is simply the product of the probabilities of all of the elements in it. In general, if the probability of getting a red is $p$, and the probability of getting a blue is $q$, then the probability of getting $r$ reds and $b(=n-r)$ blues in a particular sequence is $p^r q^{n-r}$. If you have studied a little classical statistics, you may be wondering why we are considering particular sequences, rather than families of sequences all yielding $r$ red and $b$ blue poker chips. Two answers are appropriate. One, the more important, is that we are in fact always observing particular sequences, not classes of sequences, and it is only the probability of the *particular* sequence of observations given the hypotheses that we are interested in. The other is that it makes no difference anyhow; the binomial coefficient that would have to be included in order to allow us to treat all classes of sequences yielding $r$ red and $b$ blues would simply cancel out of all subsequent calculations.

We shall work with Equation 3.7, the odds-likelihood ratio form of Bayes' theorem. We are, then, interested in the likelihood ratio appropriate to our datum, that is, the probability of that datum on one hypothesis divided by its probability on the other hypothesis. One hypothesis is in general characterized by some parameter $p$, which represents the proportion of red poker chips in the bookbag; the other hypothesis is characterized by the parameter $p'$ ($\neq p$), some proportion of red chips different from $p$. The likelihood ratio, then, is simply

$$\frac{p^r q^{n-r}}{p'^r q'^{n-r}}$$

In the particular example, however, $p = q'$ and $q = p'$. That fact permits considerable simplification of the likelihood ratio as follows:

$$\frac{p^r q^{n-r}}{q^r p^{n-r}} = \frac{p^{r-(n-r)}}{q^{r-(n-r)}} = \left(\frac{p}{q}\right)^{2r-n}$$

And, $2r - n = r - (n - r)$ is the difference between the number of reds and the number of blues in the sample. In the particular example, the ratio $p/q$ is $.7/.3$, or $7/3$. So the likelihood ratio relevant to this example is simply $(7/3)^4$. Since in the example the prior odds are 1, the posterior odds are numerically equal to the likelihood ratio, and therefore are 29.6. Decoding into posterior probabilities, the correct posterior probability that this is the predominantly red bookbag after seeing 4 more red chips than blue is 0.97.

Unless you are an exceptionally accurate probability estimator, the number you wrote down is nowhere near as large as 0.97. A typical estimate for that situation would fall in the region between 0.75 and 0.80. This illustrates a finding that has been universal in experiments comparing men with Bayes' theorem as information processors: men are incapable of extracting all of the certainty from information that Bayes' theorem indicates is in that information. To put it another way, men are conservative information processors. Experimental data supporting this conclusion are presented in Figure 3.6. This figure demonstrates the behavior of 5 typical subjects in a bookbag-and-poker-chip experiment using bags of 70–30 composition. Subjects made estimates of posterior probabilities, using a response device that consisted of two slanting troughs and 100 disks that could be set in these troughs. They started

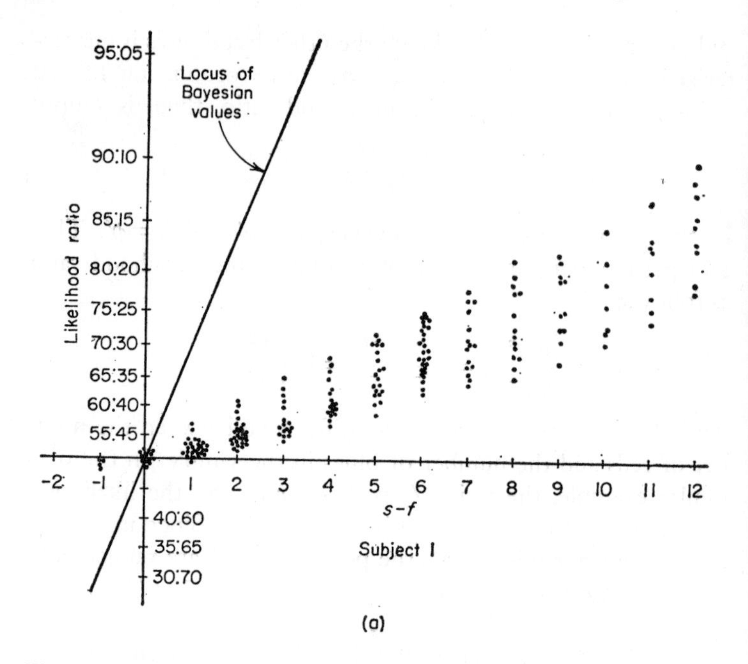


*Figure 3.6.* Estimates of 5 subjects, expressed in log likelihood ratios, as a function of the difference between the number of successes and the number of failures.

with the disks distributed in proportion to the prior probabilities for the two hypotheses they were considering; in the example you just tried, there would have been 50 disks in each trough. They moved disks from one trough to the other as they collected data; since the total number of disks is 100, this compels them to make their estimates add up to 1.

The independent variable in Figure 3.6 is labeled successes minus failures and is, if the bookbag were predominantly red, simply the difference between the number of red and the number of blue poker chips in the sample. (It is called successes minus failures rather than red minus blue simply because for some situations the predominantly blue rather than the pre-

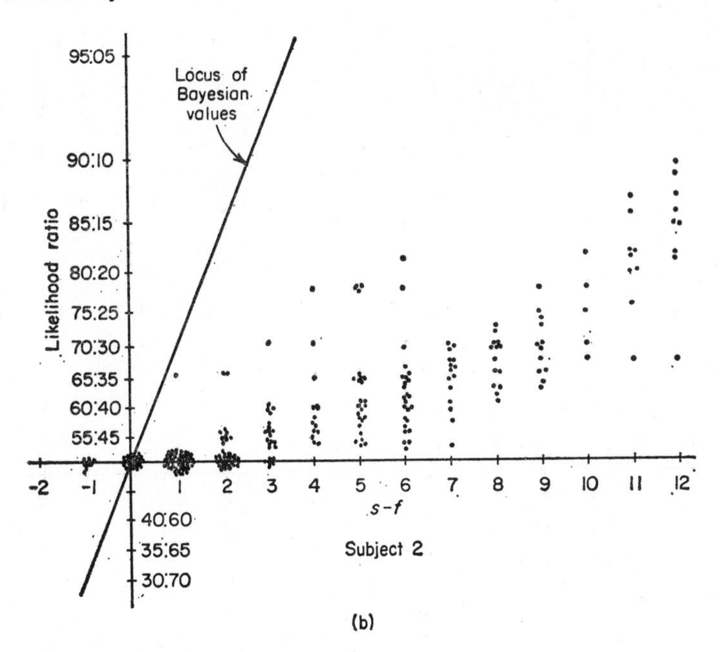


*Figure 3.6*, continued.

dominantly red bookbag was in fact chosen; successes simply means draws of the predominant color.) The dependent variable in Figure 3.6 is the logarithm of the inferred likelihood ratio. What we mean by inferred likelihood ratio is simply the posterior odds divided by the prior odds; if the subject were a perfect information processor, then calculation of posterior odds from his probability estimates followed by division of them by the prior odds should yield the appropriate likelihood ratio. The reason why we display the logarithm of the inferred likelihood ratio rather then the inferred likelihood ratio itself is that perfect performance would be a straight line in log likelihood ratio, as Equation 3.7 would indicate. This makes it exceptionally convenient to compare actual performance with ideal performance. It is apparent that a straight line passed through each subject's data would have considerably less slope

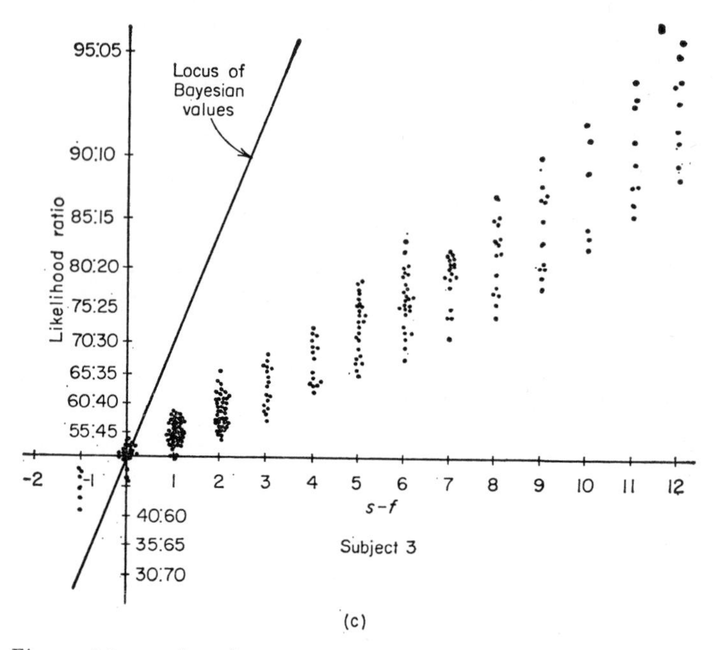


*Figure 3.6*, continued.

than it would have if they were perfect information processors. This simply displays again the conclusion that we have already stated: men are inefficient, conservative information processors. This experiment has been replicated a number of times; the results have been the same. Other, much more complicated experiments have used multinomial data-generating processes with 12 possible observations and 4 hypotheses, normal data-generating processes, and several other situations. In all of these experiments, men have been highly conservative information processors; the more complex the display, the more conservative the human performance.

Why are men so conservative in these tasks? Many speculations can be proposed; some of them can be checked experimentally. One obvious hypothesis is simply that men are im-

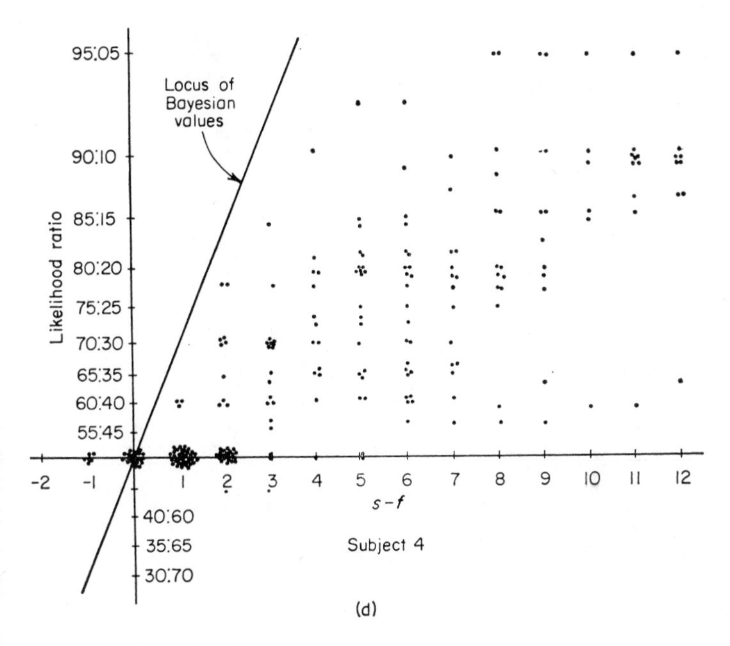


*Figure 3.6*, continued.

pressed by the fact that probabilities must lie between 0 and 1. As the data push their opinions up nearer and nearer to these limits, they become increasingly reluctant to change opinions in the face of further information, since they are getting closer and closer to the point at which their opinions cannot change any further. One very easy way to check on this hypothesis is to ask men to make their estimates in posterior odds instead of posterior probabilities; in posterior odds there are no such upper limits. Edwards, Phillips, Price, and Fujii performed an experiment in which three different groups of subjects used three different response modes: probability estimation, verbal estimation of posterior odds, and estimation of posterior odds displayed on a logarithmic scale. All three groups of subjects were highly conservative; however, the two odds groups were

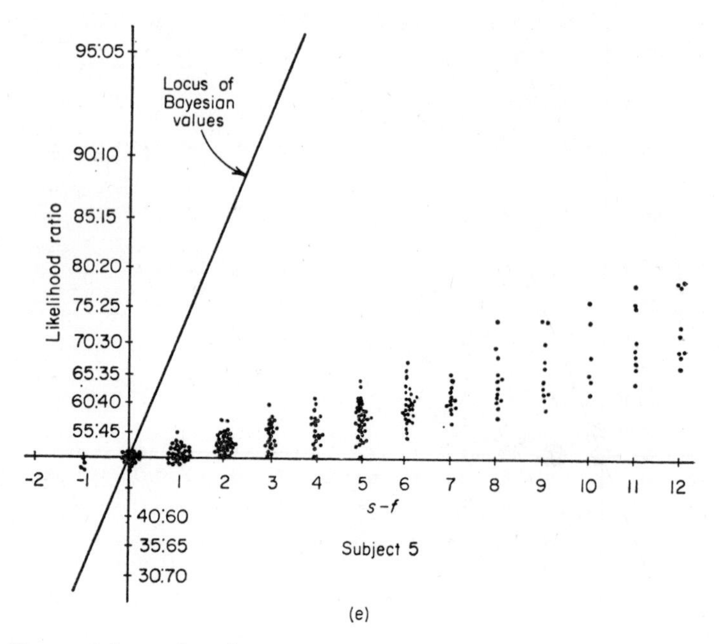


*Figure 3.6*, continued.

definitely less conservative than the probability estimation group. Other response modes, such as a scale in which the spacing is that of log posterior odds but the numbers written on the scale are posterior probabilities, are currently under study.

A second kind of hypothesis about why people are conservative in posterior probability estimation is that they have no incentive to be anything else. In these experiments, subjects have no special reason to report their "true" posterior opinions; they are simply making judgments for the purpose of furthering science and pleasing the experimenter—or perhaps simply to earn money. This hypothesis can be studied in several ways: One is to apply a payoff function to probability estimates. The basic idea is to pay the subject an amount of money contingent on the relation between which hypothesis was true and how high he estimated the posterior probability of that hypothesis.

Three different payoff functions are particularly interesting. The linear payoff function specifies that the amount of money paid is directly proportional to the posterior probability estimate. For linear payoff functions the subject should determine which hypothesis he considers more likely and estimate the posterior probability of that hypothesis as one, regardless of what he really thinks it is. Thus, a linear payoff should encourage very unconservative behavior. Two other payoff functions of considerable interest are the logarithmic and the quadratic. In the logarithmic function, the amount paid to the subject is proportional to the logarithm of his posterior probability estimate; in the quadratic payoff function, that amount is proportional to the square of his posterior estimate. For both logarithmic and quadratic functions it is optimal, under the assumption that utilities are approximately linear with money, for the subject to give as his estimate his true posterior probability, whatever that may be. These functions, then, while not conducive to conservatism, are substantially less punishing to it than is the linear payoff function.

Phillips studied the effects of these three classes of payoff functions in an unpublished bookbag-and-poker-chip experiment. All three experimental groups, and the control group which received no payoff, were conservative. But the linear payoff group was not as conservative as the other groups; in fact, subjects in this group were often too extreme. The quadratic and no-payoff groups were about equally conservative, while the logarithmic group fell between the no-payoff and linear payoff groups. Moreover, all subjects in the experimental groups learned to be less conservative in the course of the experiment. In other words, these payoff conditions do reduce the size of the conservatism effect.

Other more fundamental explanations of the conservatism phenomenon are necessarily more speculative. One difficulty with the mathematics of Bayes' theorem is that it assumes a stationary environment, that is, an environment whose characteristics do not change while you observe them. But whether the real world is changing or not is often a matter of point of view. In fact, the statement that intellligence consists of finding ways of looking at a changing world so that it seems to be unchanging is almost a definition of intelligence. Quests for laws underlying the changes that we observe in our environment are not always successful, and yet we must function in that environment. One rule that permits us to function might be: never get too sure too quickly. The conservatism effect might simply be the result of this rule. If so, the rule is too general, since in these experiments it is being applied to a situation in which its use is inappropriate.

A somewhat similar speculative explanation is that in most real-world situations different observations are not so loosely linked to one another and to the hypothesis that they bear on as in the case for bookbags and poker chips. When networks of relationships not involving the truth of one of the hypotheses being considered link one datum to another, then it is not appropriate to use Bayes' theorem in its simplest form to process these data; in the formal language of mathematics, the assumption of conditional independence is violated. (Note for the statistically sophisticated: conditional independence is not the same thing as lack of correlation. This kind of independence is a relationship that involves not only the data but also hypotheses, so that two data that are correlated for one hypothesis may be independent for a different one. Here too intelligence helps; hypotheses with respect to which data are conditionally independent are highly desirable.)

Whatever the merits or demerits of a built-in tendency to conservatism in information processing in daily life, such a tendency is clearly a hindrance to human effectiveness in information-processing systems. Such systems have no need for built-in, conservative, information-processing biases; they can provide much less automatic, much more rational biases in rather different ways. Consequently, the finding of human conservatism raises some problems for the design of man-machine systems intended to perform information processing in a more or less optimal way. We conclude this chapter with a survey of these problems.

## INFORMATION-PROCESSING AND DECISION-MAKING SYSTEMS

Man-machine systems come in all degrees of size and complexity. The number of men required to operate such a system may range from one to thousands; the machines that collaborate with these men range in complexity from paper and pencil to the largest of digital computers with elaborate and complicated input and output devices. The basic ideas that we will discuss apply to all of these systems, from one man with paper and pencil on up, but the technique of their implementation will of course depend on the kind of system being considered. The most fertile field for application, we believe, is in business decision making; the problems of business often come in naturally numerical form, the issues at stake are sufficiently important to justify a considerable amount of expense to improve the technique of making decisions, and some of the Bayesian ideas have been most elaborately worked out in business contexts. Nevertheless, we shall use a military example, in part because we happen to know more about it than about business examples and in part because it illustrates some of the speed advantages of Bayesian information processing, a class of advantage not likely to be as important in business contexts. We shall use as our example the North American Air Defense System (NORAD). Both our description of the current system and our proposal for future systems to perform the same tasks are to some degree fanciful. We are unrealistic in part because many of the realistic details are classified, and in part because the system is extremely complicated. Most of the complications make the fundamental issues we are concerned with harder to see.

Imagine a large room, about 100 feet from floor to ceiling. On one wall of that room, there is a huge map of North American and the North Polar regions. On the floor of that room are a large number of projection devices capable of projecting various kinds of information onto the map. Set high in the wall opposite the map is a glass-enclosed booth rather like a director's booth in a television studio. In that booth in times of stress sits the general who commands NORAD. To complete the popular image of that general's job, he should have set into the desk in front of him a large red button. There is in fact no button, but several large red phones serve a similar purpose. Surrounding this central room are many communications links tying it with various kinds of information sources in the outside world. Information from all over comes to this room, some of it from spies, some of it from men who sit in Washington and read European and Asiatic newspapers, some of it from radar systems of various kinds scattered all over the world and some of it from still other, still more exotic information sources. As a result, the map is filled with information. It is the general's task to observe and interpret all that information and decide whether or not the time has come to make that phone call.

The question that the general wants to answer is really a very simple one. Are we at war or are we not? In principle, it should not require all those vast masses of information to determine whether or not we are at war; some very simple information source, such as a microphone buried in Brezhnev's psychoanalyst's couch, would be quite enough. But no such straightforward way of answering the question exists, so far as we know, and so the general must try to make large quantities of information only peripherally related to his basic problem substitute for small quantities of information speaking directly to that problem. That is, he must substitute quantity of information for quality of information. This substitution of quantity for quality of information is the essence of a process that is coming to be called diagnosis or diagnostic information processing. The name is of course intended to suggest medical diagnosis, another example of such a process, but diagnostic information processing is obviously a widespread human activity, occurring in many contexts other than medicine and war.

What has modern technology done to help the general assimilate and use all the information available to him? It has provided him with more and more exotic artificial sense organs (for example, radar) with which to gather information. It has provided him with instant communication facilities to bring more and more information more and more quickly to where he can observe it; it has provided him with unparalleled display facilities for making that information accessible to his senses; it has provided him with computers and other machines that can store and retrieve that information very quickly and accurately so that if he forgets something he can quickly be reminded of it. But it has provided him with nothing whatever to assist him in figuring out what all that information means. The tool that he uses to interpret that mass of information is exactly the same tool that Alexander the Great used to perform the same task: his own trained and experienced intelligence.

To get a worm's eye view of the general's task, consider only one hypothesis and two data. The hypothesis is that the Russians are about to launch a land attack on West Berlin. Two data bearing on this hypothesis might conceivably have come to his attention. One of them is that last Tuesday a major in the Russian army got drunk in an East Berlin bar and declared that Willy Brandt, the Mayor of West Berlin, has only a month to live. The other is that a squadron of destroyers and destroyer escorts set sail from Murmansk yesterday. (Actually, neither of these data would be likely to come to the general's attention; both are too trivial in themselves to deserve that much consideration. We choose trivial examples deliberately to illustrate one feature of our proposal.) How might the general, or a system, revise opinion about the hypothesis that the Russians are about to initiate a land attack on West Berlin on the basis of these two items of information? A human being, looking at these data, would presumably dismiss them as of negligible importance. A drunken major seldom blurts out genuine state secrets, mostly because he seldom knows any. And a squadron of destroyers and destroyer escorts sailing from Murmansk is, with very high probability, doing so for routine training purposes. Nevertheless, these data have some minor bearing on the question at hand; a really efficient information-processing system should be able to use them. How?

Clearly two different questions must be answered in order to use these data. One of them is: How much impact does either datum, considered alone, have on opinion about the hypothesis that the Russians are about to attack West Berlin. This question, we believe, is entirely one for human judgment; we see no possibility of developing any mathematical model or formal mechanism for interpreting such qualitative, verbal data in the light of equally qualitative, equally verbal hypotheses. The second question, however, is: How can the separate impacts of these two distinct data be combined. Here, the answer is quite different. Bayes' theorem is a formal data-combining mechanism. To use it for that purpose, simply calculate after the first datum the posterior probability of the hypothesis, use that posterior probability as the prior probability for the next calculation, and then calculate the posterior probability after the second datum. (Alternatively, treat the two data as a single datum by multiplying their probabilities given each hypothesis together beforehand; either procedure leads to the same result.)

The general's task, then, like processing in general, can be subdivided into two separable subtasks: the assessment, for each datum and each hypothesis considered separately, of the impact of that datum on that hypothesis; and the aggregation of the impacts of all of the data so far received into a current posterior distribution over all of the hypotheses being considered. The first of these two tasks, we feel, must be performed by men; but the second is easy to mechanize by means of a formal rule for information aggregation, Bayes' theorem.

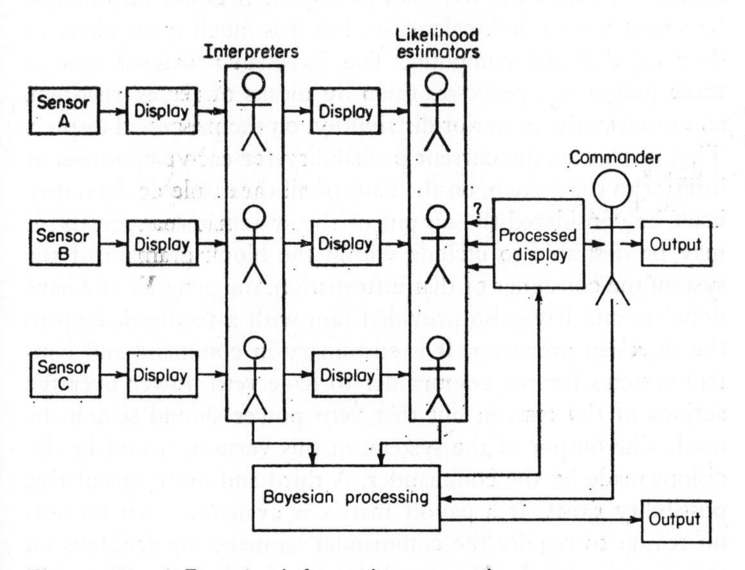


*Figure 3.7.* A Bayesian information-processing system.

This analysis suggests a system design; Figure 3.7 is a block diagram of it. Several information sources provide information to the system. This information is first filtered for completely irrelevant items and put into some reasonably standard format by trained interpreters and then is passed on to the set of operators called likelihood estimators. The task of these men is to assess the impact of each datum on each hypothesis of interest to the system in a manner that permits the use of these assessments of impact in Bayes' theorem. A number of different kinds of techniques for making such judgments are formally equivalent and equally good from the point of view of the mathematics of Bayes' theorem; choice among them is one of the numerous problems of human engineering in the design of such a system.

The judgments of the likelihood estimators are passed on to something called the Bayesian processor. It could in principle be a man with a desk calculator, but it is much more likely to be a large digital computer. The Bayesian processor accepts these judgments, processes them by means of Bayes' theorem, and displays the posterior distribution on the processed display. That display of the current probability for each hypothesis of interest to the system, on the basis of all the available data, may itself be considered the output of the system. Alternatively, it may be desirable to include within the block diagram of the system the consumer of that information, the general. We have done so, and have also provided him with a feedback loop to the Bayesian processor. It is customary in command and control systems for the commander to have veto power over the actions of the system; but that veto power should seldom be used. The output of the system, in this version, would be decisions made by the commander. A third and more speculative possibility exists. If a payoff matrix is available, then there is no reason to require the commander to make his decisions on the spot; he can in effect make them ahead of time by controlling the numbers that go into the payoff matrix, and the Bayesian processor can implement his value system in decisions simply by applying the principle of maximizing expected value. This is probably the best way of using a diagnostic system if a payoff matrix is available or can be made available.

Many researchable questions require attention before we can say for sure that such a system will work. For example, we have indicated in the block diagram a possible feedback loop whereby the likelihood estimators can look at the processed display of posterior probabilities. The question mark above that feedback loop is intended to imply that we doubt its desirability. It seems to us quite possible that these likelihood estimators would take the trend of the system's opinions too seriously and pay more attention to it than to the content of the data in making their estimates, and thus would produce an unstable system. The logic of the system does not require that feedback loop. On the other hand, it is very difficult to prevent the operators of one part of the system from knowing what is going on in other parts of the system; it is much too easy to sneak down the hall during a coffee break and bootleg a look at the processed display. Consequently, it is of some importance to discover experimentally whether that feedback actually has significant advantageous or harmful consequences.

Will this Bayesian system work? It will if and only if the likelihood estimators can do their jobs. Formal research addressed to that question is in progress. We have conducted some informal studies of ourselves and our colleagues as likelihood estimators, and have found that it is fairly easy to obtain a high degree of interpersonal agreement on likelihood ratios. It is very nearly impossible to estimate $P(D \mid H)$. The reason why is very simple: the size of $P(D \mid H)$ is markedly influenced by irrelevancies. This means that the level of detail with which the datum is specified is crucial to the magnitude of $P(D \mid H)$, whether the specifications are diagnostically relevant or irrelevant. However, the likelihood ratio is free of this objection. The magnitude of the likelihood ratio is not affected by the level of irrelevant detail, but is affected by only those details relevant to the diagnosis between the two hypotheses that define that particular ratio. At present, our best guess is that the optimal quantity for likelihood estimators to estimate is likelihood ratios taken as numbers greater than one (which means that the estimator must specify in each case which hypothesis is favored by the ratio), and displayed with a logarithmic spacing. But this conclusion is very preliminary, quite likely to be modified or reversed by more formal studies.

It will be extremely difficult to establish that a Bayesian system (or any diagnostic system, for that matter) works effectively. Such systems in the real world are extremely expensive; it is usually impossible to compare one real diagnostic system with another. A simulation is much more feasible, and three simulations of Bayesian systems are now in existence in different laboratories around the country. However, there is always some uncertainty about the degree to which a simulation in fact reproduces realistically the characteristics of the setting and system it is supposed to simulate. It should not reproduce them too realistically, since the reason for using a simulation rather than the situation itself is that the real situation is both too expensive and too complex to perform effective research in.

But the most difficult problem is to determine what the criterion of good performance should be. The natural one for a Bayesian system would be that the posterior probability of the true hypothesis should become high as quickly as possible. However, it is not enough to ask whether or not the Bayesian system comes up with the right answer, since it cannot hope to do so all the time, and any system can do so some of the time. The real question is whether it does better than alternative systems that might have been used instead. Consequently, a study intended to evaluate a Bayesian system must compare it with alternative systems. A natural alternative to a Bayesian system is for the commander to use Alexander the Great's technique for information processing: he looks at the data and makes up his mind. Another alternative is a system in which operators look at the data and directly estimate posterior probabilities for the hypotheses of interest. We are currently engaged in research attempting to compare the performance of versions of these three systems.

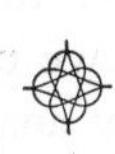

# THE PROBLEM OF REAL PAYOFF MATRICES

Diagnosis is one half of the decision-system problem; action selection is the other half. In discussing our Bayesian system, we pointed out that there were several alternative ways of translating its output into choices among courses of action. Probably the best way of doing this is to have a payoff matrix and choose among the available courses of action by applying the principle of maximizing expected utility. But where can that payoff matrix come from?

The problem of real payoff matrices is the problem of multi-dimensional value systems. We have already used the example of two applicants for a job as your secretary. One requires $100 a month more salary than the other, takes shorthand at only 50 words per minute but is a gorgeous, unmarried red-head; while the other, middle-aged and matronly, works for less and can take shorthand at 150 words per minute. The two courses of action available in this example are quite straight-forward; the dimensions along which values vary are well-defined, but synthesizing these dimensions is the problem. Do you prefer your secretary to be gorgeous, unmarried, and con-sequently likely to be lured away from you, or would you sooner have a comfortable matron who is likely to stay around longer? Whichever way your preference goes on that dimen-sion, how many words per minute in shorthand are you will-ing to sacrifice for the more preferred combination of per-sonal characteristics? And how much difference in salary do these personal and business characteristics justify? In a prob-lem like this, it is not difficult to obtain four or five or ten dif-ferent payoff matrices, one for each value dimension. The ba-sic requirement, then, for a solution to the multidimensional value problem is that of reducing many different payoff ma-trices to one.

The solution that we shall propose to this problem is the same in strategy as the solution that we proposed to the diagnostic problem. That is, we begin by analyzing the tasks into two subtasks. One is the evaluation of each possible combination of an act and a state on each of the value dimensions considered separately; it, we believe, is an inescapably human function. The other subtask is to combine these judgments about the separate value dimensions into a single payoff matrix; as was the case for diagnosis, we believe that this subtask can be done best by machine. Unfortunately, no obvious formal mechanism like Bayes' theorem exists for making these combinations.

Yntema and Torgerson (1961), concerned with this problem, have proposed a formal combining device that seems satisfactory for the purpose. It is true of many value dimensions that you consistently prefer either more to less or less to more, at least over the range of the dimension on which realistic possibilities fall. For example, most people prefer more money to less, less sickness to more, and so on. In many cases where all of the component value dimensions have this characteristic, very little error will be made by neglecting the interactions among them. The ultimate utility of each outcome is then simply the weighted sum of the utilities of the individual components. In symbols:

$$U(C) = aU(D_1) + bU(D_2) + cU(D_3) + \ldots$$

Where $U(C)$ is the utility of the composite, that is, of the actual outcome being considered, $U(D_1)$ is the utility of the first value dimension for that particular outcome, $U(D_2)$ is the utility of the second value dimension for that outcome, and so on, and $a$, $b$, $c$, and so forth, are simply positive weighting constants that determine how important each dimension is in the composite.

Yntema and Torgerson applied this technique to value judgments made by pilots concerning the relative desirability of various amounts of ceiling, visibility, and fuel left when land-ing a plane. Even though these value dimensions might reasonably be expected to interact, since, for example, a high ceiling will do you little or no good if you have essentially no visibility, they found that this simple additive mechanism served very well to predict the choices that pilots would make among the composite situations. Of course, Yntema and Torgerson were concerned with hypothetical rather than real choices, and they were attempting simply to reproduce, rather than to improve on, a decision-maker's decisions. The same sort of technique, however, should be even more applicable where the goal is to make the decision that in some way best carries out a decision-maker's value system, rather than the decision that he would have made himself. This is a subtle and important distinction. To take the decision-maker out of the system altogether would be impossible, since it is, after all, human values that the system must serve. But the primary role of the decision-maker should be to specify those values, a task that requires human judgment, rather than to concern himself with the details of their implementation, a task that we can reasonably attempt to automate.

Little research has been done on the real-world payoff matrix problem, and much of what has been done is not relevant to this particular approach to it. Nevertheless, we believe that this approach holds promise of providing satisfactory real-world payoff matrices, and thus of making possible a truly effective use of the output of a Bayesian system.

## A FUNCTIONAL ANALYSIS OF DECISION MAKING

In part as a summary, and in part to make clear the functional analysis that has been the topic of this chapter, Table 3.1 presents that analysis in abbreviated form. We have dis-

TABLE 3.1. A Functional Analysis of Decision Making

| Function | *Performed by* | | | *When performed* | |
|---|---|---|---|---|---|
| | *men* | *machines* | *both* | *ahead of time* | *now* |
| Recognize the existence of a decision problem | x | | | x | |
| Identify available acts | x | | | x | |
| Identify relevant states that determine payoff for acts | x | | | x | |
| Identify the value dimensions to be aggregated into the payoff matrix | x | | | x | |
| Judge the value of each outcome on each dimension | x | | | x | |
| Aggregate value judgments into a composite payoff matrix | | x | | x | |
| Identify information sources relevant to discrimination among states | x | | | x | |
| Collect data from information sources | | | x | | x |
| Filter data, put into standard format, and display to likelihood estimator | | | x | | x |
| Estimate likelihood ratios (or some other quantity indicating the impact of the datum on the hypotheses) | x | | | | x |
| Aggregate impact estimates into posterior distributions | | x | | | x |
| Decide among acts by using principle of maximizing expected value | | x | | | x |
| Implement the decision | | | x | | x |

cussed all of the functions in Table 3.1 except Function 1 and Function 7. Function 1 is simply to realize that something needs to be done; in a sense, it need not be listed here, since one would not attempt to apply a functional analysis unless one realized one had a problem. Function 7, the identification of relevant information sources, consists mostly of deciding whether or not the information that could be obtained from any given source is worth the cost of obtaining it. This, of course, is a form of decision problem, too; the same techniques that we are here proposing for other decision problems can be applied to it. In fact, the Bayesian approach offers some elegant mathematical tools for determining whether or not in any particular case the collection of data is worthwhile. However, it seems likely that in most real-world contexts the identification of relevant information sources will be done with relatively little reference to formal analyses, primarily because in the kinds of problems illustrated by the commander of NORAD, the cost of making a mistake is so high that any datum that might help is worth collecting provided only that its processing does not overload the system.

No existing system designed for information processing and decision making has defined its task in terms of this kind of analysis. Nevertheless, many elements of this analysis are common to the thinking of the designers of future versions of such systems and we believe that in the long run some such analysis will probably be the basis for the design of formal systems for information processing and decision making.

## REFERENCES

Bernoulli, D. Specimen theoriae novae de mensura sortis. *Comentarii Academiae Scientiarum Imperialis Petropolitanae*, 1738, *5*, 175-192. (Trans. by L. Sommer in *Econometrica*, 1954, 22, 23-36.)

Davidson, D., P. Suppes, and S. Siegel. *Decision-making: an experimental approach.* Stanford: Stanford University Press, 1957.

deFinetti, B. La prévision: ses lois logiques, ses sources subjectives. *Ann. Inst. Poincaré,* 1937, 7, 1-68. Translated in H. E. Kyburg, Jr., and H. E. Smokler (Eds.). *Studies in Subjective Probability.* New York: Wiley, 1964.

Erlick, D. E. Judgments of the relative frequency of a sequential series of two events. *J. exp. Psychol.,* 1961, *62,* 105-112.

Erlick, D. E. Judgments of the relative frequency of sequential binary events: Effects of frequency differences. WADC Technical Report 59-580, October, 1959.

Erlick, D. E. Judgments of the relative frequency of two random sequential events: Effects of duration of observation. WADD Technical Report 60-673, September, 1960.

Erlick, D. E. Judgments of the relative frequency of two random sequential events: Effects of rate of presentation. WADD Technical Report 60-714, March, 1961.

Mosteller, F., and P. Nogee. An experimental measurement of utility. *J. polit. Econ.,* 1951, *59,* 371-404.

Philip, B. R. Generalization and central tendency in the discrimination of a series of stimuli. *Can. J. Psychol.,* 1947, *1,* 196-204.

Preston, M. G., and P. Baratta. An experimental study of the action-value of an uncertain outcome. *Am. J. Psychol.,* 1948, *61,* 183-193.

Ramsey, F. P. Truth and probability. In F. P. Ramsey, *The foundations of mathematics and other logical essays,* New York: Harcourt Brace, 1931. Reprinted in H. E. Kyburg, Jr., and H. E. Smokler (Eds.). *Studies in Subjective Probability,* New York: Wiley, 1964.

Robinson, G. H. Continuous estimation of a time-varying probability, *Ergonomics,* 1964, 7, 7-21.

Savage, L. J. *The foundations of statistics.* New York: Wiley, 1954.

Shuford, E. H. Percentage estimation of proportion as a function of element type, exposure time, and task. *J. exp. Psychol.*, 1961, *61*, 430-436.

Stevens, S. S., and E. H. Galanter. Ratio scales and category scales for a dozen perceptual continua. *J. exp. Psychol.*, 1957, *54*, 377-409.

Von Neumann, J., and O. Morgenstern. *Theory of games and economic behavior*, 1st ed. Princeton: Princeton University Press, 1944.

Von Neumann, J., and O. Morgenstern. *Theory of games and economic behavior*, 2d ed. Princeton: Princeton University Press, 1947.

Yntema, D. B., and W. S. Torgerson. Man-computer cooperation in decisions requiring common sense. *IRE Trans. Hum. Fact. Electronics*, 1961, HFE-2, 20-26.

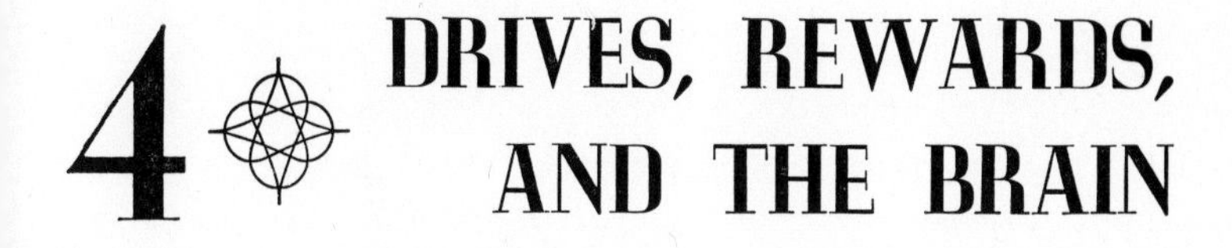

# 4 DRIVES, REWARDS, AND THE BRAIN

JAMES AND MARIANNE OLDS

UNIVERSITY OF MICHIGAN

Our knowledge of the areas in the brain that are related to drives and rewards derives from the use of relatively gross techniques; accordingly, it is relatively naïve and empirical. On the other hand, what we know makes us guess at more and search for more. In the following pages we trace out a progress from simple to somewhat more detailed guesses, based on experiments that proceed from the very gross to the somewhat less so.

For a first concept of the relation of the emotional or motivational substrates to the rest of the brain, one need not have a detailed picture of the central nervous system (CNS). It is sufficient to know that in a nonprimate mammal the CNS is laid out in the following order from back to front: (1) spinal cord, (2) hindbrain, (3) midbrain, and (4) forebrain (see Figure 4.1).

The forebrain may be thought of as being divided into five parts: (1) the hypothalamus, which is the lower part just in front of the midbrain; (2) the thalamus, which is the upper part just in front of the midbrain; (3) the olfactory bulb, which is anterior to both thalamus and hypothalamus. Above and surrounding the rest of the brain (and dwarfing it) are two thick shells of cortex: (4) the older, and in some places the inner shell, which arises mainly out of the olfactory bulb and hypothalamus is called paleocortex or rhinencephalon; and (5) the newer shell, which arises mainly out of the thalamus is called neocortex or sometimes merely *the* cortex. Through the

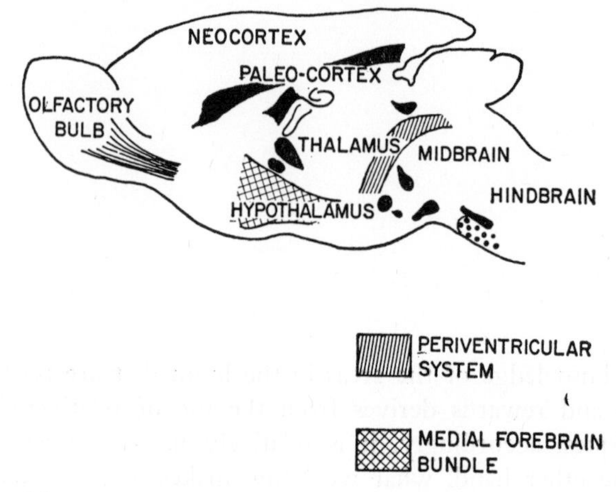


*Figure 4.1.*

center of the brain runs the ventricle, filled with fluid; in some places it is like a rivulet, in others it is like a system of lakes.

## SELF-STIMULATION AND ESCAPE

### MIDBRAIN AND FOREBRAIN SYSTEM

One possible view of the brain's emotional system is that two anatomical regions, proximally associated throughout much of the midbrain and forebrain, might be radically different in function and phylogenetic origin. One, the periventricular system, follows the ventricles from the midbrain and probably even farther back; this system intrudes into the forebrain through the medial area and then proceeds forward to include several of the paleocortical structures. The other, the medial forebrain bundle system, starts in the olfactory bulb and follows two courses, the first through olfactory pathways to the paleocortical structures and the second through the broad medial forebrain bundle to the basolateral hypothalamus and basolateral midbrain regions. The periventricular and medial forebrain bundle systems appear clearly in Figure 4.1, which is redrawn from Gurdjian (1927).

If the regions are different in phylogenetic origin, one might guess from their physiological and anatomical connections that the development of the periventricular system was based on a primitive somesthetic receptor system, and that the development of the medial forebrain bundle system was based on a primitive olfactory or chemical receptor system. Because of their points of origin, one might speak of the periventricular system as the midbrain system and of the medial forebrain bundle system as the forebrain system. From effects of electric stimulation, it could be surmised that the midbrain system has to do more with aversive behavior and the forebrain system with appetitive behavior.

For several reasons it may be guessed that neural activity in, and behavior emanating from, the midbrain system might be reflex (triggered by changes in the environment). If so, it would tend to entail negative feedback; that is, it would look as though it were directed toward counteracting the environmental changes that caused it and thus it would shut itself off. From the adaptive point of view, one might imagine its being engaged only by stimuli that constituted imminent threats to survival or health. In a sense therefore one might say the midbrain system was directed toward survival. Similar reasons suggest that behavior released by the forebrain system might be operant behavior (triggered by internal programming mechanisms). From observation of the properties of operant behavior one might guess that it would often involve positive feedback; that is, it would produce environmental conditions that would reinforce the behavior and a vicious circle would be possible. From the adaptive point of view, it might be directed toward the "hoarding" of scarce substances (like body fats), toward storage within the organism of substances not yet needed but likely to be so in the future. These supposed differences are set forth in Figure 4.2.

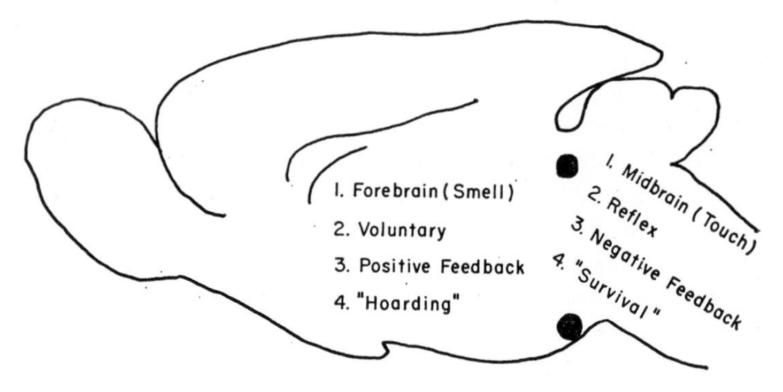


*Figure 4.2.* Functional differentiation of midbrain and forebrain behavior mechanisms.

Some facts that could be presented in support of this theoretical differentiation are (1) different effects of electric stimulation, (2) different effects of pharmacological variables, (3) different effects of temporary decortication, and possibly (4) different principles governing neural patterns.

## AVERSIVE AND APPETITIVE REACTIONS

The characteristic behaviors associated with the primitive property of irritability inherent in living matter and with intense stimulation of the somesthetic system in mammals are negative avoiding reactions. These aversive reactions are far simpler to explain on a cause-effect basis than are appetitive or homing reactions. Possibly because of this, a tendency to parsimony has led to many attempts to show or suggest that apparently appetitive reactions are nothing but disguised aversive reactions (Miller, 1957).

Empirically, reward and punishment seem to be quite different mechanisms for controlling behavior. Yet these mechanisms are rarely observed in conflict; pleasure and pain are rarely reported as occurring simultaneously, and the same behavior often seems intended to avoid punishment *as well as* to pursue reward. If the mechanisms are dual, some method of interaction or reciprocal correlation seems to be worked out within the organism to prevent conflicts.

Experiments in which aversive reactions were produced by electric stimulation of the brain (ESB) have yielded information about anatomic structures that may be related to mechanisms of negative reinforcement (Delgado, 1955; Delgado *et al.*, 1954; Hess, 1954; Olds and Olds, 1963; Roberts, 1958a, 1958b, 1962). Recently these have been combined with studies of positive reinforcement produced by ESB (Olds and Milner, 1954) to further the analysis of relations between the mechanisms of punishment and those of reward.

Many studies (Bower and Miller, 1958; Brown and Cohen, 1959; Roberts, 1958b) that showed elicitation of appetitive and aversive reactions from stimulation of the same point were taken as evidence for a single mechanism, while studies (Olds, 1960; Olds and Peretz, 1960; Olds and Olds, 1963) that showed differentiation of appetitive from aversive points were taken as evidence for a dual-motive mechanism. Studies of interactions suggested possible mechanism of reciprocal correlation (Olds and Olds, 1962).

## BASIC METHODS

*Escape test.* When rats were stimulated repeatedly in the midbrain system, they became active and learned to escape from the stimulation (Olds and Peretz, 1960). Given access to a lever which would turn off the stimulator for a few seconds, the animals learned to press the lever regularly, thus keeping the stimulus turned off for a large proportion of the time (Travis and Olds, 1959).

The method of experiment is portrayed in Figure 4.3. One-half second stimulus trains were applied at the rate of 1 per

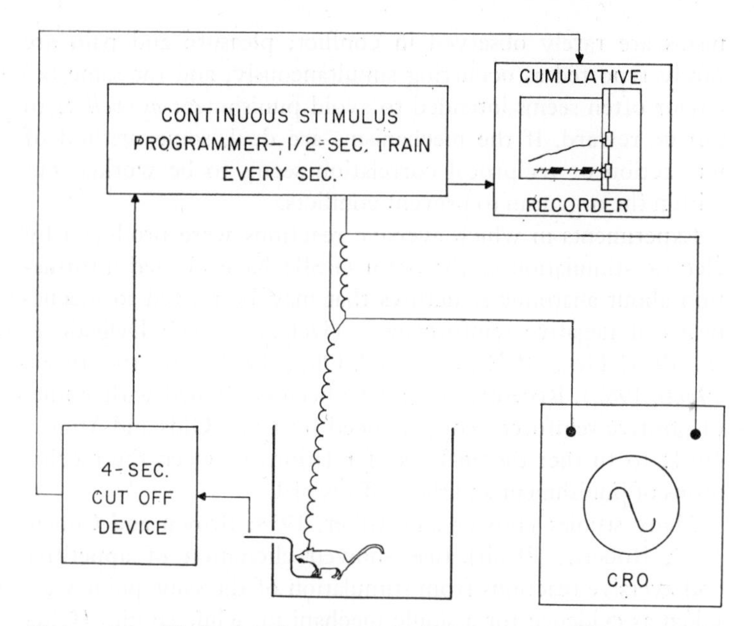


*Figure 4.3.* Methods of escape test. Programmer delivers stimuli to brain at rate of 1 per second. Animal's response terminates programmer for 4 seconds. Recorder converts response rate into slope of curve (45° = 100 rpm). Baseline of recorder marks periods of regular stimulation (wide line) and periods of escape from stimulation (thin line).

second and terminated for a period of 4 seconds after each response of the animal. Thus, during an 8-minute period, 480 stimulations were delivered in the absence of a response. As shown in Figure 4.4, with electrodes in different places this method yielded four different stimulus-response patterns: (1) maximum stimulation with no response, (2) considerable stimulation with random response, (3) less stimulation with unskilled escape behavior, and (4) minimum stimulation with skilled escape behavior.

When electrodes were placed in the midbrain system, as shown in Figure 4.5(a), or in a series of related places, Pattern

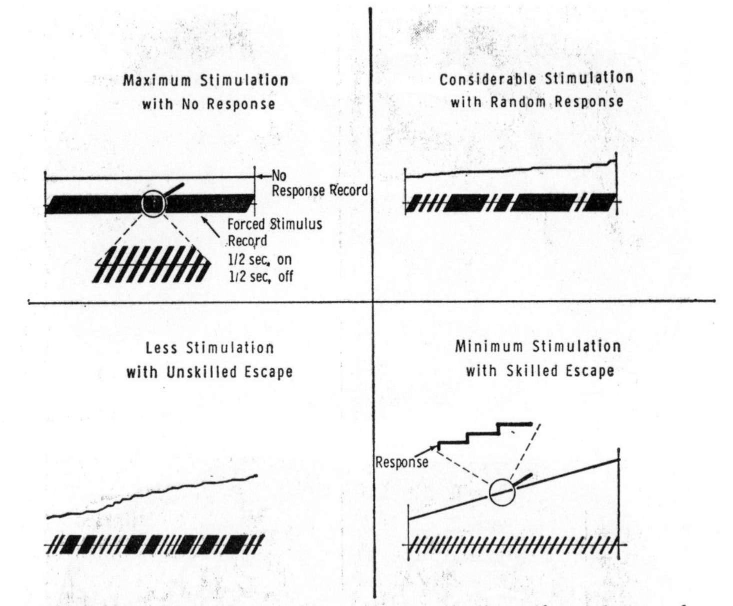


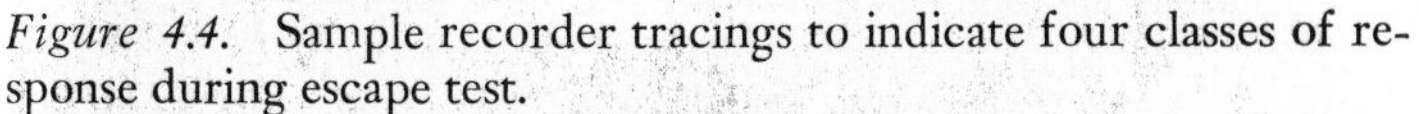

*Figure 4.4.* Sample recorder tracings to indicate four classes of response during escape test.

4 eventually appeared. The animals responded skillfully, receiving a minimum of stimulation. When electrodes were placed in the forebrain system, as shown in Figure 4.5(b), or in a set of related places, Pattern 1 soon appeared. The animals responded far below a chance level, receiving a maximum of stimulation.

*Self-stimulation test.* When electrodes were implanted in the forebrain system and a circuit was arranged to make a brief train of electric stimulation occur as a regular consequence of some response in the behavior repertory of the rat, that response soon came to predominate, occurring eventually at its maximum possible rate (Olds and Milner, 1954; Olds *et al.*, 1960; Olds and Olds, 1963). In this and many other kinds of experiments (Olds, 1958b), the electric stimulation appeared

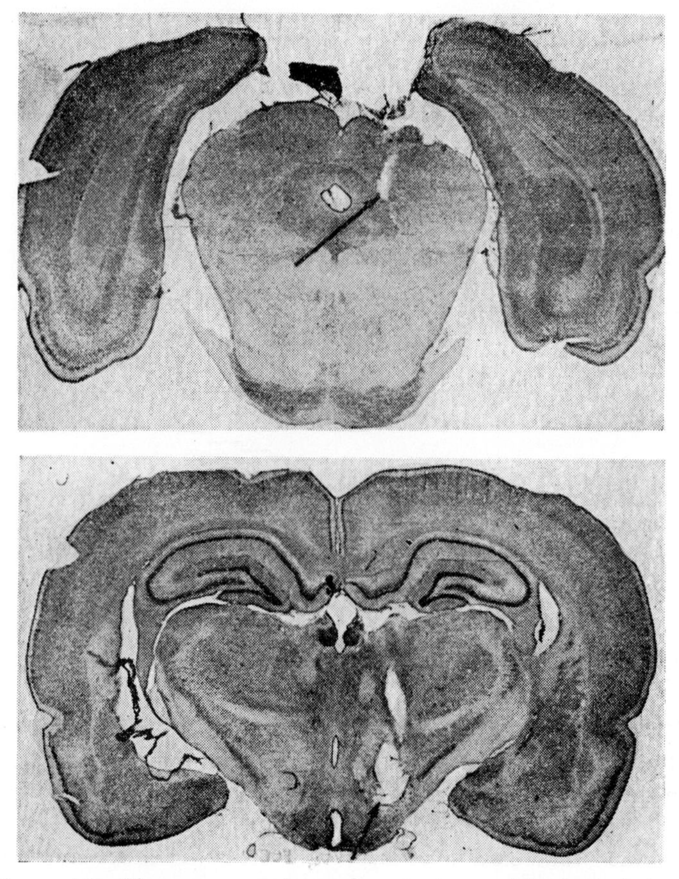

*Figure 4.5.* Transverse sections of rat brain at midbrain and forebrain levels showing electrode track in midbrain system (top) and in forebrain system (bottom).

to serve as a maximal source of animal gratification; in the parlance of the behavioral psychologist, it was a source of "positive reinforcement."

The method of the self-stimulation test is portrayed in Figure 4.6. One-half-second (or 1/4-second) stimulus trains

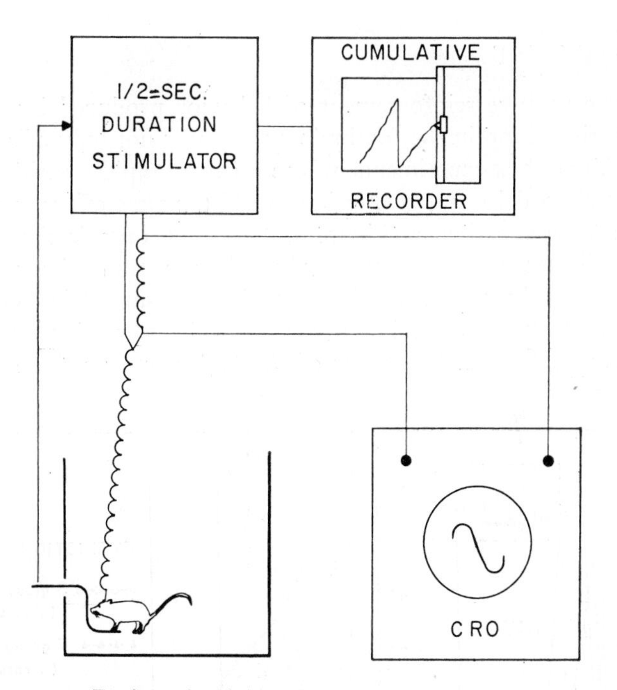


*Figure 4.6.* Design of self-stimulation test.

were applied automatically whenever the rat depressed the lever. The animal had to release and press again to get more.

When stimulation was applied in this fashion to the part of the midbrain area shown at the top of Figure 4.5, the animal quickly learned to stay away from the lever most of the time. No more than 1 or 2 responses occurred in an 8-minute period after the animal had become accustomed to the apparatus. On the other hand, when stimulation was applied in the forebrain system, as shown in the lower half of Figure 4.5, the animal quickly learned to press the lever very regularly. Rates for an 8-minute period ranged from 600 up to 1200 responses and even higher (Bures *et al.*, 1961).

## MAZE TEST

The positive reinforcement of behavior produced by electric stimulation in the forebrain system was not only effective in Skinner box experiments, where it caused rapid repetition of a simple pedal response, but it also had the same effect as food in a maze experiment (Figure 4.7), causing organization of a complicated response pattern when electric stimulation of the brain was given as a reward after each maze run (Olds, 1956b).

Two groups of animals were run in a version of the Lashley III maze. Eight rats of the "S" group received only

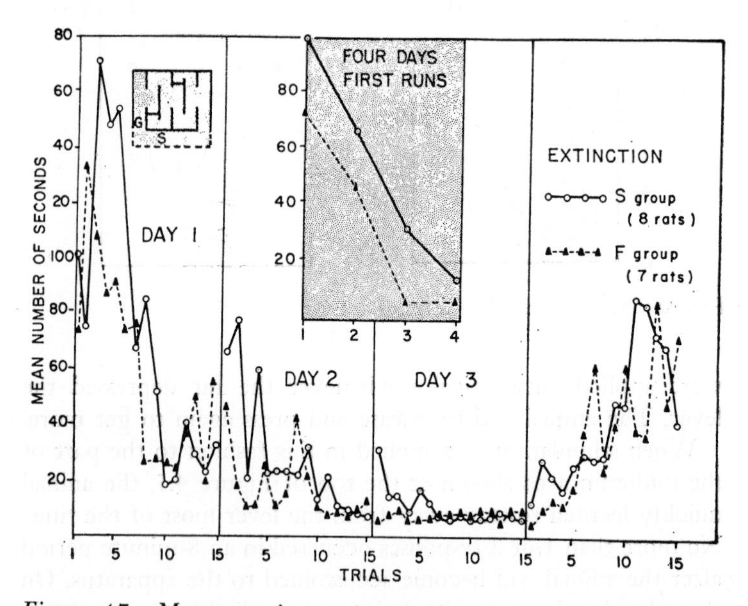


*Figure 4.7.* Maze experiment. Average learning curves of 2 groups of rats run in a maze during a 4-day test; both groups were under 23-hour food deprivation. At the end of the maze, Group S received electrical stimulation in the forebrain systems and Group F received food. On Days 1 to 3 the rats were rewarded; on Day 4 they were not. The large insert shows average time of initial trial for the 2 groups on each of the 4 test days.

forebrain stimulation in the goal box. Seven rats of the "F" group received only food. Both groups were hungry. The S group showed a reduction in maze running time whether the change was measured within the course of a day or from day to day. The animals learned slightly faster for a food reward but ran faster for ESB reward. When the ESB reward was withdrawn on the fourth day, extinction appeared just as it did when the food reward was withdrawn.

## DISORGANIZING EFFECTS OF STIMULATION

A strong relation of forebrain stimulation to organized behavioral chains was also indicated by its capacity to disorganize them. In the aforementioned maze experiment, the forebrain stimulus was presented in the "reinforcing" position of an orderly behavior sequence. In that position it seemed to augment or cement the organization. On the other hand, when forebrain stimulation was presented randomly in the course of organized behavior chains reinforced by food, it had a disorganizing influence.

A discrimination reversal test (Figure 4.8) was used to study the disorganizing influence of ESB on associative behavior. In a 3-foot-long box, 2 pedals were placed at one end and a food magazine at the other. A response on the "correct" pedal caused a pellet to be released at the food magazine; the response also cut off the mechanism so that the pellet had to be eaten (at which time a photobeam was triggered) before a second response would be rewarded. This forced the animal to shuttle from food end to pedal end of the box in order to get food. The correct pedal was changed from day to day; one day the correct pedal was the wide plastic lever on the left, the next day it was the long white metal lever on the right, and so on. The aim of this method was to have the animals learn and relearn approximately the same associative problem day after day, with the level of difficulty remaining relatively high even after long practice, and to have the animals train and test them-

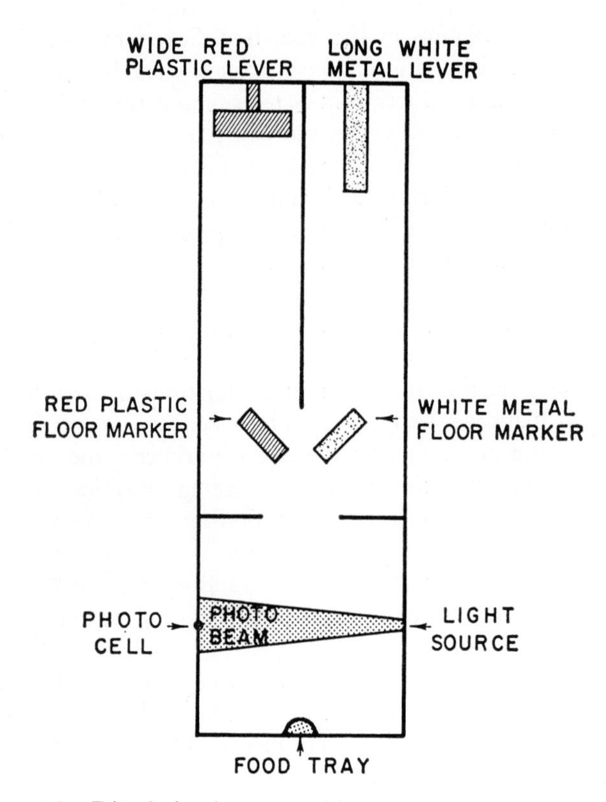


*Figure 4.8.* Discrimination reversal box.

selves without the intervention of the experimenter to start each trial. The long delay between response and reward served to maintain the difficulty level. Tests were made only after long preliminary training had eliminated progressive improvement.

After pretraining, electric stimulation was introduced in midbrain or forebrain structures to find whether it would disrupt performance of this simple associative task. The electric stimulation was applied in trains of 0.5-second every 3 seconds for the whole period of the test. The animals were scored in terms of the number of trials needed on a given day to meet a criterion of 10 consecutive correct responses. With electrodes in the midbrain system, stimulation produced no change in these scores, but with electrodes in the forebrain system radical interference was produced. Scores during stimulation deviated from control scores by more than three standard deviations. Thus the same forebrain electric stimulation that had organized associative patterns when given as reinforcement disorganized similar patterns when applied on an uncontingent basis.

From the foregoing data one may perhaps conclude that at certain points in the forebrain system electric stimulation had definite effect both in organizing and disorganizing associative behavior, whereas stimulation in the midbrain system had much less effect on such behavior.

## ADAPTIVE FUNCTIONS

The data have indicated that escape behaviors were elicited by the stimulation of structures supposed to be in the midbrain system and operant responses were reinforced by the stimulation of structures supposed to be parts of the forebrain system. Response patterns involving choice were relatively little affected by midbrain stimulation. They were greatly affected by forebrain stimulation; they were reinforced (organization was promoted) by forebrain stimulation when it was made contingent on performance of a response pattern, and disorganized by uncontingent application of the same stimulus.

Three speculative questions arise: (1) as to the functional significance that might lie behind such a dual-motive arrangement, (2) as to the phylogenetic origin of the duality, and (3) as to actual mechanisms that might be involved. Without any particular evidence, it can be supposed that the aversive system may be a device for actual escape from destructive conditions already imposed. Its phylogenetic origin, if the central nervous system may be regarded as a set of invaginated receptor systems, would be the somesthetic apparatus and particularly the pain system which warns the organism of imminent threat. Its mechanism would involve action during stimulation and cessation on withdrawal of the stimulus. The behavior would look as if it were directed toward a goal, namely stimulus withdrawal, because it would start on commencement of stimulation and continue until stimulus withdrawal occurred. One might speak of negative feedback only because the behavior would cause a change of state in the environment, which in turn would shut off the behavior. By the same reasoning, it could be guessed that the adaptive function of the forebrain system was to lead the organism forward toward scarce substances of the environment, to lead the organism forward even at times when there was no immediate threat to survival by their lack. The scarcity of these objects would imply that by waiting to the last minute the organism would likely die, but by getting them before the need was imminent they would be available when needed. Phylogenetically, this system would derive from the olfactory receptor system, placed up front to help the animal to "home" on food. The mechanism might entail positive feedback in that the behavior leading to reinforcement would be repeated until reinforcement ceased. Thus the behavior would in turn produce more of the same behavior.

# CORTICAL INFLUENCE ON OPERANT AND REFLEX BEHAVIOR

## SPREADING DEPRESSION AND BEHAVIOR

When the cerebral cortex is subjected to certain strong stimulations of electrical, chemical, or mechanical variety, waves of "spreading depression" (SD) move out from the point of stimulation to encompass the entire hemisphere, that is, half of the neocortex (Leão, 1944). These waves produce dysfunction of the whole hemisphere and a resulting abnormal function in other CNS structures which lasts from 20 minutes to several hours, depending on the severity of the initiating stimulus. The process is reversible.

A well-known and outstanding series of studies by Bureš, Burešova, and their collaborators (1958, 1959, 1960) has utilized SD as a tool in brain-and-behavior research. These studies have contributed substantially to the understanding of cortical influences on midbrain and forebrain motive systems. Before this contribution is discussed, some of the basic SD behavioral experiments need to be mentioned.

Bureš, Burešova, and Zahorova (1958) showed that simple alimentary and avoidance conditioned responses (CRs) were abolished during bilateral waves of spreading depression produced by application of potassium chloride (KCl) on the cortex through small holes. Repeated waves of spreading depression elicited by 25 percent KCl lasted 3 to 5 hours and abolished the conditioned responses for the entire period.

In studying the interaction of the cerebral hemispheres in learning, Bureš and Burešova (1960) showed that avoidance CRs elaborated during unilateral SD in the left hemisphere were not evidenced during retention tests with SD in the other hemisphere. A habit was taught to animals with both hemispheres intact, and then was extinguished by teaching the animals an incompatible habit during SD in the left hemisphere. On retest the animals with left SD displayed the incompatible CR while the animals with right SD displayed the original CR. Bureš concluded that conflicting information may be stored independently in the two hemispheres.

Bureš and Burešova also suggested that intervening trials with both hemispheres intact might somehow help the memory trace to move from one hemisphere to the other. Russell and Ochs (1961) demonstrated that one trial with both hemispheres intact was sufficient to move the trace from one side to the other. Bureš concluded that the memory trace, once formed, could be transmitted only to those parts of the brain that were activated when the animal was performing the conditioned response.

The Bureš group showed that there is some tendency for SD to abolish escape and feeding responses (1959). This was true even though SD did not affect the normal posture and mobility of the animals. The group also showed a possible path of these cortical influences on reflex behaviors. When units in the mesencephalic reticular formation were studied during SD experiments, an augmentation in the frequency of firing at these subcortical levels occurred at the beginning of the SD wave (1959). Thus a cortical-reticular inhibitory influence appeared to have been removed.

## SPREADING DEPRESSION AND THE THEORY OF SELF-STIMULATION

The work of Bureš in the subcortical direction was relevant to the problem of separation and interaction of dual-motive systems. In fact, SD analysis caused a basic reformulation of the problem. What began as a distinction between appetitive and aversive behavior first changed to a distinction between voluntary and involuntary behavior, and then, by increase in scope, to one between operant and reflex behavior. The term "operant" denotes all voluntary-like behavior which obeys the law of effect, that is, survives in the animal's repertory on the basis of its adaptive consequences (Skinner, 1938). The reflex category includes all environmentally triggered behavior, whether of the unconditioned or the conditioned reflex type. The operant category contains a far larger proportion of appetitive behavior than aversive, while the reflex category is similarly overbalanced in the direction of aversive responses.

## DETAILS OF BEHAVIOR DURING A FOUR-CONTINGENCY TEST

Many animals have been prepared with probes which permit alternation between stimulation in the purely aversive mid-brain system and stimulation in the purely rewarding fore-brain system. A four-contingency method was used (see Figure 4.9), applying in continuous repetition, a cycle of four different 2-minute tests: (1) rewarding stimulus with self-stimulation test, (2) aversive stimulus with self-stimulation test, (3) rewarding stimulus with escape test, and (4) aversive stimulus with escape test. After each 8-minute cycle, another cycle was started.

During Test 1 classical self-stimulation appeared (see Figure 4.10). During Test 2 there was rarely any behavior at all because the animal did not choose to self-stimulate via the aversive midbrain electrode. The detailed behaviors presented during Tests 3 and 4 need mention for a clear understanding of the effects observed under SD. During Test 3, with stimulation in a pure appetitive area (for example, Animal No. 2 in Figure 4.10), the animal was very active; particularly, there was sniffing, but there was also avid forward movement and manipulation of all encountered objects. The manipulation encompassed every item in the test chamber except the lever that would terminate the brain shocks. The animal avoided the lever at a far better than chance level, often moving toward it but not depressing it. One could use the term "operant avoidance behavior" to describe it; the animal appeared to "purposefully" avoid the termination of brain shocks (Bureš *et al.*, 1961).

Similarly, during Test 4, with electrodes in a pure aversive area there was a great deal of unconditioned behavior. However, the animal did not sniff and often did not move forward; instead it backed up and sprang toward the top of the testing chamber, obviously attempting to escape. This unconditioned escape behavior moved the animal about the cage and regu-

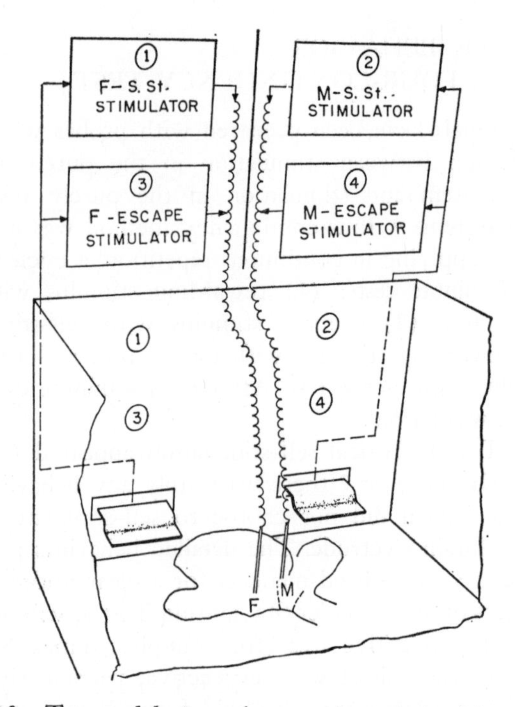


*Figure 4.9.* Two-pedal, 4-contingency box. Animal is repeatedly presented with the following cycle: (1) 2 minutes of F (forebrain) self-stimulation; (2) 2 minutes of M (midbrain) self-stimulation; (3) 2 minutes of F escape; and (4) 2 minutes of M escape. The F electrodes are those implanted in forebrain system; M electrodes are those in the midbrain system. During Periods (1) and (3) the left lever, and during Periods (2) and (4) the right lever, turns the stimulus on or off. Indicator lights above the pedals are turned on as the corresponding program is presented.

larly brought it into contact with all objects, including the escape lever. This gross responding yielded lever depression at a greater than chance level, but it was "unskilled escape behavior" and could be thought of as unconditioned and reflex in nature.

It was only with considerable training that this gross behavior

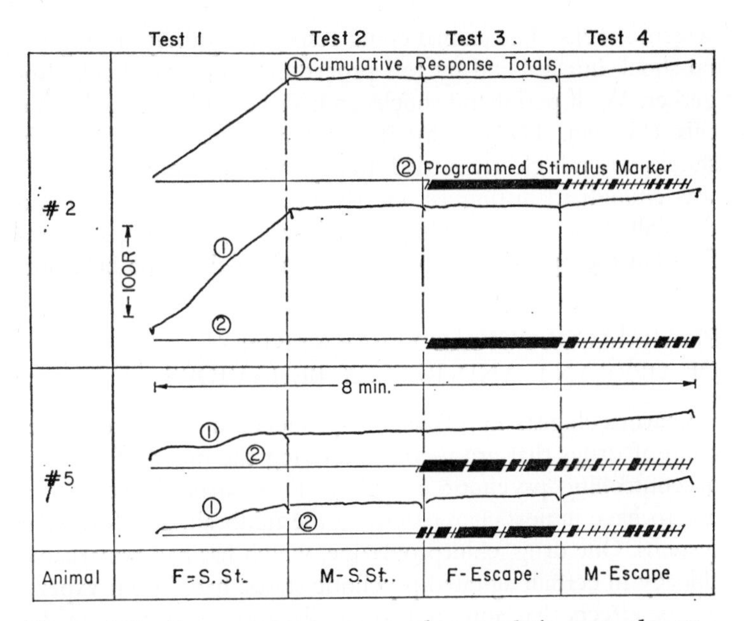


*Figure 4.10.* Four-contingency records: cumulative recorder tracings for 2 animals. In each case, 2 complete cycles are given to indicate the stability of the behavior. The top line, (1), in each cycle represents the response speed in terms of slope (45° = 100 rpm). Vertical dotted lines mark the end of the 2-minute periods. The baseline, (2), in each cycle has a stimulus marker activated during escape. If the escape stimulus goes continuously (½ second on, ½ second off), the marker produces a continuous black bar. Each 4-second (or longer) period of escape is indicated by a break in this black bar.

gave way to a skilled performance of the escape response. When this finally occurred, the animal waited patiently at the pedal while the stimulus was off, already prepared to respond, and then it responded quickly each time the brain shock occurred. When the animal developed this behavior, the number of brain shocks actually delivered became very small—a minimal number so far as the experiments were concerned. Complete avoidance did not occur with midbrain system shocks. The animal could respond regularly during the no-shock interval and by this procedure avoid the shock altogether. With peripheral shocks animals could be trained to do this (Sidman, 1953); why it did not occur with midbrain shocks was not clearly settled. In any event, for our purposes it was enough to distinguish clearly between the unskilled and the skilled escape responding, which were spoken of as the reflex and the operant components of the final escape behavior.

## PHARMACOLOGICAL SEPARATION OF OPERANT AND REFLEX BEHAVIORS

Pharmacologists have recently produced a variegated spectrum of drugs that are useful in altering the mood of patients or controlling psychotic agitation. These drugs have turned out to have important relations to the midbrain and forebrain systems. One drug, chlorpromazine, which has had remarkable efficacy in certain agitated psychotic states, had, in our experiments, effects that appeared to parallel those of spreading depression.

Earlier work indicated a chlorpromazine effect that was greater against forebrain reward than against midbrain escape behavior (Olds, 1959; Olds and Travis, 1960). The interpretation that the drug acted selectively against positive reinforcement was first called to question by the experiments of others. Work of Gavlichek (1958) and Cook and Weidley (1957) made it clear that chloropromazine also acted selectively against some aversive behaviors and could spare reflex responses of the alimentary system.

On retesting chlorpromazine in the four-contingency apparatus the tendency was readily apparent for self-stimulation to be counteracted immediately and for some escape behavior to continue (Olds, 1960). Closer inspection of the data revealed two additional effects (see Figure 4.11). First, the skillful component of the escape response disappeared almost si-

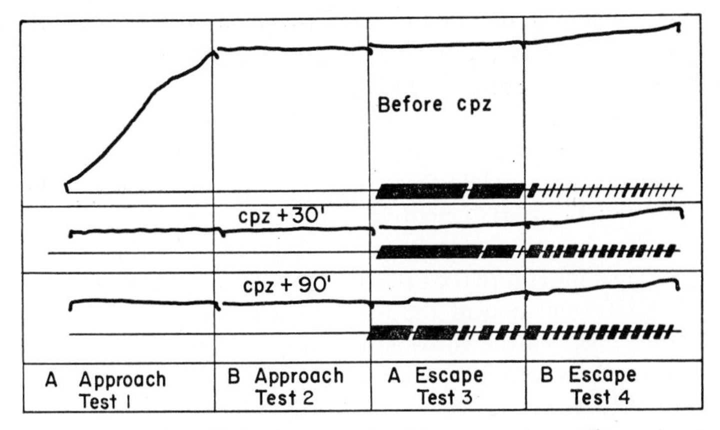


*Figure 4.11.* Detailed picture of chlorpromazine effects in 4-contingency box with forebrain system (A) and midbrain system (B) electrodes. The first tracings were taken before injection of chlorpromazine; the second, 30 minutes after i.p. injection; and the third, 90 minutes after injection at the height of the chlorpromazine effect.

multaneously with the disappearance of self-stimulation; only unskilled escape behavior survived. The animal returned under chlorpromazine to his original gross escape efforts, performing the jumping responses with great force. Pedal responses still occurred, but largely because the animal moved so much in its unconditioned escape efforts that it could not miss the pedal.

Second, during the forebrain escape test, an event occurred which seemed surprising when it was first observed. While response rates in all other tests were depressed, Test 3 showed a response increment (Figure 4.11). The fact was surprising only if one forgot that the animal was always responding during Test 3; almost all possible responses except the pedal response occurred. When one thinks of this as an active pedal-avoidance response, the problem answers itself: when all other operant responses failed, operant avoidance during Test 3 failed, too; the animal no longer refrained from turning off the hypothalamic shocks. In other words, there was a shift from no response to the random pedal tendency.

This detailed study seemed to make it clear that operant behavior was counteracted by chlorpromazine; reflex behavior was spared. Thus while there seemed to be a clear anatomical distinction between appetitive and aversive responses, there seemed to be a pharmacological support for a distinction between operant and reflex behavior. However, we continued to seek a reformulation of the problem which might yield congruence between the anatomical and the pharmacological distinctions. It was here that the SD studies were most fruitful.

## SD SEPARATION OF OPERANT AND REFLEX BEHAVIORS

The SD tests on self-stimulation were initiated in our laboratory by Bureš when he visited this country in 1959 to attend the second Macy conference on *The Central Nervous System and Behavior* (Bureš, 1959). He spent several days starting our series of tests, and then, after he had returned to his own laboratory, he, together with Burešova and Fifkova, undertook a set of physiological investigations to study neural activity at appetitive and aversive centers during the SD period. In these studies microelectrodes were placed in the same general area as our stimulating electrodes. The combined results were published in *Physiologia Bohemoslovenica* (Bureš *et al.*, 1961). Of this study we shall discuss first the behavioral half and then the physiological half.

*Methods of the SD Behavioral Test.* Ten male albino rats were used. Each had in the midbrain and forebrain system electrodes pretested to yield dependable escape and self-stimulation behavior, respectively.

After a long period of pretraining in the four-contingency apparatus, rats anesthetized with ether were prepared, as shown in Figure 4.12. Openings 3 millimeters in diameter were

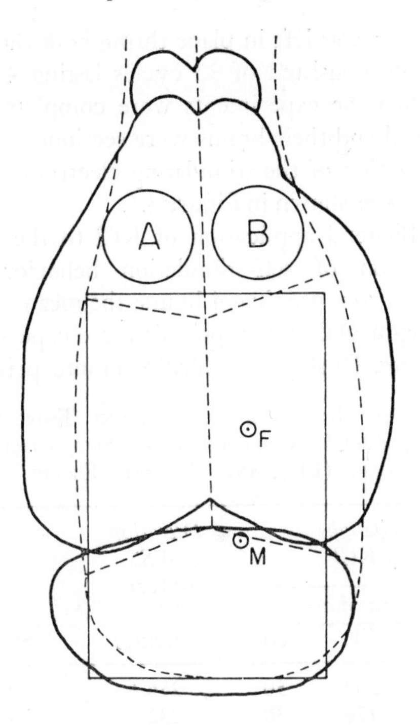


*Figure 4.12.* Preparation in SD behavioral experiments. This shows the rat brain as it would look from above; dotted lines indicate places where bones of the skull join. A placque holding F and M electrodes covered almost the whole surface of the skull. Openings at A and B were used for application of 25 percent KCl (Bureš *et al.*, 1961).

made above the frontal regions of both hemispheres. Skin was then replaced over the skull and fastened with one loose suture.

By the following morning the rats had recovered. The suture was clipped and the blood clot removed from the openings before preliminary testing. Then 4 complete cycles (32 minutes) of testing were run as controls. After this, 22 percent KCl was applied bilaterally with 2 x 2 millimeter filter papers.

The filter paper was left in place throughout the remainder of the test, which consisted of 32 cycles lasting 4 hours and 16 minutes. When the experiments were completed, the animals were sacrificed and their brains were sectioned and stained for precise localization of the stimulating electrode tips. Electrode tracks appeared as shown in Figure 4.5.

*Results.* Bilateral application of KCl to the cortex caused total elimination of self-stimulation behavior for periods ranging from 1 to more than 4 hours; the mean was 2.33 hours. Effects on tegmental and hypothalamic escape behavior were far less definite. During the third 8-minute period after KCl

TABLE 4.1. Response Rates during Third 8-minute Interval after KCL Application for Self-stimulation (SS), Forebrain Escape (FE), and Midbrain Escape (ME) Tests*

| *Behavior changes caused by KCl* | | | | *Duration of SS effect in minutes* | *Mean Control rpm on Day 30**** | | |
|---|---|---|---|---|---|---|---|
| Rat No. | Percent of control SS | FE | ME | | SS | FE | ME |
| 1 | 0 | 200 | 50 | 256+ | 99 | 3 | 10 |
| 2 | 1 | 170 | 30 | 232 | 76 | 4 | 7 |
| 3 | 0 | 125 | 35 | 128 | 82 | 8 | 12 |
| 4 | 7 | 115 | 50 | 132 | 68 | 1 | 22 |
| 5 | 0 | 100 | 60 | 240 | 66 | 0 | 10 |
| 6 | 0 | 100 | 90 | 64 | 22 | 3 | 9 |
| 7 | 0 | 95 | 0 | 104 | 108 | 6 | 6 |
| 8 | 0 | 80 | 50 | 112 | 75 | 3 | 5 |
| 9 | 0 | 50 | ** | 88 | 45 | 3 | 0 |
| 10 | 0 | 20 | 0 | 60 | 37 | 5 | 19 |
| Mean | 1 | 106 | 41 | 140 | | | |

* The tests were given as percentage of control rates taken earlier on same day. Also, the duration of the self-stimulation effect is given in minutes from the time of KCl application to the time when the SS rate rose above 10 responses per minute (rpm). In the last 3 columns mean control rates for cycles 1-12 on Day 30 are given in responses per minute.

** Control rate taken earlier the same day was 0.

*** Day 30 was the day preceding the KCl test.

application the mean Test 1 self-stimulation rate was 1 percent of control; the Test 3 (forebrain "escape") rate was 106 percent of control; and the Test 4 (midbrain escape) rate was 41 percent of control (Table 4.1). Even though midbrain escape behavior was depressed and sometimes eliminated by KCl, in all cases there were periods during which the midbrain response continued after total disappearance of forebrain self-stimulation (Figures 4.13 and 4.14). Although not recorded systematically, it was noted that unconditioned escape responses often became even more violent during periods when

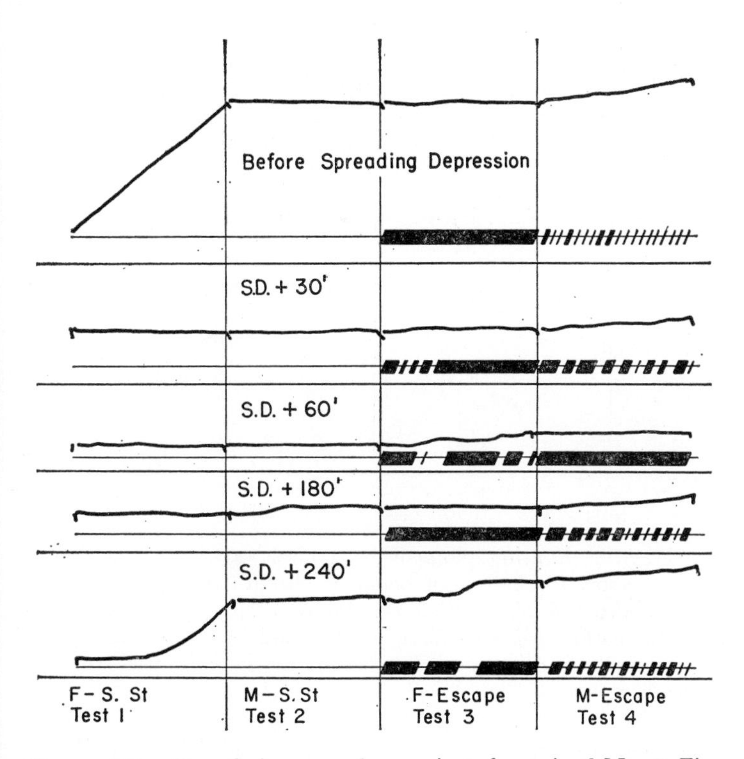


*Figure 4.13.* Cumulative recorder tracings for animal No. 5. Five complete cycles are given; the first before SD, the others ½, 1, 3, and 4 hours, respectively, after application of KCl to cortex.

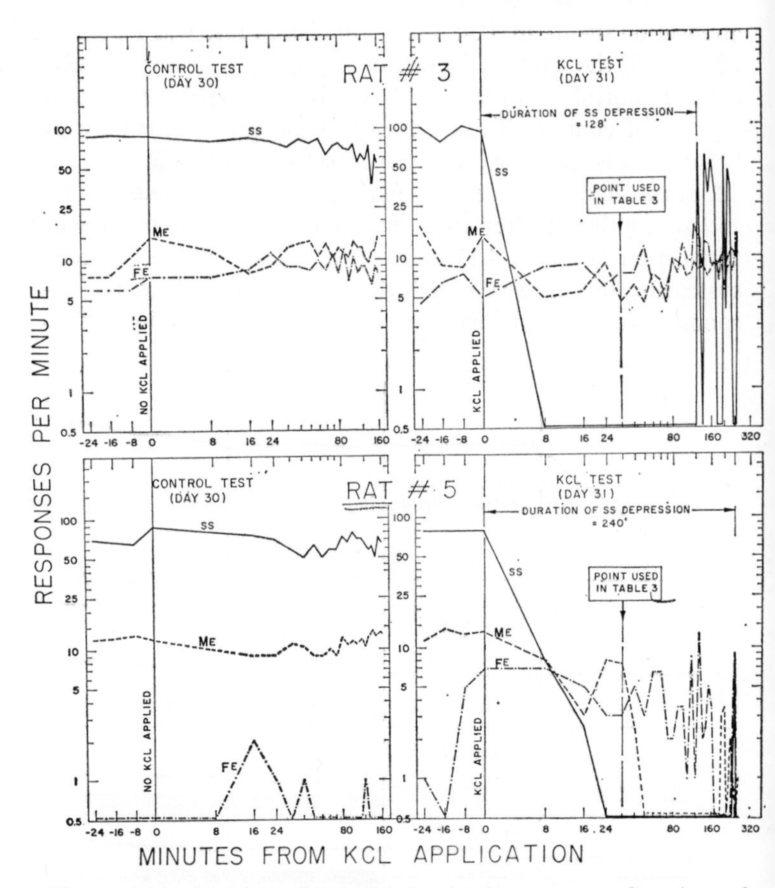


*Figure 4.14.* Log-log plots of behavioral rates as a function of time to show the course of behavior changes after application of KCl to cortex (Bureš *et al.*, 1961). Abbreviations are: SS—forebrain self-stimulation, ME—midbrain escape, and FE—forebrain escape. As the midbrain self-stimulation rate during Period 2 was usually 0, it was not plotted.

the learned escape responses were depressed. Similarly, Test 3 (forebrain escape) responding always showed some periods of augmentation after KCl application. The general tendency of

Test 3 escape to increase was obscured in several cases by augmentation in Test 3 escape behavior which occurred on the day of SD tests but before application of KCl (Figure 4.14, Rat No. 5). This occurrence presumably was a consequence of opening the skull on the previous day and removing the blood clot on the day of the test.

From this data it seemed reasonable to conclude that voluntary or operant behaviors disappeared as a group during spreading depression. This included all self-stimulation, the pedal avoidance during Test 3, and the skilled pedal behavior during Test 4. Only a reflex or unlearned component of the escape behavior usually survived.

Thus SD divided behavior along the line dividing operant from reflex, rather than along the line dividing appetitive from aversive responses. It was surprising, therefore, to find that an anatomical distinction which appeared to follow the appetitive-aversion line resulted from the SD single-unit tests of Bureš, Burešova, and Fifkova (Bureš *et al.*, 1961).

## SD SEPARATION OF FOREBRAIN AND MIDBRAIN UNITS

*Methods.* In this case (Bureš *et al.*, 1961) steel microelectrodes were lowered into the midbrain location where stimulation produced escape behavior, and the forebrain location where stimulation yielded appetitive behavior. When single-unit responses were observed, a baseline response frequency was established and then a mild (2 percent) KCl application was made unilaterally in the cortex to study the effects on the unit response rates. This milder application produced a cortical slow wave of 1 to 5 minutes, and a brief unilateral cortical depression lasting from 10 to 20 minutes (Figure 4.15). In other tests (Rüdiger and Fifkova, 1963), a similar SD caused a 10- to 20-minute impairment of self-stimulation when SD and self-stimulation electrodes were on the same side of the brain.

*Results.* The most common effect on units recorded at

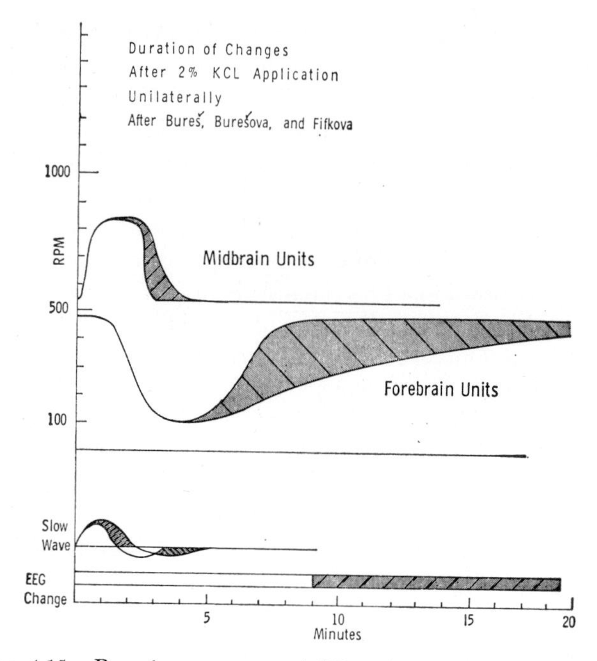


*Figure 4.15.* Rough summary of SD unit experiments of Bureš, Burešova, and Fifkova (Bureš *et al.*, 1961). In all cases shading is used to indicate the area of variability.

midbrain escape points was an increase in response rate, which amounted to more than 50 percent and which coincided quite well in time with the period of the cortical slow wave. The onset of the increase came immediately after the commencement of the slow wave, and the return to normal came at about the same time as the termination of the slow wave. The slow wave is only the beginning of the SD. The change in midbrain units did not continue to the end of the SD.

With electrodes at the forebrain reward point, however, the results were quite different: there was a depression rather than an augmentation. The onset of the effect was delayed for about 2 minutes and the hypothalamic unit depression was extended through time to the end of the EEG depression (Figure 4.15).

SD physiological tests thus showed a selective depression of unit activity in the anatomical region associated with self-stimulation, while SD behavioral tests showed a selective depression of all operant behavior of both self-stimulatory and aversive origin. It thus appeared that, in some complicated fashion, the anatomical region of self-stimulation might be involved in both appetitive and aversive behaviors insofar as these were operant. This suggested specifically that the self-stimulation area, by some interaction with the aversive area, might be involved in the mediation of operant escape behavior. From the data on hand, the most likely form of this relationship appeared to be an inhibitory action directed from the area where stimulation yielded aversive effects to the area where stimulation yielded appetitive ones.

The time relationship involved in the unit behaviors (Figure 4.15) indicated at least the possibility of such an inhibitory relation. These were such that the advancing cortical wave might have caused the burst of midbrain firing immediately. This burst in the midbrain system might then have mediated the hypothalamic depression.

Other considerations also suggested that such a pathway might be involved. Several physiological investigations (for example, Adey, 1958, and Hugelin and Bonvallet, 1957) demonstrated a cortico-midbrain inhibitory influence that could explain a midbrain burst resulting from cortical depression. But no cortico-hypothalamic facilitatory influence had been demonstrated that could explain a forebrain-reward systems depression following a cortical depression. While the possibility of such an influence was taken seriously, the alternative hypothesis also had to be given serious consideration, that the excessive activity at the midbrain escape point inhibited activity in the forebrain reward area.

Such an inhibitory relation would offer a means of rendering equivalent the reinforcing events following the hypothalamic self-stimulation response and the midbrain escape response. In each case the reinforcing event would have caused augmented activity in the lateral hypothalamus; in the case of self-stimulation it would have resulted from direct stimulation; in the tegmental case it would have been a release or rebound from inhibition. From this theoretical basis it was suggested that possibly the learned component of the escape behavior was sustained by the same mechanism as the self-stimulation, and therefore both could be expected to disappear together under pharmacological or physiological manipulations which impaired lateral hypothalamic function. This, of course, was precisely what the pharmacological and SD experiments had indicated.

## DISCUSSION

*Mediation of aversive operants by self-stimulation mechanisms.* In both the pharmacological and SD experiments the manipulations appeared to act selectively on the brain areas associated with self-stimulation, and it appeared that these were not merely substrates of appetitive behavior but rather substrates of all operant responses. This suggested an inversion of the classical drive-reduction theory which has had such a long history in behavioral psychology (Miller, 1957). The contention would be that aversive reactions, at least the ones that obey the "law of effect," might be appetitive mechanisms in disguise. The drive-reduction view seems to hold just the opposite, namely, that all apparent pursuit tendencies actually represent the organism's thinly veiled tendency to escape from the gnawing internal drive state.

## A PHYLOGENETIC FABLE

The greatest barrier to common acceptance of the view that homing reactions and spontaneous behaviors have mechanisms of their own quite different from the simpler reflex ones is possibly the difficulty involved in answering two simple questions: If homing mechanisms exist, how do they work? If they work, how did they come to pass?

Not only do we lack valid scientific answers to the questions but we also have some trouble imagining the form that the answers might take. An appropriate conclusion to this discussion on SD might be another approximate answer in the form of a phylogenetic fable (Figures 4.16 and 4.17).

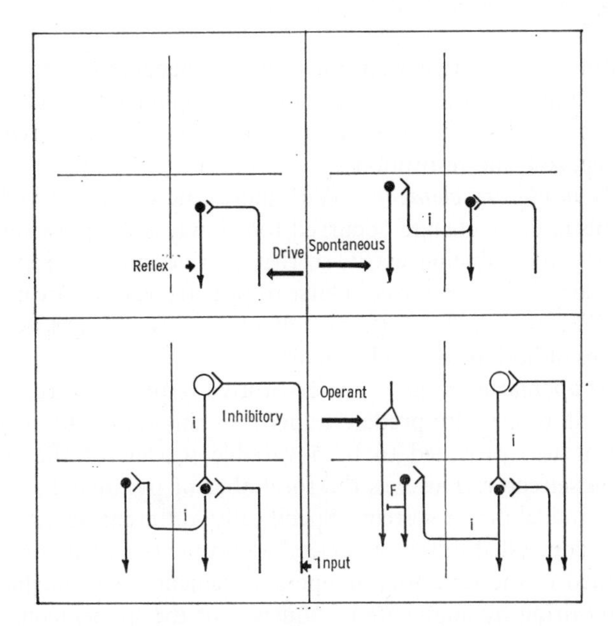


*Figure 4.16.* A phylogenetic fable.

*The reflex element.* There was first a reflex arc that did nothing until drive was imminent. This was the forefather of the ergotropic and sympathetic response system (the response systems involved in fight, fright, and flight).

*The spontaneous element.* During periods of no-drive, time was wasted so that an evolutionary trend yielded a spontaneous

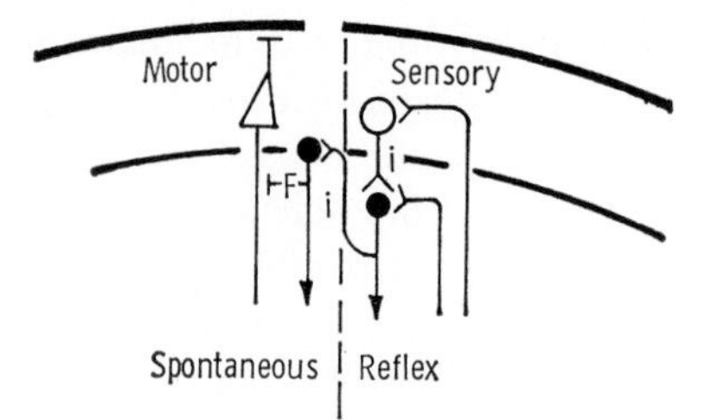


*Figure 4.17.* Design for a simple brain.

restitutive device that went into action whenever there was no drive. This was the forefather of the trophotropic and parasympathetic response systems (the response systems involved in sleep, rest, and restitution).

*The inhibitory element.* With increasing complexity of the organism, drive change occurred too slowly after presentation of the drive-reducing event, so that a drive inhibitor sensitive to sensory input (sensitive at first to primary rewards) came to pass. This was the forefather of olfactory, visceral, and sensory systems of both paleo- and neocortex.

*The operant element.* The restitutive responses were, however, still too rigidly predetermined; for this reason an operant element was provided to be a variable servant of the spontaneous effector. This was the forefather of pyramidal and extrapyramidal motor systems. Specifically, different operant elements controlled different skeletal adjustments which could be included in the repertory if operant elements were facilitated during firing by augmented frequency of the spontaneous elements.

Thus a 4-quadrant brain design might be imagined (see Figure 4.17). The quadrants would contain (1) reflex, (2) spontaneous, (3) inhibitory, and (4) operant elements. The aversive electrodes would be thought to affect the reflex units; hence the reflex quadrant would be the midbrain system. Since the self-stimulation electrodes would be affecting the spontaneous units, the spontaneous quadrant would represent the focus of the forebrain system. Primary rewards from the environment would be projected to the inhibitory (sensory) cortices and from there inhibit or counteract the reflex drive-units. Thus the inhibitory or sensory quadrant would be the sensory aspect of the paleocortex. Gross directions of behavior would originate in the operant elements. Thus the operant or motor quadrant would be the motor aspect of the paleocortical or extrapyramidal systems. While not relevant to our argument, it seems possible that if such an arrangement existed, temporary connections might be formed among the dendritic elaborations of the motor and sensory cortical units.

Imagination aside, the drug and SD experiments suggested (1) that there might be a dependence of all operant behavior on the same set of elements (those at the self-stimulation focus), and (2) the cortex might inhibit units at an aversive point (that is, units in the supposed midbrain system), and these in turn might inhibit those at the self-stimulation focus.

# THE ANATOMICAL SUBSTRATE

## POINTS OF REFERENCE IN THE BRAIN

In the following discussion some more detailed points of reference in the brain will be needed repeatedly. To establish these points, the following brief review and elaboration of the basic organization of the central nervous system is given. In most mammals one finds in front of the spinal cord: (1) the medulla oblongata or hindbrain; (2) the mesencephalon or midbrain; (3) the cerebellum, growing like a mushroom planted on the upper boundary between medulla and midbrain; (4) the diencephalon or between-brain, in front of the midbrain; and (5) the telencephalon or endbrain, located in front of the diencephalon and consisting of the olfactory bulb, some subcortical nuclei, and the cerebral cortex (see Figure 4.18).

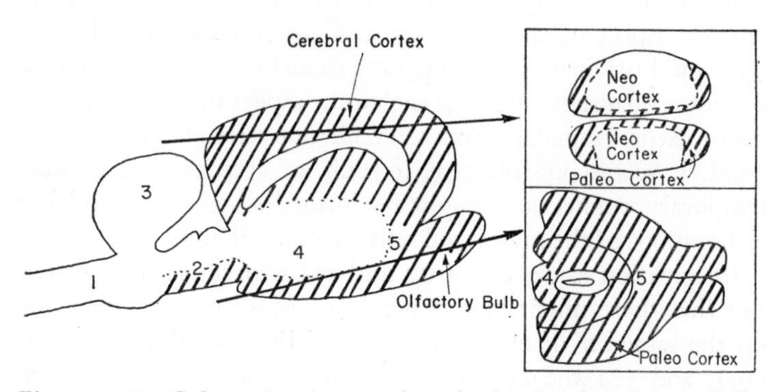


*Figure 4.18.* Schematic picture of rat brain showing (1) medulla, (2) midbrain, (3) cerebellum, (4) diencephalon, and (5) telencephalon, with olfactory-chemoreceptor systems shaded. In the upper horizontal section the maner in which paleocortex surrounds neocortex is shown. In the lower horizontal section the manner in which paleocortex surrounds lower diencephalon (hypothalamus) is shown.

The cerebral cortex may be conceived of as blossoming above the boundary between the diencephalon and olfactory bulbs in a fashion similar to that in which the cerebellum sits above the medulla and midbrain. The cerebral cortex, however, is far larger and hence spreads out over many of the previously mentioned structures, covering many of them completely. The main distinction in the cortex is that between the borders that make up the paleocortex and the neocortex (which makes up much the larger—in-between—parts of the cortex). The paleocortex is phylogenetically related to the olfactory system and may still be involved in processing information derived from receptors specialized for detecting chemical changes in the blood and cerebrospinal fluid. The rest of the cortex is related mainly to somesthetic, auditory, visual, and motor systems. In the diencephalon a similar distinction exists between the hypothalamus, the lower (ventral) part which is heavily related to olfaction, chemoreception, and to the paleocortex; and the thalamus, the upper (dorsal) part that is similarly related to the neocortex. The same dorsal-ventral relation has also been shown in the midbrain where in dorsal areas somesthetic, auditory, and visual information is processed, but where in ventral areas there are fibers from olfactory, rhinencephalic, and hypothalamic systems.

## THE FOCUS OF POSITIVE REINFORCEMENT

Positive reinforcement produced by ESB was originally discovered with electrodes placed in a boundary region between the rhinencephalic systems of telencephalon and the related systems of hypothalamus (Olds and Milner, 1954).

It was first thought to be mainly related to the rhinencephalon. Experiments showed that positive reinforcing effects could be produced by stimulating some parts of almost all rhinencephalic structures (Olds, 1956a). In rats it became clear that more than half the electrodes placed at random in the rhinencephalon would yield positive reinforcement.

Later studies showed that the focus of the phenomenon, if maximum responding for a minimum ESB could be taken to indicate a focus, was not in the rhinencephalon but rather in the hypothalamus or midbrain or possibly even farther back (Olds, 1956a; Olds, Travis, and Schwing, 1960; Olds and Olds, 1963). In fact, there is a pair of long tubes extending from olfactory bulbs and rhinencephalon which pass along the two outer edges of hypothalamus and into similar (ventrolateral) areas of midbrain. While much of the area between, and surrounding, these tubes seem to yield positive reinforcement when ESB is applied, the tubes themselves appear to comprise the focus of the phenomenon, if maximal effects from minimal stimulation is used as the criterion. The forebrain system is thus subdivided into two parts: the olfactory-cortical (rhinencephalic) part which forms a mild reward field, and the olfactory-midbrain (hypothalamic) part which forms an intense reward focus (see Figure 4.19).

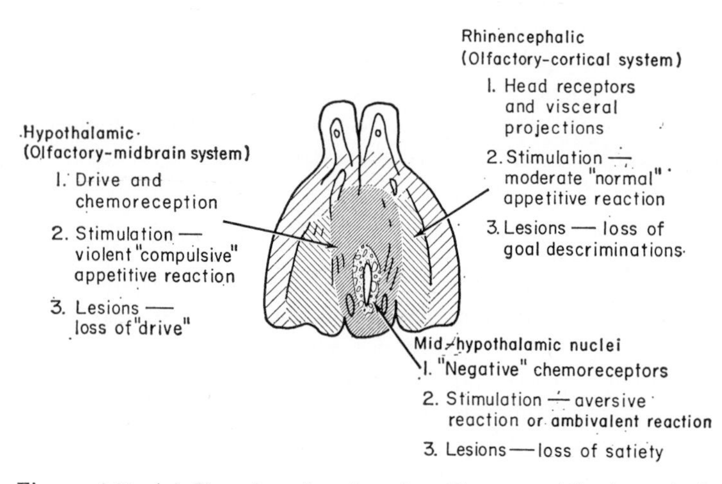


*Figure 4.19.* (a) Drawing showing the olfactory-midbrain and olfactory-cortical systems and the midhypothalamic nuclei.

A number of differences between the positive reinforcement produced by hypothalamic ESB and that produced by rhinencephalic ESB have been observed. As these differences appear to be important both for an understanding of the internal organization of the positive reinforcement mechanism and for an understanding of its integration into larger brain systems, we shall list and discuss four of them here. (1) In experiments where each response was followed by one ESB reward, response rates were far higher with hypothalamic than with rhinencephalic stimulation. Animals would press a lever 10,000 times an hour to stimulate lateral hypothalamus, but only about 500 times an hour, under the same conditions, to stimulate the septal or amygdaloid areas, both of which are subdivisions of the rhinencephalon (Olds, Travis, and Schwing, 1960). (2) The animals' "appetites" for lateral hypothalamic stimulation

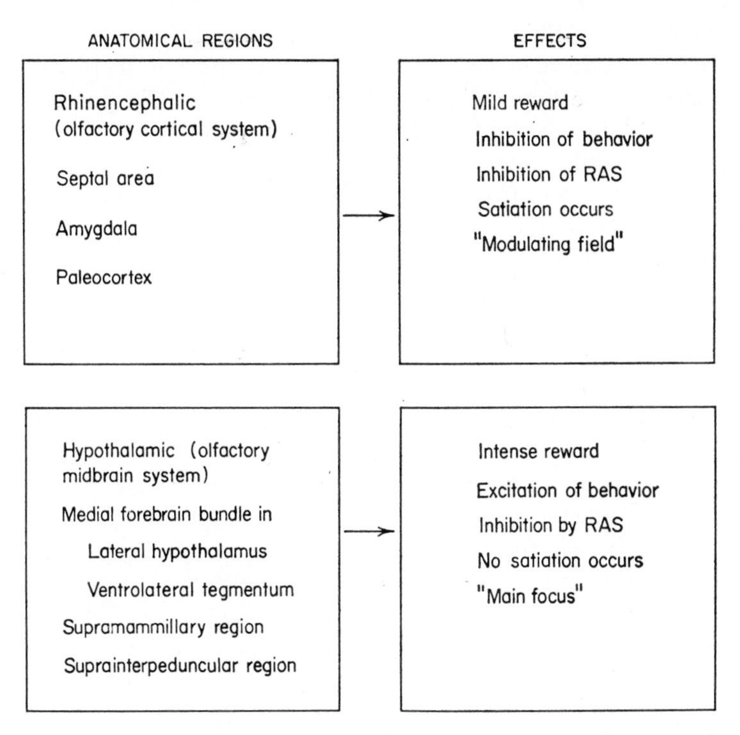


*Figure 4.19*, continued. (b) Two kinds of brain stimulus reward.

often seemed relatively insatiable, whereas a definite satiation point was usually reached in experiments with rhinencephalic stimulation. Animals stimulated themselves in the septal area several thousand times and then stopped for the day; animals stimulated themselves in lateral hypothalamus hour after hour, maintaining a rate of several thousand responses per hour and stopping only when a state of physical exhaustion appeared (Olds, 1958). (3) The ESB reward produced by hypothalamic stimulation seemed to be accompanied by a heightened general activity level (Roberts, 1958), whereas the ESB reward produced by rhinencephalic stimulation seemed often to be accompanied by some inhibition of general activity (Olds,

1956b). (4) While there were some apparent pain- or anxiety-relieving effects of ESB reward in rhinencephalon, there were places in the hypothalamus where ESB reward did not have these effects (Brady, 1961).

These differences were best understood when compared with earlier data from lesion and ablation experiments, which suggested that the effects of rewarding and punishing stimuli in the environment were lost if rhinencephalic parts of the system were ablated (Kluever and Bucy, 1939; Schreiner and Kling, 1953). On the other hand, control of the system by chemical or hormonal states or by visceral conditions of drive or satiety were lost if diencephalic parts of the system were destroyed (Teitelbaum, 1955; Teitelbaum and Stellar, 1954). Such data suggested that the rewarding stimuli from the environment might be projected first to rhinencephalic systems of telencephalon and from there might exercise influence over a hypothalamic focal point. However, they seemed also to indicate that states of organic need had influence via the hypothalamus, and this suggested that the hypothalamus, like the rhinencephalon, represented an input stage to the system and that both influences might be combined at a third focal point not yet localized.

## THE AMBIVALENT REACTIONS AND SIGN INVERSIONS

The involvement of these two subdivisions with an aversive system was first suggested by the observation that ESB in many brain areas yielded both positive and negative reinforcement (Roberts, 1958). Observations of this kind have now been made by many others (Lilly, 1958; Bower and Miller, 1958; Brown and Cohen, 1959; Olds, 1960). One may speak of the ESB in these cases as yielding ambivalent reactions; we believe that the ambivalent reactions were divided into two types, one of which made reasonably good sense but not the other. In the sensible case, the animal responded to turn the stimulus on sparingly in an experiment where it had to respond to get stimulated. But when the same animal was stimulated repeatedly by the apparatus, the stimulus appeared to be "on" too much of the time and the animal responded by turning it off part of the time (cf. Lilly, 1958). In such cases one may suppose that in very small doses it was positively reinforcing but in larger doses it was negatively reinforcing.

The kind of ambivalent reaction we observed more often (Olds and Olds, 1953) did not make such good sense. The animal appeared to respond to turn the stimulus on even though each application of the stimulus seemed aversive. It was as though the animal could not stay away from the stimulus even though it could not stand it. The stimulus appeared to be both rewarding and aversive at the same time. In these cases, the animals often pressed the pedal regularly in the positive reinforcement experiment but at the same time struggled to escape from the field. Very energetic efforts were made to escape from the test chamber, and when these were successful the animal would not come back of its own accord. But when the animal was brought back and forced to remain in the test chamber, it did maintain a substantial rate of "positive reinforcement" behavior (still struggling futilely to escape). We spoke in these cases of "mixed reactions." It was difficult to view this more common type of ambivalent reaction without concluding that two normally incompatible patterns were being elicited simultaneously. It seemed that two mutually inhibitory systems were possibly stimulated in these experiments; therefore we supposed that the electrodes in these cases might be placed on a boundary between locations yielding positive and those yielding negative reinforcement. To test this, we studied the topographic distribution in the diencephalon of points yielding positive reinforcement, negative reinforcement, and ambivalent and neutral reactions (Olds and Olds, 1963). From rat to rat, test points were spaced 1 millimeter apart and each point was tested first for positive reinforcement and second for negative reinforcement produced by electric stimulation.

The results did not accord with our expectation that ambivalent reactions would be evoked by stimulation in an anatomical boundary region between areas yielding pure positive and those yielding pure negative reinforcement; they showed instead an unexpected and considerably more interesting distribution. As expected, there were points yielding positive reinforcement without any negative reinforcement, and vice versa. And there were points yielding ambivalent reactions. But to our surprise, the mixed effects did not fall on a topographic boundary.

To understand the organization discovered, one may imagine a black box with two large multichanneled cables entering from different sides, along with innumerable smaller cables. The black box appeared to be mainly a junction point between the two very large cable systems. The finding was: (a) stimulation of one of the cables yielded pure positive reinforcement, (b) stimulation of the other cable yielded pure negative reinforcement, and (c) stimulation of the black box itself yielded the mixed responses. The black box was the midline system of hypothalamic nuclei, all of which appeared to be involved. The two large cables were the medial forebrain bundle and the periventricular system of fibers (Ariens-Kappers, Huber, and Crosby, 1936). The medial forebrain bundle system is the lateral hypothalamic tube, also called the olfactory-midbrain system. It makes up the focus of the forebrain system. Gross anatomy suggests that its main function is to connect the hypothalamic nuclei with the talencephalon; however, it may have an even more extensive range of connections. While commonly thought to be a two-way system the main direction of conduction of the medial forebrain bundle is probably from telencephalon toward hypothalamus. The periventricular system of fibers, sometimes called the dorsal longitudinal fasciculus of Schütz, is mainly involved in relating the hypothalamic nuclei to the nonspecific systems of the thalamus and midbrain. It also may be a two-way system, but its main direction of conduction is probably away from hypothalamus toward the nonspecific systems. From the viewpoint of the present analysis, the hypothalamic nuclei might be thought to serve mainly as a way station for the transfer of messages from the medial forebrain bundle to the periventricular system of fibers, or vice versa. The actual finding (see Figure 4.20) was:

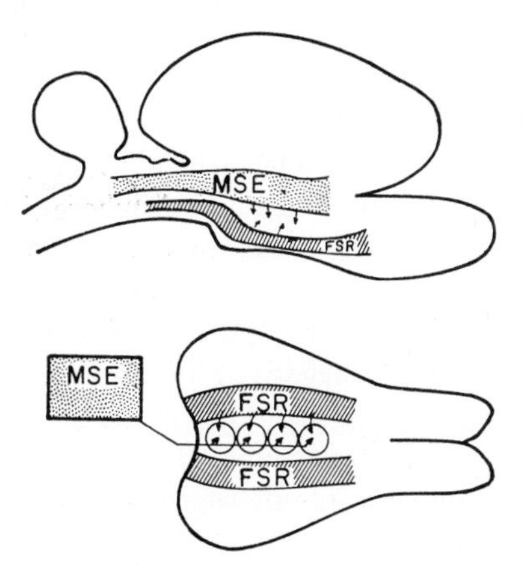


*Figure 4.20.* Schematic saggital and horizontal sections to show outcome of positive-negative reinforcement mapping study. Pure negative reinforcement behavior was produced by stimulation of the periventricular system of fibers, here labeled MSE (midbrain substrate of escape); pure positive reinforcement behavior was produced by stimulation of the lateral hypothalamic tube, here labeled FSR (forebrain substrate of reward). The nuclei (circled) into which both systems project yielded ambivalent, that is, positive-negative, reactions.

(a) stimulation of the medial forebrain bundle yielded pure positive reinforcement, (b) stimulation of the periventricular system of fibers yielded pure negative reinforcement, and (c) stimulation of all medial hypothalamic junctional areas yielded the mixed, positive-negative effects (Olds and Olds, 1963).

A marked difference between hypothalamus and thalamus was also discovered by the tests. Almost every single electrode in the hypothalamus yielded positive reinforcement; that is, the medial points yielded mixed positive-negative effects and the lateral points yielded pure positive effects. No hypothalamic points yielded pure negative or neutral effects. As for the thalamus, almost every single electrode yielded some negative reinforcement. We will not discuss this division further in the present paper, but one cannot help but wonder what is the evolutionary significance of a division in which the thalamus seems more involved in aversive behavior and the hypothalamus seems more involved in homing reactions. As for the fact that the whole hypothalamus seemed to be involved in this kind of behavior control, one may ask where the specific drive centers and the opposing autonomic centers that have long been known to occupy the hypothalamus appeared in this analysis, if all of the hypothalamus were shown to be a positive (or mixed positive-negative) reinforcement system. The answer appeared to be that this was the same hypothalamus that by other tests yielded drive and autonomic responses. But a common denominator of all these differentiated areas was their involvement in reinforcement of behavior, both positive and negative, but particularly positive.

Other possible sign inversions between afferent and efferent fiber tracts were suggested by the data, although many of them were open to question owing to the small number of cases studied, the small size of the tracts involved, and the consequent question of whether stimulation of the tract or of the area through which it passed yielded a given effect.

The particular system involving a whole series of sign inversions is called alternatively the "Papez circuit" (Papez, 1937) or the "limbic system of MacLean" (MacLean, 1949). The actual synaptic points need not be indicated for purposes of the present discussion. For those interested, we may mention particularly the relay in the habenula in the mammillary body, and that between dentate gyrus and hippocampal gyrus (Figure 4.21). While names are not important, the structure of this particular circuit is important. The Papez circuit might be conceived of, in oversimplified fashion, as involving four fami-

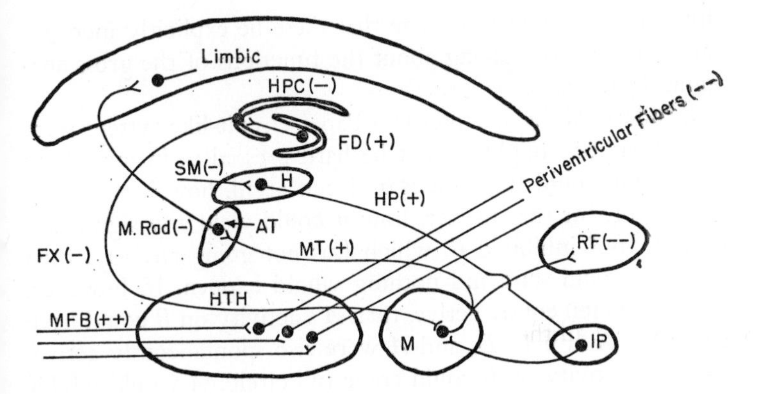


*Figure 4.21.* Possible sign inversions in highly schematic picture of the Papez-MacLean system as it might appear in sagittal section of rat brain. Stimulation of fiber systems marked with plus or minus signs is thought to yield positive or negative reinforcement behavior, respectively. The abbreviations are: Limbic, limbic cortex; HPC, hippocampus; FD, fascia dentata (dentate gyrus); SM, stria medullaris; H, habenula; HP, habenulo interpeduncular tract; IP, interpeduncular nucleus; RF, reticular formation; M, mammillary bodies; HTH, hypothalamus; MFB, medial forebrain bundle; MT, mammillo thalamic tract; M. Rad, medial radiations to the cortex and FX, fornix.

lies of neurones, *A, B, C,* and *D.* Neurones of Family A synapse on *B; B* on *C; C* on *D;* and *D* on *A* again to form a circuit. This has always been thought of as a circuit where information could circulate, maintaining its form or character while it was made available first to one and then to another relevant system. If, as we now suspect, stimulation of *A* yielded effects opposite to those caused by stimulation of *B,* and *B* yielded effects opposite to those of *C,* and so forth, then the idea of circulation of a simple message would be unsatisfactory and the possibility that inhibition rather than excitation occurred at these synapses would become more likely. A wide variety of neuroinhibitory synaptic processes has been demonstrated in the last two decades (Eccles, 1961). It is possibly in keeping with our age that these be explicitly incorporated into our theorizing about the functions of the gross anatomical pathways.

If indeed all the synapses in a Papez circuit-like system were inhibitory, one might at first be hard pressed to imagine how the system could function as a circuit at all, how it could get started, or, for that matter, how it could yield any significant output. If *A* inhibited *B*, which was not going anyway, then nothing would start and nothing would happen. If, however, *B* were spontaneously active, then *A*'s activity on *B* could have an effect. And if *C*, *D*, and *A* were also spontaneously active, then *A*'s activity on *B* could come full circle: *A* would inhibit *B* and this would release *C*, thereby inhibiting *D* and releasing *A*. The function of such a system might be unclear, but in at least one sense of the word it would "work." As for output, if each neurone acted only on its successor within such a circuit, there would be little hope of a wider range of consequences. We may, however, imagine that each member of the circuit would have both extra- and intra-circuit efferents and afferents; the existence of an abundance of collaterals in the case of most neurones makes this not unlikely. If we grant spontaneous activity and a system of collaterals, such a circuit might well serve as a complicated interaction system to mediate damping effects of positive and negative reinforcement mechanisms on one another.

## THE STRUCTURE AND FUNCTION OF A REINFORCEMENT MECHANISM

The areas so far mentioned have been (1) the paleocortical positive reinforcement areas, (2) the hypothalamic nuclei of mixed results, (3) the periventricular system of pure aversive effects, and (4) the lateral hypothalamic (medial forebrain bundle) area of pure positive effects. The hypothalamic nuclei themselves appear to deserve first place in a search for an integrative mechanism. Possibly the lateral hypothalamic area comes second.

## THE HYPOTHALAMIC NUCLEI

All the main differentiated nuclei of the hypothalamus are grouped along the midline; there are several of them and they have widely diversified functions, being related to eating, water control, temperature regulation, and so forth, and also to various autonomic adjustments (Ariens-Kappers, Huber, and Crosby, 1936). From the viewpoints of the present analysis, however, these nuclei are relatively homogeneous: they all yielded mixed positive-negative reinforcing effects, when electric stimulation was applied, and represented anatomical points for synapse between elements of the periventricular system and elements of the medial forebrain system. We will refer to these nuclei as the midhypothalamus and distinguish them from the lateral hypothalamic tube, which contains mainly the medial forebrain bundle. As may be seen, we have used the terms "lateral hypothalamus" and "medial forebrain bundle" more or less interchangeably.

The question of polarity presents itself strongly when we deal with the synapses between the medial forebrain bundle and periventricular fibers in the midhypothalamus: Which direction do the synapses conduct? In discussing direction we will use the term "downstream" to refer to the paleocortex-medial forebrain bundle-midhypothalamus-periventricular direction, and "upstream" to refer to the opposite direction. Older anatomical views suggested that the medial forebrain bundle and periventricular systems were mainly downstream channels. And while newer views (Ariens-Kappers, Huber, and Crosby, 1936) make it clear that both systems are bidirectional, it still seems likely that the main direction of conduction in this family of systems in downstream.

One suggestion is that the medial forebrain bundle contains

three kinds of elements: (1) fibers coming down from paleocortical sensory analyzers (possibly from the rhinencephalic ESB positive system), (2) fibers representing paleocortical and extrapyramidal motor systems (possibly determining the gross direction of behavior), and (3) small interstitial elements having both origin and termination in the hypothalamus itself (possibly making up the lateral hypothalamic-positive system). If we assume that the main fiber system originating in midhypothalamus is the periventricular escape system and that it is a downstream system, then it seems not impossible that it would have elements of Class 1 as its own inhibitory afferents and elements of Class 3 as elements inhibited by its recursive collaterals. The rhinencephalic ESB reward system would inhibit the periventricular escape system in the midhypothalamus, and the periventricular system would inhibit, via collaterals, the lateral hypothalamic ESB reward system. This medial to lateral hypothalamic inhibition could occur in the same midhypothalamic nuclei but at a different system of synapses. Stimulation in the periventricular area then could activate the periventricular fibers antidromically, thereby exciting the collateral system and bringing inhibition to bear on the lateral hypothalamic positive mechanism.

The possibility exists, therefore, that one positive system (A) inhibits the periventricular system of fibers (B), and the other positive system (C) is inhibited by it. If this should turn out to be so, it would not be impossible that the paleocortical positive points (A) would have their effect on the final-common-path of operant reinforcement (C) by virtue of this double inhibitory relation. By inhibiting B, A would cause a release of activity in C and this event would account for reinforcement of the ongoing behavioral patterns. We consider it not unlikely that if these events occurred they might all take place in midhypothalamus—the A–B synapses being the main downstream synapses occupying this area and the B-C synapses having a status involving recursive collaterals of the B (periventricular) fibers (see Figure 4.22).

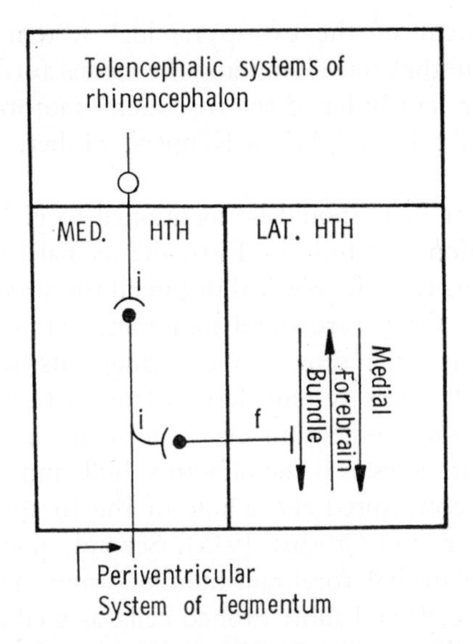


*Figure 4.22.* Schematic diagram showing supposed synapses in the hypothetical hypothalamus. The positive reinforcement mechanisms of rhinencephalon are supposed, in this diagram, to have inhibitory synapses on the periventricular neurones which originate in the medial hypothalamus. The recursive collaterals of the periventricular neurones are supposed to inhibit the "interneurones" which have positive reinforcing effects in the lateral hypothalamus.

## THE LATERAL HYPOTHALAMIC TUBE

Possibly the most marked anatomical fact about the lateral hypothalamic area (the tube that seems the core of the positive reinforcement system) is that it contains or is bounded by a very large number of downward coursing (motor?) fiber systems, both myelinated and unmyelinated. In the medial forebrain bundle itself are long axoned fibers from areas near the olfactory bulb, others from the rhinencephalic cortical systems, and still others from the extrapyramidal motor systems. Bounding the medial forebrain bundle dorsally is a second large component of the extrapyramidal system which runs through the subthalamus; bounding the medial forebrain bundle laterally is the remainder of the forebrain's motor outflow, the pyramidal tract itself (Ariens-Kappers, Huber, and Crosby, 1936).

Several other facts should be mentioned to give perspective to the discussion that follows. First, the medial forebrain bundle system runs from its cortical origin all the way to, and possibly through, the ventrolateral midbrain; it is not, however, always accorded the same name through its whole extent. Phylogenetically, this system derives from a tract connecting olfactory bulb to tegmentum. At some stages in phylogenetic development it seems as if the olfactory bulb and the long connecting tube constituted the whole of the forebrain (Ariens-Kapper, Huber, and Crosby, 1936). Second, along the whole course of the medial forebrain-bundle system are interposed small granule cells and short axoned cells, as well as the longer fibered cells (Papez, 1958). Third, juxtaposed to the medial forebrain-bundle system along its telencephalic course is a system of nuclei much like, and continuous with, the hypothalamic nuclei that bound it medially in the hypothalamus. This system of nuclei yielded mixed positive-negative reinforcing effects which were similar to those of the hypothalamic nuclei when electric stimulation was applied (Wurtz and Olds, 1963), and therefore it seems they may be part of the same system with, and similar in function to, the hypothalamic nuclei. Fourth, arising more or less on the other boundary of the tube (the dorsolateral boundary in diencephalon) is the system of extrapyramidal nuclei, nuclei that often yield neutral effects when stimulated electrically (Ariens-Kapper, Huber, and Crosby, 1936).

In forming hypotheses about the relation of structure and function in this long, tubular, and double-bounded system, two preliminary suppositions seem reasonable: (1) that the general function is relatively homogenous over the whole extent, with the posterior pole having priority only in the fact that much of the output of the system must pass through this point; (2) that the paleocortical and extrapyramidal systems under discussion

*Figure 4.23.* Brain sections showing approximate actual organization of the medial forebrain bundle, periventricular systems of fibers, and granule cells. Paleocortical "sensory" (round) and "motor" (triangular) neurones are suggested as passing through the medial forebrain-bundle area. The hypothesis is indicated that paleocortical "sensory" fibers innervate the periventricular system via the medial hypothalamic nuclei, but that "motor" fibers bypass the medial nuclei heading further downstream in the lateral tubular area. Periventricular fibers as seen in the sagittal (lower) section originate in the medial hypothalamus and rise dorsally into the midthalamus and midbrain. In the horizontal section, these same fibers are imagined as having "recursive" collaterals which innervate the "granule" cells of the medial forebrain bundle. While these granule cells are here indicated as being entirely in the lateral hypothalamic tube, it does not seem impossible that they might better be imagined as crossing over from the medial to the lateral hypothalamus, as indicated more schematically in Figure 4.22.

have an organization not totally unlike that of the neocortex, with some neurones specialized to receive incoming sensory messages (as possibly occurs in what is called "Layer 4" of neocortex), and others specialized to determine behavioral direction (as in "Layer 5").

If fibers from both kinds of neurones traveled in the medial forebrain bundle, those of the first type (sensory) might enter the midline nuclei to form the inhibitory afferents of the periventricular fibers making up the connection we have already spoken of. The motor fibers, on the other hand, might travel on downstream to influence the basic directions of behavior (see Figure 4.23).

If this kind of organization existed, it does not seem impossible that interaction between the short or granular neurones of the medial forebrain bundle and the longer axoned motor fibers might be at the crux of the reinforcement process. It would not be impossible, that is, if the medial forebrain-bundle

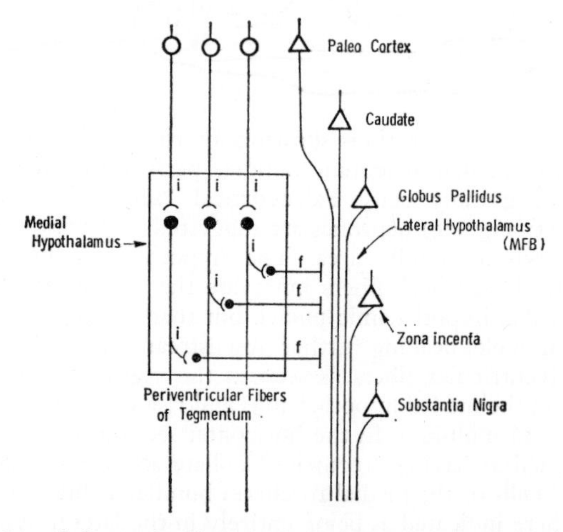


*Figure 4.24.* Schematic diagram indicating the possible sources of origin of the medial forebrain-bundle motor systems in paleocortical and extrapyramidal structures.

motor fibers were the entities to be reinforced, and the medial forebrain-bundle smaller units did the reinforcing. If this were so, it is of course still not apparent why the axons of the reinforced fibers would mingle with the granule and short-fibered reinforcing neurones. As the extrapyramidal motor system has sources of origin of its fibers distributed repeatedly along the axis of this system, it might be that at each level nearby small fibers acted upon the soma-dendritic systems of the extrapyramidal neurones taking origin nearby (see Figure 4.24). On the other hand, it would not be impossible to suppose that spontaneous activity of the longer fibered neurones might be somehow controlled by periaxonal influences. The notion of activity triggered at the initial segment or at the first "node of Renvier" in axonal systems currently has wide acceptance (Eccles, 1961). This forces one to think seriously of the possibility that activity might be generated or modulated at other axonal stages.

## INTERACTIONS

In a series of experiments interactions among the parts of the brain involved in the control of operant or voluntary behavior were investigated. Physiologically, this control undoubtedly consists of mechanisms for the facilitation of some behaviors and the inhibition of others. Only to the layman does it appear in terms of reward and punishment, pleasure and pain. An animal repeats those behaviors that result in certain consequences and eliminates those that result in others.

The layman thinks of appetitive consequences as having survival value and of aversive consequences as presenting conditions that are noxious or dangerous to the survival of the organism. From the point of view of the physiological mechanisms of behavior, however, both sets of conditions must be projected to regions of the brain that somehow have facilitatory or inhibitory control over the same ongoing stream of voluntary or operant behavior.

One great difficulty dogging the attempt to understand these mechanisms lies in the fact that the behaviors involved are facilitated or inhibited by conditions which arise after the behaviors are performed (see Figure 4.25). The appetitive or

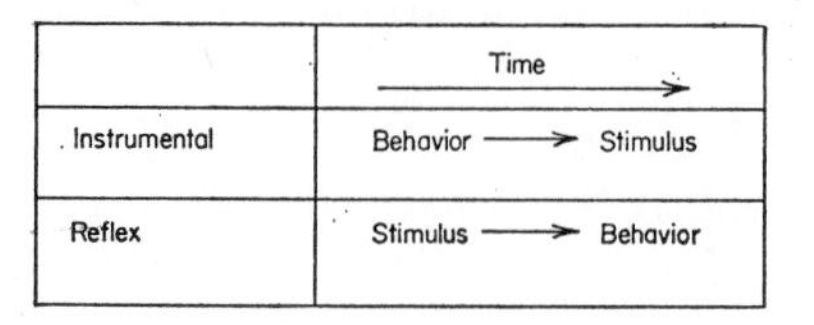


*Figure 4.25.* Instrumental conditioning: the behavior investigated occurs first and the controlling stimulus second. The latter serves to modify later repetition frequency of the behavior. Instrumental behavior differs from reflex in that the main environmental control over behavior comes first in the reflex case, second in the instrumental case (after Skinner, 1938).

aversive consequence follows the behavior and serves to modify its later repetition frequency, not its present occurrence; for the event is completed by the time the controlling consequence ensues. Although the mechanism is conceived of as a link forged between the behavior and its facilitatory or inhibitory consequences, it is quite clear that it is not the behavior, as an ephemeral or transient event, which becomes so linked but some behavior control element within the organism whose active state yields the behavior. Similarly, it is not the reward or punishment as a particular stimulus situation that becomes associated with the behavior control element, but rather some neural mechanism whose aroused state constitutes the rewarding event. Thus what appears to the layman as a problem of controlling behavior by manipulation of rewards and punishments is seen at the physiological level as a problem of associating behavior control elements with neural mechanisms that have the capacity to modify the repetition frequency of the behavior.

Even though we can reach general agreement on the problem stated thus in its most general terms, it is by no means similarly easy to agree on the neural structures that constitute the behavior control elements. Classical studies make it almost a matter of course that the pyramidal and extrapyramidal motor systems have something to do with behavior, and it is not at all unlikely that units or circuits comprising one or both of these systems constitute the behavior control elements for which we search. However, there is no certainty about which of these units or circuits might be involved, nor in what manner. Besides this, we have yet to understand the other pole of the association, namely, the neural mechanisms which have the capacity to modify behavior repetition frequencies. Experiments that have contributed to this understanding concern us now.

As suggested in the preceding section, it appears possible that there is an interstitial system in the medial forebrain bundle, that is, the lateral hypothalamus, whose activity serves to facilitate *ongoing* motor mechanisms and possibly to reinforce the firing pattern of *antecedently active* motor systems. This interstitial system might be thought of as the final common path of a reinforcement mechanism which controls all the voluntary or operant behavior of the organism. We might consider it to be spontaneously active, controlled inhibitorily by input from drive centers of medial hypothalamus, drive centers that project downstream via the periventricular system of fibers. These medial drive centers might be visualized as coming under dual control. On the one hand, they would be directly responsive to chemicals and hormones in the blood or interstitial fluid. In the sense of being without excitatory synapses, they would be similar to the interstitial fibers of the medial forebrain bundle. On the other hand, they might be under inhibitory control from fibers coursing downward from the structures of the rhinencephalic "visceral brain." These would be the paleocortical sensory fibers, which in turn receive projections from the visceral, olfactory, and gustatory receptors. It can be seen in Figure 4.24 that both normal reward mechanisms and reward mechanisms instigated by stimulation of paleocortical structures should be milder and more satiable than reward mechanisms instigated by direct stimulation of the interstitial systems of the medial forebrain bundle. This is because both normal and paleocortical rewards would have access to the final common pathway only via a double inhibitory synaptic relation. Similarly, the supposed negative reinforcement achieved by stimulation of periventricular fibers might be simply an artifact of their inhibitory relation to the final common pathway. There would be operant behavior directed to terminate periventricular stimulation, because such termination would release a spontaneous medial forebrain-bundle discharge. The interstitial fibers, being the final common path for periventricular escape behaviors and for both mild and intense self-stimulation behaviors, would be in such a controlling position that any chemical or physiological manipulation that would cause them to be greatly depressed would wipe out all operant behaviors.

## DOUBLE-STIMULUS EXPERIMENTS

The proposed double-inhibitory relation suggested that stimulation of paleocortical self-stimulation points might inhibit periventricular escape behavior, and that stimulation in periventricular escape points might inhibit medial forebrain bundle self-stimulation behavior. The effects of stimulating medial forebrain bundle on periventricular escape behavior were not clearly indicated by the proposal.

To test the possibility that stimulation of the rhinencephalic positive ESB mechanisms would cause inhibition of the periventricular escape system, negative reinforcement behavior was produced with ESB in periventricular system as the aversive stimulus. Tests were made (Routtenberg and Olds, 1963) for modification of this behavior by continuous application of

ESB in the positive system. The rhinencephalic positive system was used for application of the positive stimulus. The behavior produced by the aversive stimulus was suppressed or inhibited in several of these tests. Although the experiments are not completed, still it seems that we may tentatively conclude that stimulation in the earlier discovered, milder, paleocortical positive area yielded positive reinforcement which served at the same time to reinforce instrumental, and to suppress or inhibit aversive, behavior.

The other aspects of the proposed double-inhibitory systems were bolstered somewhat by similar, earlier experiments which might be taken as demonstrating an inhibitory relation from periventricular system to lateral hypothalamus, and suggesting in a new way a dependence of periventricular escape behavior on the medial forebrain bundle (Olds and Olds, 1962). These were experiments in which the rewarding effects of lateral hypothalamic stimulation were tested during simultaneous application of a continuous and uncontingent train of stimuli to the periventricular system, and similar experiments in which periventricular escape behavior was tested during application of a continuous and uncontingent train of stimulation to lateral hypothalamus.

The surprising outcome seemed to indicate antagonism from periventricular system to hypothalamus, but synergism from hypothalamus to periventricular system (see Figure 4.26). Stimulation in the periventricular system served to inhibit the rewarding effects or at least the appetitive behavior caused by stimulation of the lateral hypothalamus, but continuous stimulation in the hypothalamus served to augment escape behavior driven by stimulation of the periventricular escape point. There is no proof that the inhibitory effect emanating from periventricular stimulation was a consequence or a cause of the aversive character of this stimulation. Other aspects of interpretation may also be open to question. But it is quite clear that this apparently anomalous result of synergism in one direction and antagonism in the other was not incompatible with the hy-

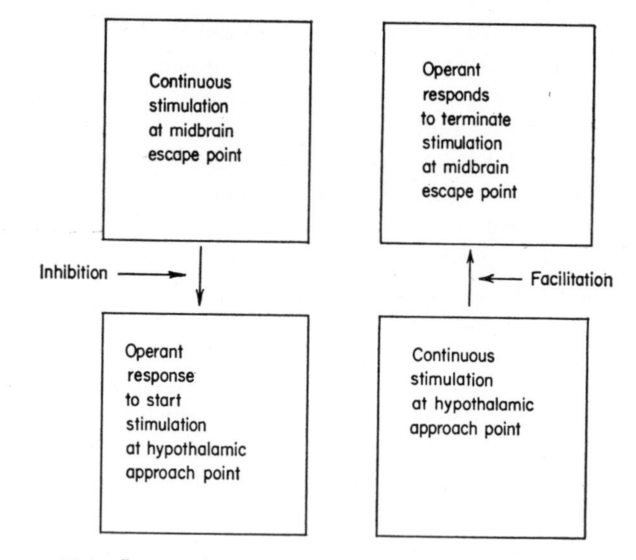


*Figure 4.26.* Interaction experiment.

pothesis of an inhibitory mechanism playing against a background of spontaneous activity in the lateral hypothalamus, a spontaneous background which, however, could be augmented in a relatively abnormal way by electric stimulation. In such a case, periventricular stimulation would engage the inhibitor. The escape response, by diminishing the inhibitor, that is, by terminating the periventricular stimulus, would augment the spontaneous activity of the lateral hypothalamus. Stimulation of the lateral hypothalamus during periventricular escape behavior might simply augment the power of the reinforcing event: it might create a larger background of spontaneous hypothalamic activity to be disinhibited. In such a case, the so-called escape response would result in a larger amount of hypothalamic activity.

Thus these data are compatible with the view stated above, namely, that the operant component of behavior comes under final control of a lateral hypothalamic mechanism, a mechanism which might itself be under inhibitory control from other parts of the brain. The double-stimulus experiments thus were in general harmony with the picture of a chain or loop of neurones whose alternate members yielded motive effects of opposite sign, each inhibiting its successor, at least some members of the chain or loop being spontaneously active, and having collaterals to provide for output.

Contributing to the view of a sequence of negative interactions between two different kinds of motive systems were experimental programs coming mainly from other laboratories.

## ELECTROPHYSIOLOGICAL EXPERIMENTS

Porter and his colleagues (1959) studied electrophysiological correlates of brain stimulus reward. Most significant among their findings was the indication that seizures caused by the rewarding stimulus, when it was applied in one rhinencephalic area, seemed to foster the rewarding effect, but seizures caused by the rewarding stimulus, when it was applied in another rhinencephalic area, seemed to counteract or terminate the rewarding effect. In other words, the appetitive behavior sustained by reinforcement of electric stimulation in the first area, the hippocampus, continued as long as the stimulus had the capacity to produce periodic seizures, but, if adaptation occurred so that the hippocampal stimulus no longer yielded occasional seizure episodes, the animal lost interest and would no longer press a pedal to stimulate the hippocampus. In the second area, the amygdala, it was quite the other way around; the animal responded regularly to stimulate the amygdaloid electrodes, but lost interest as soon as the amygdaloid stimulus produced a seizure episode. The animal appeared to shy away from the pedal which yielded the amygdaloid stimulus for periods as long as 24 hours after the amygdaloid seizure, although it pressed avidly for the stimulus up to the point in time when a seizure was produced. In both cases there were different effects of the electric brain stimulus when it yielded seizure discharges: the hippocampal stimulus was only rewarding if it produced seizure discharges and the amygdaloid stimulus was rewarding unless it produced seizure discharges. Now considering (1) the findings just summarized, (2) the proximity of these two rhinencephalic areas, and (3) the fact that not only appetitive but also aversive effects of electric stimulation derive from both structures, albeit from slightly different areas, it is easy to imagine that here, again, opposing mechanisms might be proximally placed, with mutual inhibitory synapses, so that whenever one mechanism was rendered inoperative by seizures the opposing mechanism came into play.

## FEEDING CENTER EXPERIMENTS

Another set of experiments suggested evidence for negative interaction of the two systems at the hypothalamic level. These were the experiments on the excitatory and inhibitory eating centers of the hypothalamus (Anand, 1961). It is well known from a great deal of early work on hypothalamic feeding mechanisms that a so-called satiety center exists in the ventro-medial hypothalamus where ablation causes overeating and electric stimulation may cause cessation of eating. A so-called feeding center also exists in the lateral hypothalamus where ablation causes permanent cessation of eating, and electric stimulation causes instrumental and consummatory responses related to food. Recent work (Margules and Olds, 1962; Hoebel and Teitelbaum, 1962; Miller, 1961) showed that the lateral hypothalamic feeding center constituted one part of the lateral hypothalamic reward system. Thus stimulation produced both eating and positive reinforcement. The feeding center of the lateral hypothalamus appeared to be one among a larger set of places in the brain where electric stimulation yielded positive reinforcement. Similarly, while not quite so clear, electric stimulation of ventro-medial hypothalamus yielded aversive effects (Olds, 1960) or ambivalent effects (Olds and Olds, 1963). It did not seem at all unlikely that the periventricular fiber system which was stimulated by means of electrodes in the midbrain had some of its origin in this same ventro-medial area (Krieg, 1932; Crosby and Woodburne, 1951). Therefore it was possible to imagine that stimulation of the hypothalamus at the satiety point had some of the same aversive consequences as stimulation in the midbrain escape points. In any event, several experiments indicated both pure aversive effects and ambivalent aversive effects from the stimulation of medial hypothalamic regions (Olds, 1960; Roberts, 1958b; Hoebel and Teitelbaum, 1962).

The hunger experiments directed at this same area (Anand, 1961) made it appear not at all unlikely that part of this medial region constituted a glucose receptor which might function to inhibit the lateral hypothalamic feeding mechanism. This medial-to-lateral inhibitory relation was suggested by lesion experiments and by EEG experiments of Anand and his several different collaborators. They were also indicated in experiments on individual medial and lateral neurones (Anand *et al.*, 1962; Oomura *et al.*, 1964). The same relations were clearly demonstrated in the work of Hoebel and Teitelbaum (1962), which indicated that inactivation of the ventro-medial area by local injection of procaine caused augmentation of both rewarding effects of lateral hypothalamic stimulation and eating behavior caused by lateral hypothalamic stimulation; a diminution of both of these effects was caused by stimulation in the ventro-medial hypothalamus (Figure 4.27). These interactions paralleled precisely the effects of excesses of hunger and satiety: the hungry animal yielded more eating behavior and also a greater rewarding effect of lateral hypothalamic stimulation; the animal that had been preloaded with an excess of food showed a diminution in eating behavior caused by lateral stimulation and a diminution in the rewarding effect of this same stimulation. These feeding mechanisms appeared to demonstrate in a functional context a one-way inhibitory relation between a periventricular system whose stimulation caused aversive behavior and a lateral hypothalamic mechanism whose

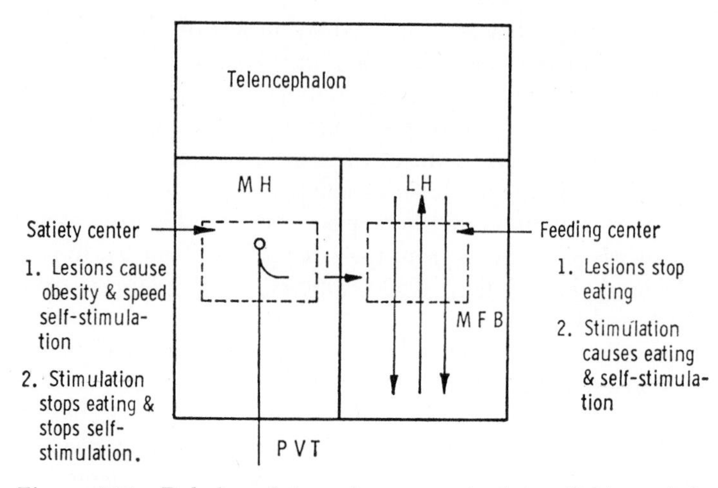


*Figure 4.27.* Relation of the satiety center in the medial hypothalamus to the feeding center in the lateral hypothalamus.

stimulation caused appetitive behavior. In this case, it was interesting but not quite anomalous that aversion appeared to correlate with an excess of satiety; psychology has tended to emphasize those aversive mechanisms associated instead with an excess of hunger.

## LESIONS ON SELF-STIMULATION

In order to establish relative priority of different parts of the positive reinforcement system, a series of ablation experiments was carried out to find whether one ESB reinforcement area was essential to the reinforcement behavior resulting from stimulation at another similar area. The first series of experiments of this nature was carried out by Ward (1960, 1961), who showed that extensive ablations in various rhinencephalic structures did not adversely affect the positive reinforcement produced by ESB in the ventro-lateral regions of tegumentum (see Figure 4.28).

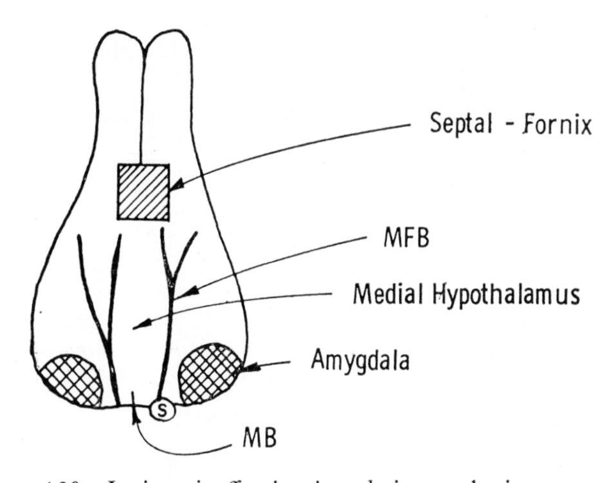


*Figure 4.28.* Lesions ineffective in relation to brain-stem reward behavior (after Ward, 1960, 1961). Lesions destroying the septal area and fornix columns of the rhinencephalic system were ineffective in one experiment. Here the ineffective lesions are shown projected onto a horizontal section which passes through the medial forebrain bundle. In both experiments stimulation was at the point marked S in the medial forebrain bundle behind the mammillary bodies (MB).

We extended this work recently by experiments intended to discover whether anterior or posterior parts of the lateral hypothalamic tube could be considered essential to the ESB positive reinforcement process. Because the tube runs in anterior-posterior direction all the way from olfactory cortical areas through to midbrain areas, and because stimulation of all parts appeared to yield very strong positive reinforcement, one could not help but wonder whether the effects of the stimulation had access to behavior control mechanisms via the outflow directed toward rhinencephalon and neocortex or via the outflow directed toward midbrain.

Electrodes were implanted in anterior and posterior parts of the tube and their positions were verified by making ESB positive reinforcement tests. In the cases where these tests indicated that both electrodes were in the positive reinforcement system, large electrolytic lesions were made either at the an-

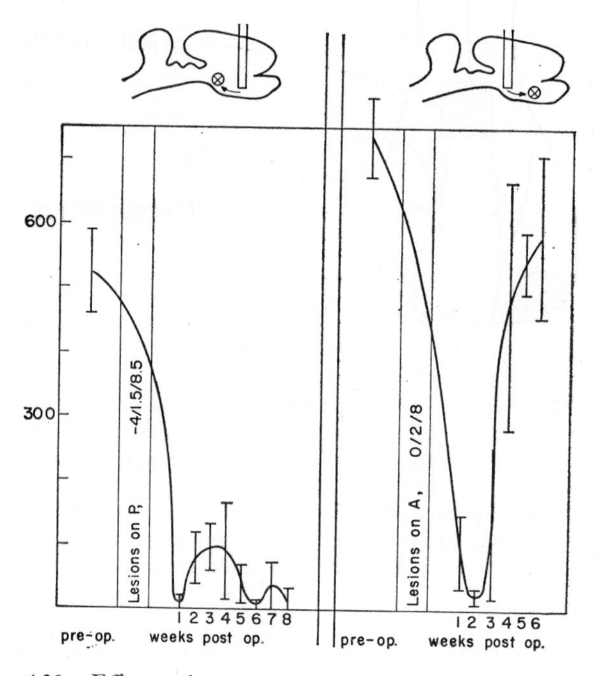


*Figure 4.29.* Effects of anterior and posterior lesions in the lateral hypothalamic tubes. Each vertical line represents the range of 5 scores taken over the period of 1 week. Each score indicated the response output for an 8-minute period on a positive reinforcement behavior test. In the left-hand case stimulation in the anterior part of the lateral tube served as reinforcement, and lesions were placed in the posterior part (lesions on P); in the right-hand case stimulation was in the posterior part and lesions were placed in the anterior part (lesions on A). In both cases there was a sharp drop in positive reinforcement behavior lasting 2 to 3 weeks. In the case of anterior lesions, however, there was recovery so that in the fourth week behavior at the top of the range was of the same order of magnitude as before the lesions. For further analysis, each animal was given a score representing the top of its fourth-week range as a percentage of the low point of its range in the pre-lesion week.

terior or the posterior point. In each case a companion lesion was made at a site symmetrically opposite that point in the other side of the brain. (Generally, lesions must be bilateral to be effective.)

Lesions were made by passing 2 milliamperes of D.C. current for 15 seconds; the lesion size was approximately 1 millimeter (compare Krieg, 1946). The electrode site used for making the lesions was no longer tested. Tests were made after the lesions for ESB positive reinforcement from stimulation of the remaining (anterior or posterior) electrode site. In all cases there was a period of 2 or 3 weeks during which positive reinforcement behavior did not appear on stimulation of the remaining electrodes (see Figure 4.29). In 7 of 10 cases with anterior lesions, however, performance recovered so that positive reinforcement behavior rates were of the same order of magnitude as before the lesions. In none of the cases with posterior lesions was there similar recovery.

The results appeared to indicate that the positive reinforcement system had a posterior focus. At least, the posterior part of the lateral hypothalamic tube was essential in some way to the positive reinforcement produced by stimulating the anterior part, but the anterior part was not similarly essential. One might imagine that information had to exit in the direction of the midbrain in order for the positive reinforcement phenomenon to appear, or that the posterior part of the lateral tube was a final common path for positive reinforcement.

## LESIONS ON ESCAPE

If this area were also a final common path for negative reinforcement, if, that is, operant behavior apparently motivated by termination of the negative stimulus were actually motivated by a burst of released activity in the positive substrate, then the operant aspect of this particular aversive behavior would be heavily dependent on the integrity of the positive mechanism for its maintenance. Lesions in the positive area might therefore attenuate or obliterate this aversive behavior. In the other direction, however, if there were an inhibitory action from the negative substrate on the positive, there might even be augmentation of positive behavior after lesions in the negative substrate.

The experiments on this problem so far have been preliminary. In 6 cases the effects of periventricular (escape) lesions on positive reinforcement were studied; in another 8 cases the

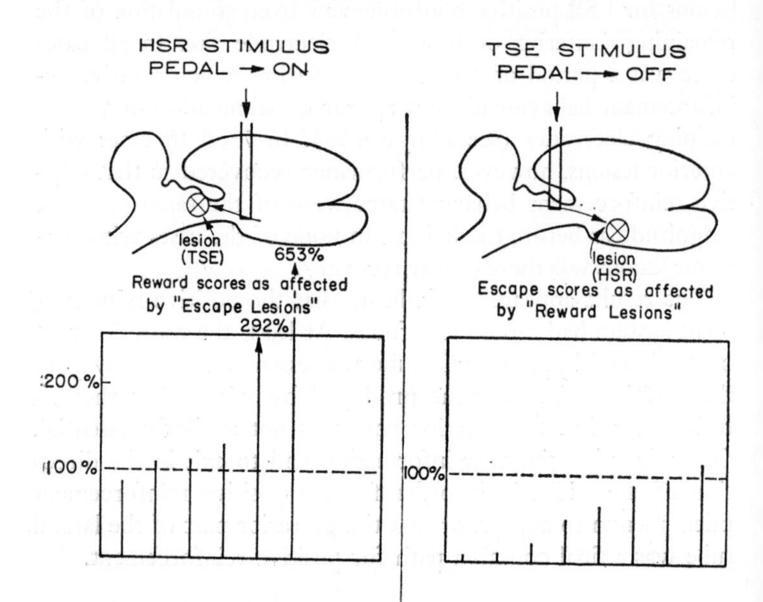


*Figure 4.30.* Effects of lesions in positive and negative reinforcement producing areas on the behavior produced by electric stimulation in the "opposing" area. Lesions of tegmental substrate of escape did not depress the positive reinforcement behavior; in fact, two cases showed augmentation. Lesions in the hypothalamic substrate of reward did cause significant depression in the negative reinforcement behavior. In each case the best performance 4 weeks after the lesion is given as a percent of the worst performance the week prior to lesion.

effects of medial forebrain bundle (positive reinforcement) lesions on ESB negative reinforcement were studied. Small bilateral electrolytic lesions were produced by means of electrodes previously tested for ESB reinforcement; a second set of electrodes in the opposing system was used to test the effectiveness of the lesions. The results were in the predicted direction (see Figure 4.30). There was no single case where periventricular (escape) lesions produced an appreciable deficit in ESB positive reinforcement behavior. In 2 out of 6 cases, there was a very great augmentation. On the other hand, there was no case where medial forebrain bundle (positive) lesions produced appreciable augmentation of ESB negative reinforcement behavior. In 5 of these 8 cases, there was a major deficit in negative reinforcement behavior; in 3 of these cases, ESB escape disappeared altogether.

While the data indicate only partial effects in some cases, the possibility remains that ESB escape was entirely dependent on the ESB positive reinforcement mechanism, for the small electrolytic lesions might easily have missed the crucial area in certain cases; histological verification of these lesions had not been carried out as yet.

## THE INHIBITORY CHEMICAL CONTROLS

In the preceding sections we have guessed that a positive reinforcement system in lateral hypothalamus might be inhibited by stimulation in periventricular system, and that a release of the suppressed neural activity might occur on termination of the periventricular stimulation. It is clear that this implies not a dormant system in lateral hypothalamus but one that is spontaneously active. One might imagine a spontaneous neural activity level which would be temporarily suppressed by inhibitory input and would perhaps return suddenly to normal or even yield a supernormal burst upon termination of the inhibitory input. The activity might be analogous to that of the "off" fibers in the retinal ganglion (compare Hartline,

Wagner, and Ratliff, 1956). A study of the effects of excitatory and inhibitory transmitter substances directly applied to the positive reinforcement substrate has cast some light on the problems of spontaneous activity and inhibitory control (Olds, Yuwiler, Olds, and Yun, 1964).

Many attempts to stimulate by direct application of the supposed neurotransmitters, acetylcholine, epinephrine, and serotonin, failed in our laboratory after the volume of the directly applied fluid was reduced clearly below the level that permitted stimulation by means of saline alone. With these small volumes stimulation was achieved, however, by means of various substances which caused a depletion of ionic calcium in the interstitial fluid. Most neural fiber systems may be vizualized as prone to continuous spontaneous discharge but for the presence of ions that control activity; this is much as an atomic pile would be in continuous activity but for the rods that control the reaction. In the case of nerve fibers, the "rods" that control activity are calcium ions; any momentary reduction in these ions results in a burst of activity just as if a stimulating current had been applied (Brink, 1954). To cause a depletion of ionic calcium it is only necessary to use a substance that unites with calcium to form a precipitate or to form a soluble complex. A wide variety of such substances has been used to stimulate the hypothalamus, such as sodium phosphate, sodium bitartrate, sodium pyrophosphate, and sodium versenate (EDTA). These are listed in ascending order of their efficacy as stimulators; this is also the order of their tendency to withdraw ionic calcium from the interstitial fluid.

After these experiments with calcium bonding substances, the neurohumors were tried again for excitatory and inhibitory effects in the lateral hypothalamic (reward) substrate, mixing them with sub- and suprathreshold concentration of sodium pyrophosphate. In these experiments, serotonin, epinephrine, and norepinephrine, which are among the supposed neurohumors found in very high concentrations in this area of the brain (Vogt, 1957), counteracted very strongly the excitation produced by high concentration of the calcium binder, pyrophosphate (see Figure 4.31). The supposed neuroinhibitory substance, gamma amino butyric acid, had similar (but weaker) action. Acetylcholine did not have any marked capac-

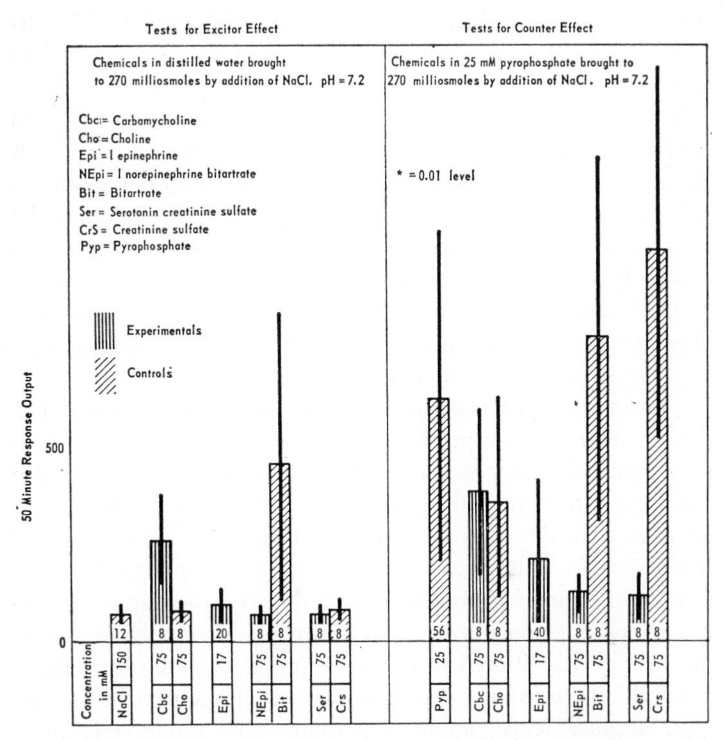


*Figure 4.31.* Test for A excitor effects and B countereffects with chemicals in water brought to 0.272 osmoles by addition of NaCl. Each animal was assigned a score equal to the best of the three 50-minute response totals. The histogram shows the mean of the scores for all animals tested with a given solution. Variability indicated is the standard deviation. The number of animals tested is indicated inside the base of each column. The chemicals used are indicated below the columns, with concentration in mm. Epinephrine was tested in 17 mm concentrations because higher ones yielded a precipitate.

ity to counteract the effects of suprathreshold pyrophosphate nor to augment the action of subthreshold concentrations. None of the chemicals mentioned above had any excitatory power when mixed with saline or distilled water. The possibility that the main neurotransmitters in this area (for example, serotonin, epinephrine, and norepinephrine or related substances) might have inhibitory function was therefore taken seriously.

That there were no excitatory transmitters, however, was far from demonstrated. The failure to stimulate or inhibit with acetylcholine suggested that possibly it was being counteracted effectively by cholinesterase. Therefore the acetylcholine-like compound, carbamylcholine, which resists cholinesterase, was tested. It produced effective chemical activation when applied to the lateral hypothalamus whether mixed with subthreshold concentrations of pyrophosphate or merely with saline enough to make an isotonic solution (see Figure 4.31).

The outcome of these experiments therefore suggested (1) that the substances especially related to the hypothalamus possibly had inhibitory action, but (2) that the area might also yield excitatory responses related to acetylcholine. One might suppose that this area of the hypothalamus, like some other brain systems (Marrazzi and Hart, 1957), was positively sensitive to cholinergic substances and negatively sensitive to epinephrine, norepinephrine, and serotonin. Because the latter are heavily distributed in this area, however, one might guess that inhibitory input to the area played a large part in its control. Because acetylcholine is perhaps more moderately present in this area according to histochemical maps (Burgen, 1955), one might guess that excitatory input was less important.

## UNIT REINFORCEMENT EXPERIMENTS

These experiments have been conducted in an effort to establish an interaction between the positive reinforcement system and some central responses which might be said to be reinforced. Single-unit responses were recorded with microelectrodes whose uninsulated surface was conical with length about 10$\mu$ and maximum diameter about the same. Large neurones have a diameter considerably larger than this. Repetitive spikes of constant wave shape recorded with these microelectrodes were presumed to be the responses of individual neurones in the brain. These were chosen for reinforcement because they were clearly identifiable responses which appeared to be emitted by the animal on a more or less random basis. Thus they appeared to meet the criterion of Skinner (1938) for operant behavior.

It would take too much time to recount the long and sometimes difficult course of the unit reinforcing experiments. It is sufficient to say they have been underway for six years and they have not yet produced a substantial and readily repeatable set of findings. In order that the reader may be cautious in evaluating the material to be presented, he should know that the total number of "reinforceable" neural responses thus far observed has been in the order of 30 or 40. Largely because of this small number, it has been very difficult to demonstrate conclusively that any augmentation in response frequency was a consequence of positive reinforcement rather than direct elicitation or toning up of the brain by background stimulation.

In the experiments that follow, efforts were made to circumvent this problem and the methods used indicate at least a fruitful path for further work.

Chronic animals were prepared with a positive reinforcing macroelectrode in the lateral hypothalamic tube. Behavioral tests were made to validate the location of the electrode. Then animals were anesthetized with pentobarbital and placed in a stereotaxic instrument. Exploration was made by means of 2 microelectrodes glued together with a separation at the tips of about 100 microns (Verzeano and Negishi, 1960). These were placed through a trephine opening and advanced through the

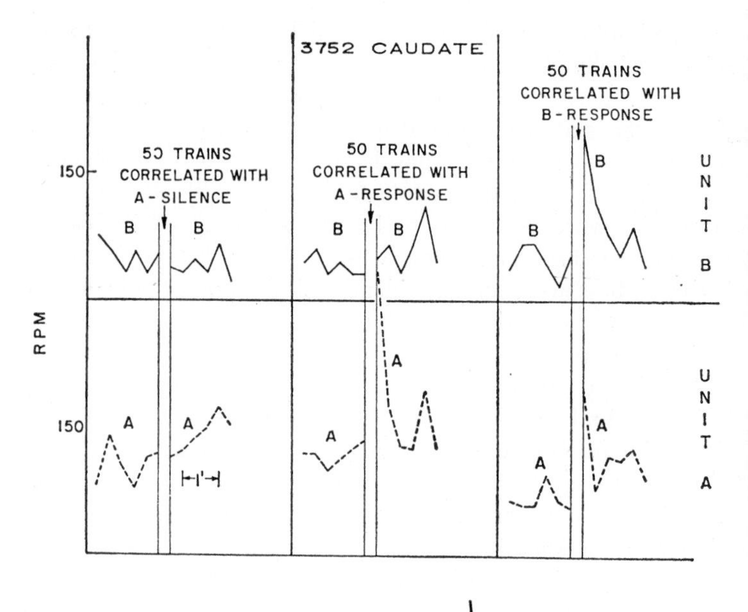


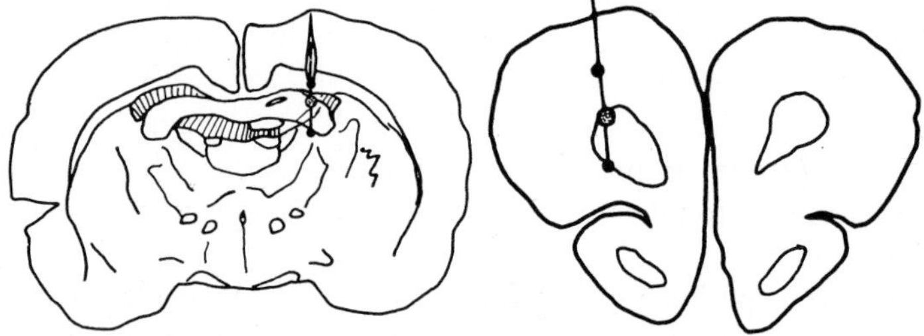

*Figure 4.32.* Data (top) and histological localization (bottom) in successful single-unit reinforcement experiments. Each curve indicates the changing response rate of a single-unit response in responses per minute (rpm). Actually, points were determined every 20 seconds and converted to rpm by multiplying response output by 3. Each of the gaps indicates an interposed period during which 50 one-half-second trains of 50 $\mu$a (60-cycle sine wave) stimulation was applied via the lateral hypothalamic (positive reinforcing) electrodes. Curves for the B and A units were generated simultaneously. Three procedures were applied successively: (1) reinforcement for "stopping" the A response, (2) reinforcement for "making" the A

brain by means of a micromanipulator. The potential difference between each microelectrode and a large ground electrode in the brain were amplified and displayed on a twin-beam cathode ray oscilloscope; they were also recorded on a two-channel magnetic tape recorder. Movement of the microelectrodes was continued until neural responses of constant form and repetitive character were observed on both channels. These were considered to be extracellular responses of single-brain cells if (a) they were negative with respect to ground, (b) the duration was in the 0.3 to 1.5 microseconds range, (c) their amplitude was of 300 microvolts or more, and (d) their amplitude was changed radically by micromovement of the electrode tips (in the 30 to 100 micron range).

When two different unit responses of this sort were indicated by recordings from the two proximal microelectrodes, reinforcement tests were made while the animal was still under pentobarbital anesthesia.

Two kinds of control test were used to differentiate between elicited and reinforcing effects. (1) Cessation of responding as well as responding was reinforced at a given brain point, so that the animal was reinforced first for "stopping" the unit response and later for "making" the response. (2) While

---

response, and (3) reinforcement for "making" the B response. In each case a 3-minute recording was made before and after a series of stimulations. In each case it can be seen that the electric stimulation had its first major effect in augmenting a unit response rate when it was used to reinforce the animal for making that response. In other words, the *first* large increment in each response rate appeared during the time the stimulus was correlated (as reinforcement) with that response. The 3-minute period just following a reinforcement period regularly showed a decline from a high level of responding which appears quite similar to a normal operant extinction curve. The fact should also be observed that the previously reinforced A response showed a second large increment when the B response was reinforced. This may be interpreted as a "superstitious" behavior (cf. Skinner, 1938); a similar effect has been shown in our laboratory when two skeletal operants were used.

one unit response was reinforced, the second, recorded from a nearby point, served as a control. If (a) augmentation of a unit response rate occurred during the appropriate period, and if (b) no similar augmentation occurred during the period of reinforcement for "stopping" or during the period of reinforcement of the other unit response, then the unit response rate in question was considered to be under operant control. In several cases two neighboring unit responses have been shown by this method to be under operant control. Many have failed this test. In two cases there was satisfactory histological localization of brain areas yielding such operantly controlled unit responding. In one, microelectrodes were in fibers of the olfactory-cortical system; in the other, microelectrodes were in fibers of the extrapyramidal system. In both cases each of the two neighboring unit responses appeared to be under operant control (Figure 4.32). In these experiments, and in previous experiments, there were many cases where electrodes were histologically determined to be in the neocortex. In these cases a failure of control of unit responses by reinforcing methods seemed to be the rule (Olds and Olds, 1961).

While the results are far from conclusive, it does not seem impossible that paleocortical and extrapyramidal motor fibers had their response frequencies determined somehow by electric stimulation in the lateral hypothalamic tube, provided that this stimulation was correlated in a "reinforcing" fashion relative to the neural responses in question.

## THEORY OF OPERANT BEHAVIOR

A current (and highly tentative) view of mechanisms in operant behavior might involve four systems (see Figure 4.33). System B would be an aversive mechanism phylogenetically related to the somesthetic receptor system; it would have caudal origin, entering from spinal cord and medulla through the midbrain and midline diencephalon. It would be inhibited by System A which would be a "homing" mechanism phylo-

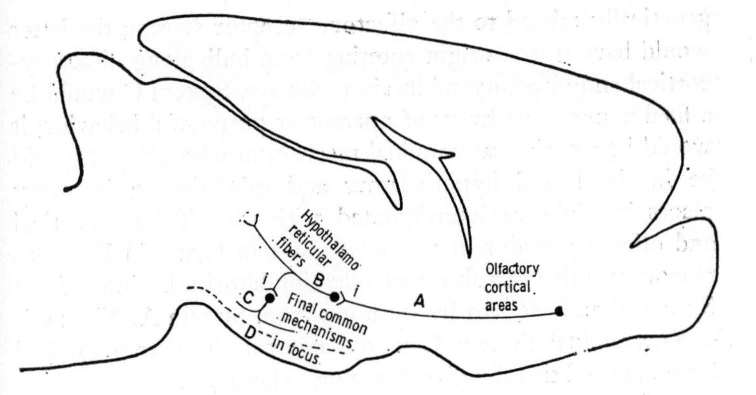


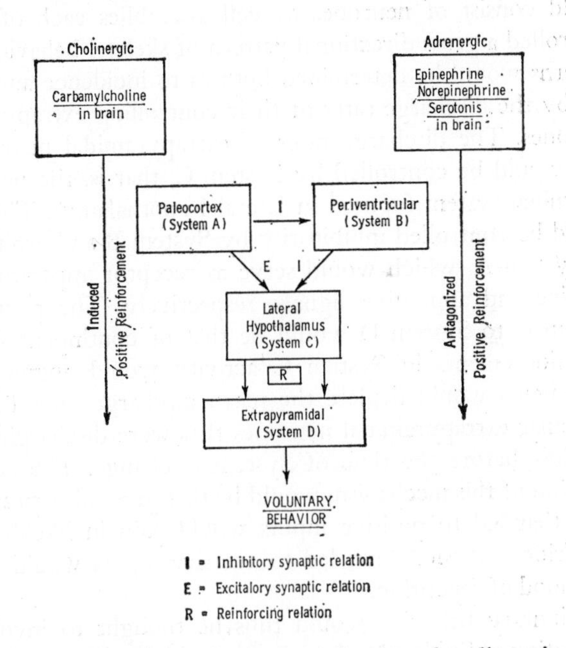


*Figure 4.33.* (a) above; (b) below. See text for discussion. The reinforcing relation in diagrammed in Figure 4.34.

genetically related to the olfactory receptor system; the latter would have rostral origin entering from bulb along olfactory-cortical and olfactory-midbrain pathways. System C would be a final common pathway of operant or purposeful behavior; it would be a periextrapyramidal mechanism whose focus would be in the lateral hypothalamus and subthalamus; in many places it might be interdigitated with the olfactory-cortical and olfactory-midbrain pathways. System C would be spontaneously active but also controlled inhibitorily by input from System B and excitatorily by input from System A. The periextrapyramidal System C would control the extrapyramidal System D and thereby give direction to behavior.

In simplified form, the resulting picture of operant behavior would be this: System D, the extrapyramidal system, would consist of neurones or cell assemblies each of which controlled a gross directional pattern of skeletal behavior; such patterns would be determined both as to incidence and intensity by the discharge rates of their controlling extrapyramidal neurones. The discharge rates of extrapyramidal neurones in turn would be controlled by System C, that is, the periextrapyramidal system focused in lateral hypothalamus. The latter would be controlled inhibitorily by System B and excitatorily by System A, which would serve as receptor apparatuses for aversive and appetitive signals, respectively. The relation of System C to System D would be that of contingent facilitation: increments in System C activity would augment and decrements would deplete the mean discharge rates of those particular extrapyramidal neurones that were discharging rapidly just before the time of System C change. The adaptive function of this mechanism would be that gross directional patterns that led to positive inputs would gain in likelihood of repetition and those that led to aversive inputs would lose in likelihood of repetition.

Voluntary behavior would thus be thought to involve an interaction of System D, the extrapyramidal system, which controlled gross directional patterns of skeletal behavior; System

C, a lateral hypothalamic periextrapyramidal system which had control over the response rates of extrapyramidal neurones; and Systems B and A which served as receptor systems for

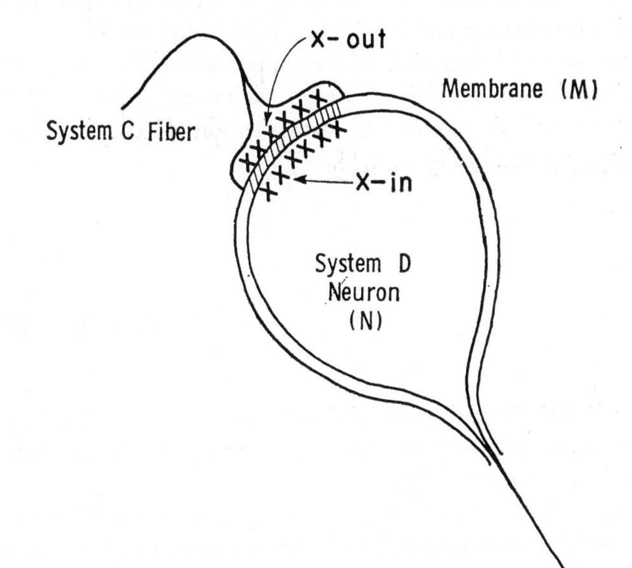


*Figure 4.34.* Membrane M might be activated after repeated discharge of extrapyramidal neuron, N, that is, during the "high sodium pumping phase." M (when activated) would be a self-adjusting membrane permeable to X; it would adjust to terminate flow of X out or in during the activation period. There would be neither flow nor adjustment during the inactive period. Thus on sudden excess of X-out during the period of activated membrane there would be an influx of X which would gradually diminish if X-out were maintained at a constant level. If, on the other hand, a sudden depletion of X-out occurred during the activation period, there would be an efflux of X. Also, X-in would tend to augment the firing rate of N. The amount of X-out would be determined by the spontaneous or controlled discharge rate of the antecedent "reinforcing" unit of the periextrapyramidal mechanism (system C in Figure 4.33 (b). The latter, as indicated, would be controlled negatively by system B activity; and positively by activity emanating from the olfactory-visceral projection system A.

aversive and positive signals, respectively, and exercised inhibitory and excitatory control over the lateral hypothalamic System C.

The synapses relating Systems A, B, and C would be of the classical excitatory and inhibitory type. That synapse relating C to D would be special. The relations would be: A to B inhibition, B to C inhibition, A to C excitation, and C to D "reinforcement." A possible characterization of the latter relation is suggested in Figure 4.34.

## REFERENCES

Adey, R. W. Organization of the rhinencephalon. In H. H. Jasper *et al.* (Eds.), *Reticular Formation of the Brain.* Boston: Little, Brown, 1958. Pp. 621-644.

Amassian, V. E., and J. W. Hardress. Spatiotemporal patterns of activity in individual reticular neurons. In H. H. Jasper *et al.* (Eds.), *Reticular Formation of the Brain.* Boston: Little, Brown, 1958, pp. 69-108.

Anand, B. K. Nervous regulation of food intake. *Physiol. Rev.*, 1961, *41*, 677-708.

Anand, B. K., G. S. Chhina, and S. Baldev. Effect of glucose on the activity of hypothalamic "feeding centers." *Science*, 1962, *138*, 597, 598.

Ariens-Kappers, C. V., G. C. Huber, and E. C. Crosby. *The comparative anatomy of the nervous system of vertebrates including man.* New York: Macmillan, 1936.

Bower, G. H., and N. E. Miller. Rewarding and punishing effects from stimulating the same place in the rat's brain. *J. comp. physiol. Psychol.*, 1958, *51*, 669-674.

Brady, J. V. Motivational-emotional factors and intracranial self-stimulation. In D. E. Sheer (Ed.), *Electrical stimulation of the brain.* Austin, Texas: University of Texas Press, 1961, 413-430.

Brink, F. The role of calcium in neural process. *Pharmacol. Rev.*, 1954, *6*, 243-298.

Brown, G. W., and B. D. Cohen. Avoidance and approach learning motivated by stimulation of identical hypothalamic loci. *Am. J. Physiol.*, 1959, *197*, 153-157.

Bureš, J. Private communication, 1960.

Bureš, J. Reversible decortication and behavior. In M.A.B. Brazier (Ed.), *The central nervous system and behavior.* Transactions of the Second Conference. New York: Josiah Macy, Jr. Foundation, 1959, 207-248.

Bureš, J., and O. Burešova. The use of Leão's spreading depression in the study of interhemispheric transfer of memory traces. *J. comp. physiol. Psychol.*, 1960, *53*, 558-561.

Bureš, J., O. Burešova, E. Fifkova, J. Olds, M. E. Olds, and R. P. Travis. Spreading depression and subcortical drive centers. *Physiol. bohemoslov.*, 1961, *10*, 321-331.

Bureš, J., O. Burešova, and A. Zahorova. Conditioned reflexes and Leão's spreading cortical depression. *J. comp. physiol. Psychol.*, 1958, *51*, 263-268.

Burgen, A. S. V., and F. C. MacIntosh. The physiological significance of acetylcholine. In K. A. C. Elliot *et al.* (Eds.), *Neurochemistry: The chemical dynamics of brain and nerve.* Springfield, Illinois: Charles C. Thomas, 1955. Pp. 311-389.

Cook, L., and E. Weidley. Behavioral effects of some psychopharmacological agents. *Ann. N. Y. Acad. Sci.*, 1957, *66*, 740-752.

Crosby, E. C., and R. T. Woodburne. The mammalian midbrain and isthmus regions. Part II. The fiber connections. C. The hypothalamo-tegmental pathways. *J. comp. Neurol.*, 1951, *94*, 1-32.

Delgado, J. M. R. Cerebral structures involved in transmission and elaboration of noxious stimulation. *J. Neurophysiol.*, 1955, *18*, 261-275.

Delgado, J. M. R., W. W. Roberts, and N. E. Miller. Learning motivated by electrical stimulation of the brain. *Am. J. Physiol.*, 1954, *179*, 587-593.

Delgado, J.M.R., H. E. Rosvold, and E. Looney. Evoking conditioned fear by electrical stimulation of subcortical structures in the monkey brain. *J. comp. physiol. Psychol.*, 1956, *49*, 373-380.

Eccles, J. C. The mechanism of synaptic transmission. *Ergebn. Physiol.*, 1961, *51*, 299-430.

French, J. D. Corticofugal connections with the reticular formation. In H. H. Jasper *et al.* (Eds.), *Reticular formation of the brain.* Boston: Little, Brown, 1958. Pp. 491-505.

Gavlichek, V. Electroencephalographic characteristics of conditioned defensive dominant state. *Fiziol. Zhur. S.S.S.R.*, 1958, *49* (Abstract).

Gurdjian, E. S. The diencephalon of the albino rat. *J. comp. Neurol.*, 1927, *43*, 1-114.

Hartline, H. K., H. G. Wagner, and F. Ratliff. Inhibition in the eye of Limulus. *J. gen. Physiol.*, 1956, *39*, 651-673.

Hess, W. R. *Das Zwischenhirn: Syndrome, Lokalisation, Functionen.* Basel: Schwabe, 1954. P. 187.

Hoebel, B. G., and P. Teitelbaum. Hypothalamic control of feeding and self-stimulation. *Science*, 1962, *135*, 375-376.

Hugelin, A., and M. Bonvallet. Tonus cortical et controle de la facilitation motrice d'origine reticulaire. *J. Physiol. (Paris)*, 1957, *49*, 1171-1200.

Kluever, H., and P. C. Bucy. Preliminary analysis of functions of the temporal lobes in monkeys. *A.M.A. Arch. Neurol. Psychiat.*, 1939, *42*, 979-1000.

Krieg, W.J.S. Accurate placement of minute lesions in the brain of the albino rat. *Quart. Bull., Northwestern University Medical School*, 1949, *20*, 199-208.

Krieg, W. J. S. The hypothalamus of the albino rat. *J. comp. Neurol.*, 1932, *55*, 19-89.

Leão, A. A. P. Spreading depression of activity in the cerebral cortex. *J. Neurophysiol.*, 1944, *7*, 359-390.

Lilly, J. C. Learning motivated by subcortical stimulation: the start and stop patterns of behavior. In H. H. Jasper *et al.* (Eds.), *Reticular formation of the brain.* Boston: Little, Brown, 1958, 705-727.

MacLean, P. D. Psychosomatic disease and the "visceral brain"; recent developments bearing on Papez theory of emotion. *Psychosom. Med.*, 1949, *11*, 338-353.

Margules, D. L., and J. Olds. Identical "feeding" and "rewarding" systems in the lateral hypothalamus of rats. *Science*, 1962, *135*, 374-375.

Marrazzi, A. S., and E. R. Hart. An electrophysiological analysis of drugs useful in psychotic states. In H. E. Himwich (Ed.), *Tranquilizing drugs*. Washington, D.C.: Amer. Assoc. Adv. Sci., 1957. Pp. 9-21.

Masserman, J. H. Is the hypothalamus a center of emotion? *Psychosom. Med.*, 1941, *3*, 1-25.

Miller, N. E. Experiments on motivation. *Science*, 1957, *126*, 1271.

Miller, N. E. Integration of neurophysiological and behavioral research. *Ann. N. Y. Acad. Sci.*, 1961, *92*, 830-839.

Olds, J. A preliminary mapping of electrical reinforcing effects in the rat brain. *J. comp. physiol. Psychol.*, 1956a, *49*, 281-285.

Olds, J. Approach-avoidance dissociation in rat brain. *Am. J. Physiol.*, 1960, *199*, 965-968.

Olds, J. Hypothalamic substrates of reward. *Physiol. Rev.*, 1962, *42*, 554-604.

Olds, J. Runway and maze behavior controlled by basomedial forebrain stimulation in the rat. *J. comp. physiol. Psychol.*, 1956b, *49*, 507-512.

Olds, J. Satiation effects in self-stimulation of the brain. *J. comp. physiol. Psychol.*, 1958a, *51*, 675-678.

Olds, J. Self-stimulation of the brain. *Science*, 1958b, *127*, 315-324.

Olds, J. Spreading depression and hypothalamic behavior mechanisms. *Fed. Proc.*, 1962, *21*, 648-658.

Olds, J. Studies of neuropharmacologicals by electrical and chemical manipulation of the brain in animals with chronically implanted electrodes. In P. B. Bradley *et al.* (Eds.), *Neuropsychopharmacology*. New York: Elsevier, 1959. Pp. 20-32.

Olds, J., and P. Milner. Positive reinforcement produced by electrical stimulation of septal area and other regions of rat brain. *J. comp. physiol. Psychol.*, 1954, *47*, 419-427.

Olds, J., and M. E. Olds. Interference and learning in paleocortical systems. In J. F. Delafresnaye (Ed.), *Brain mechanisms and learning*. Oxford: Blackwell Scientific Publications, 1961. Pp. 153-187.

Olds, J., and B. Peretz. A motivational analysis of the reticular activating system. *Electroenceph. clin. Neurophysiol.*, 1960, *12*, 445-454.

Olds, J., and R. P. Travis. Effects of chlopromazine, meprobamate, pentobarbital, and morphine on self-stimulation. *J. pharmacol. exp. Therapeut.*, 1960, *128*, 397-404.

Olds, J., R. P. Travis, and R. C. Schwing. Topographic organization of hypothalamic self-stimulation functions. *J. comp. physiol. Psychol.*, 1960, *53*, 23-32.

Olds, J., A. Yuwiler, M. E. Olds, and C. Yun. Neurohumors in hypothalamic substrates of reward. *Am. J. Physiol.*, 1964, *207*, 242-254.

Olds, M. E., and J. Olds. Approach-avoidance analysis of rat diencephalon. *J. comp. Neurol.*, 1963, *120*, 259-295.

Olds, M. E., and J. Olds. Approach-escape interactions in rat brain. *Am. J. Physiol.*, 1962, *203*, 803-810.

Olds, M. E., and J. Olds. Emotional and associative mechanisms in rat brain. *J. comp. physiol. Psychol.*, 1961, *54*, 120-126.

Oomura, Y., K. Kimura, H. Ooyoma, T. Maeno, M. Ihi, and M. Kuniyoshi. Reciprocal activities of the ventro-medial and lateral hypothalamic areas of cats. *Science*, 1964, *143*, 484-485.

Papez, J. W. A. proposed mechanism of emotion. *Arch. Neurol. Psychiat.*, 1937, *38*, 725-743.

Papez, J. W. Visceral brain, its component parts and their connections. *J. nerv. ment. Disease*, 1958, *126*, 40-56.

Porter, R. W., D. Conrad, and J. V. Brady. Some neural and behavioral correlates of electrical self-stimulation in the limbic system. *J. Exptl. Anal. Behav.*, 1959, 2, 43-55.

Roberts, W. W. Both rewarding and punishing effects from stimulation of posterior hypothalamus of cat with same electrode at same intensity. *J. comp. physiol. Psychol.*, 1958b, *51*, 400-407.

Roberts, W. W. Fear-like behavior elicited from dorsomedial thalamus of cat. *J. comp. physiol. Psychol.*, 1962, *55*, 191-198.

Roberts, W. W. Rapid escape learning without avoidance learning motivated by hypothalamic stimulation in cats. *J. comp. physiol. Psychol.*, 1958a, *51*, 391-399.

Routtenberg, A., and J. Olds. The attenuation of response to an aversive brain stimulus by concurrent rewarding septal stimulation. *Fed. Proc.*, 1963, 22, 515 (Abstract).

Rüdiger, W., and Fifkova, E. Operant behavior and subcortical drive during spreading depression. *J. comp. physiol. Psychol.*, 1963, *56*, 375-379.

Russell, I. S., and S. Ochs. One trial interhemispheric transfer of a learning engram. *Science*, 1961, *313*, 1077-1078.

Schreiner, L., and A. Kling. Behavioral changes following rhinencephalic injury in cat. *J. Neurophysiol.*, 1953, *16*, 643-659.

Seigel, S. *Nonparametric statistics for the behavioral sciences.* New York: McGraw-Hill, 1956.

Sidman, M. Avoidance conditioning with brief shock and no exteroceptive warning signal. *Science*, 1953, *118*, 157-158.

Skinner, B. F. *The behavior of organisms.* New York: Appleton, 1938.

Teitelbaum, P. Sensory control of hypothalamic hyperphagia. *J. comp. physiol. Psychol.*, 1955, *48*, 156-163.

Teitelbaum, P., and E. Stellar. Recovery from failure to eat produced by hypothalamic lesions. *Science*, 1954, *120*, 894-895.

Thorndike, E. L. *Animal intelligence*. New York: Macmillan, 1911.

Travis, R. P., and J. Olds. Two kinds of escape from midbrain stimulation. *Amer. Psychologist*, 1959, *14*, 430 (Abstract).

Verzeano, M., and K. Negishi. Neuronal activity in cortial and thalamic networks; a study with multiple microelectrodes. *J. gen. Physiol.*, 1960, *43* (Suppl.), 177-195.

Vogt, M. Sympathomimetic amines in the central nervous system; normal distribution and changes produced by drugs. *Brit. med. Bull.*, 1957, *13*, 166-171.

Ward, H. P. Basal tegmental self-stimulation after septal ablation in rats. *A.M.A. Arch. Neurol.*, 1960, *3*, 158-162.

Ward, H. P. Tegmental self-stimulation after amygdaloid ablation. *A.M.A. Arch. Neurol.*, 1961, *4*, 657-659.

Wurtz, R. H., and Olds, J. Amygdaloid stimulation and operant reinforcement in the rat. *J. comp. physiol. Psychol.*, 1963, *56*, 941-949.

# INDEX